# THE WORLD OF WADE
## BOOK 2

## Collectable Porcelain and Pottery

by
IAN WARNER

and
MIKE POSGAY

©Copyright 1994
By Antique Publications
P.O. Box 553
Marietta, Ohio 45750

HB ISBN #1-57080-001-4
PB ISBN #1-57080-000-6

*This book is dedicated*
*to*
all Wade employees, both past and present,
whose skills, talent and dedication to their work
has given so much pleasure to
collectors
of
Wade porcelain and pottery.

# TABLE OF CONTENTS

# FOREWORD

A number of years ago when Mike Posgay and I were searching for a title for our book on Wade pottery, our good friend, the late William Heacock, saw an old Wade catalog with a line drawing of the globe, along with the word Wade, on the cover. Without a second thought, Bill suggested "The World of Wade" as a title. Five years later, *The World of Wade* is to have a sibling – *The World of Wade Book 2*. Bill Heacock, a glass researcher and author of numerous books on Victorian Pattern Glass, Fenton Art Glass and Northwood Glass, would have been elated at the success of the Wade book. We thank Bill for his suggestion for a title and for introducing us to his publisher.

*The World of Wade Book 2* is not an update or repeat of *The World of Wade*. It is rather a continuation or extension of the first book. As little as possible has been repeated, but items which are repeated are included either to show color examples or to expand on a set or series.

On a number of entries, reference has been made to a page or pages in *The World of Wade*. This occurs where further information or illustrations of a series or line may be found. This cross reference not only helps to eliminate unnecessary text repetition but will also assist readers to find information more easily.

Since *The World of Wade* was published, we have researched additional magazines and newspaper articles, helping to verify or revise dates of issue of a number of Wade items. A number of these articles, especially those written by the late Sir George Wade for the in-house magazine *"The Jolly Potter,"* have put new light on the development of the Wade Potteries. Due to this new information, we have rewritten the history of the potteries under the heading: The Development of the Wade Potteries.

The use of any company name, trade mark or logo in this book is either with permission of the copyright holder or to make identification clear.

Ian Warner and Mike Posgay

Brampton, Ontario 1994

To contact the authors please write to:
P.O. Box 93022,
499 Main Street South,
BRAMPTON, Ontario
Canada L6Y 4V8

# ACKNOWLEDGEMENTS

We would like to thank all the Wade collectors who have been so supportive and complimentary on our first Wade book. We would also like to thank all of you who have written, made telephone calls and sent information from around the world. Your contributions to this book are much appreciated. A very big "thank you" to those of you who welcomed us into your homes to photograph your collections, thereby giving other collectors a chance to see items they might not have otherwise seen. Your generosity was overwhelming.

Our special thanks go to the following who went so far out of their way to be of assistance.

We thank Sylvia and Karol Ashken and "Seppi," Surrey, England, for allowing us to photograph many unusual pieces from their collection. Your splendid hospitality definitely lifted our spirits when the weather did not cooperate for our photography sessions and time was running out.

To Catherine, John and Stuart Barlow, Nottingham, England, we extend our gratitude for your help, loan of photographs to include in this book and your continued interest in Wade collectors through your newsletter *"The Wade Collectors Club Newsletter."*

Ralph Brough, Sales Director, Wade (PDM) Ltd., Yorkshire, England, has been a constant source of information, taking time from his busy schedule to answer our many questions and keeping us up-to-date on new developments at Wade (PDM) Ltd. We thank you Ralph, for your help and continued interest.

Our thanks go to John and Elizabeth Clarke, Middlesex, England, for helping us photograph so many items from their personal collections which are included in this book.

Derek Dawe, Wade (PDM) Ltd., Staffordshire, England, has advised and helped us right from the beginning of our interest in Wade products in the 1970's. His help and continued interest in both this book and *The World of Wade* has been enormous. Without his help these books would have been far less complete. We thank you Derek. Our very best wishes for a long and happy retirement – we both will miss you on our visits to the potteries.

Roger Ellis, Sales Director (Consumer Products), Wade Ceramics Ltd., Staffordshire, England, has been of great help in our quest for information on more recent Wade products. We thank you Roger, for your continued interest and assistance.

We thank John and Roberta Feist, Florida, USA, for inviting us to their home to see their collection and for their continued support in our search for accurate information.

Jeff and Liz Fisher, Essex, England, went out of their way to make us feel welcome in their home. We thank you for letting us see and photograph your collection.

Without the help of William Harper, Staffordshire, England, our understanding of the George Wade products of the 1950's would be sorely lacking. Thank you, Bill, for your contributions to the Wade giftware lines. You have given immense pleasure to Wade collectors the world over. We would like to extend our apologies to Jean Harper for invading her house during renovations.

Our dear friends Harriet and Bruce Kellman, New York, USA, are always so supportive in our endeavors. We thank you, Bruce and Harriet, for your hospitality and above all your continued friendship.

Our thanks go to R. Alec McCullough, Staffordshire, England, whose memories and experience as a director of Wade (Ireland) Ltd., right from the early days, has been most helpful and enlightening. We thank you for your help. We would also like to thank Betty McCullough for letting us visit on such short notice and thereby upsetting their plans for the day.

Ivan McGee, Commercial Manager, Wade Ceramics Ltd., Staffordshire, England, always makes time for us during our visit to the potteries. His help searching out information on Wade products of years past and especially his help in the field of backstamps is much appreciated. It is always a pleasure to sit with Ivan in his office and listen as he reminisces about the people with whom he worked and the products with which he was associated during his years at Wade.

We thank Heather and William MacArthur, Ontario, Canada, for their friendship, help and support over the years. We also thank them for allowing us to transport such a large portion of their collection to be photographed at the studios in Marietta.

Richard and Denise Mellor, Warwickshire, England. Richard was one of the first people to write us after the publication of *The World of Wade*. He then invited us to see and photograph his collection during one of our visits to the UK. Thank you, Richard, for all your help.

Our deep gratitude goes to Carole Murdock and Valerie Moody, Colorado, USA, who have been our friends since the early days, for their interest in our books and their willingness to edit and correct anything and everything that needed to be corrected. Thank you also for allowing us to quote from your newsletter *"The Wade Watch."* We appreciate your contributions and those of your families.

We thank Ken and Margaret Neate, Oxfordshire, England, who have been of so much help to us in obtaining information for our book and for introducing us to many other Wade enthusiasts and former Wade employees. Thank you also, Ken and Margaret, for your hospitality and for helping us photograph your collection for inclusion in this book. Please know that you were the very first to write us from the UK, and that first letter developed into a lasting friendship.

Lynn Neil, Essex, England, has been in contact with us since *The World of Wade* was published. She has kept us informed on the content of her growing collection as well as her expanding family. Thank you for your help over the years.

Shawn Patterson, Ontario, Canada, is a true Wade enthusiast. His help in obtaining items to photograph for this book is truly appreciated. His indulgence in allowing us to hold on to sizable portions of his personal collection, for weeks on end, is also greatly appreciated. Many thanks, Shawn, for your help.

We would like to thank Vernon Shields, Devon, England, for searching through his memories of his many years as a joint director of George Wade and Wade Heath to answer our questions. His help added accuracy to both of the Wade books. For this help, we are deeply grateful.

Our thanks go to Libuse and Steve Smykal, Ontario, Canada, for their help and encouragement over the years and for the loan of so many pieces from their collection for photographing in Marietta.

We sincerely thank Muriel Trouton, Seagoe Ceramics Ltd., Co. Armagh, Northern Ireland, for all her help over the years for both this book and *The World of Wade*. Her assistance in searching through records of Wade (Ireland) Ltd. and for obtaining information from past employees of the pottery has been invaluable. Thank you, Muriel, for being there when we needed you.

Both William and Joan Walker, Cheshire, England, have had many years of experience with Wade Heath, and we sincerely thank them for sharing their knowledge with us. We also thank them for showing us and letting us photograph many unusual items from their collection.

Carole and John Woolner, Ontario, Canada, generously loaned us a number of pieces from their extensive collection to photograph in Marietta. Thank you, John and Carole, for your help and interest.

Our grateful thanks also go to the following individuals, firms and representatives of firms for their help and contributions to this book.

Caryl Alcock, Secretary, Wade (PDM) Ltd., Staffordshire, England
Carl and Thelma Anderson, Ontario, Canada
Maureen D. Ballentine, Ontario, Canada
B. Beanland, Company Secretary, Guinness Brewing G.B., England
Janet Berrisford, Sales Office Manager – Consumer Products, Wade Ceramics Ltd., Staffordshire, England
E.M. Bishop, Senior Product Manager, Tom Smith Group Ltd., England
Bernhard Burton, Director of Sales – Consumer Products (Export), Wade Ceramics Ltd., Staffordshire, England
Margaret Cleaver, Ontario, Canada
Barbara Cooksey, Wade Ceramics Ltd., Staffordshire, England
Glenn and Alonzo Cotton, New Hampshire, USA
Elaine and Adrian Crumpton, Buckinghamshire, England
Martin R. Edwards, Asprey PLC, England
David and Hilary Elvin, Kent, England
Gary Excell, Dorset, England
Pam Ferrazzutti, Ontario, Canada

Cynthia Findlay, Ontario, Canada
Margaret Gerwin, Ohio, USA
Andrea Goble, Ontario, Canada
Edith and Douglas Hacking, Ontario, Canada
Anne and Stuart Hampson, Lancashire, England
Tony Hemmings, Director of Sales – Consumer Products (UK), Wade Ceramics Ltd, Staffordshire, England
Ken Holmes, Wade Ceramics Ltd., Staffordshire, England
Camille Huggins, California, USA
Karen Hunter, Ohio, USA
Kevin E. Isherwood, Essex, England
Peter and Therese Jaslow, PQ, Canada
Sylvia R. Jay, Consumer Relations Manager, Lyons Tetley Limited, Middlesex, England
Sandra and Kent Jones, California, USA
Patricia Kantaroff, Ontario, Canada
Cyndy Katrynuk, British Columbia, Canada
Pat and John Keating, Sussex, England
Carol M. and Kimberly Korn, Michigan, USA
Louise Lae, California, USA
Richard and Denise Melia, New Jersey, USA
Ken and Rose Mellor, Warwickshire, England
Edith, Stefan, Edward and Vladimir Mlynar, Austria
Lindsay Mouat, Senior Product Manager, Lever Rexona New Zealand Limited, New Zealand
Lesley Penniston, Staffordshire, England
Arthur Pratzky, Western Australia, Australia
Elva and Arthur Roach, Western Australia, Australia
Janet Robinson, New Zealand
Brian Rose, Ontario, Canada
Barrie, Iris and Leonie Sadler, North Devon, England
Philip G. Schepp Jr., California, USA
Mary Ann Sloan, Oregon, USA
Russell Schooley, West Sussex, England
John Stringer, Co. Armagh, Northern Ireland
Taunton Cider plc., Taunton, Somerset, England
Jill Thomas-Clark, Assistant Registrar, The Corning Museum of Glass, Corning, New York, USA
Fay Thompson, Ontario, Canada
Sabina Waldman, Austria
Glen Willis, Ontario, Canada
Virginia Wright, The Corning Museum of Glass, Corning, New York, USA
Jenny Wright, Department Secretary – Consumer Products, Wade Ceramics Ltd., Staffordshire, England
Judith Wooten, Wade Ceramics Ltd., Staffordshire, England
Vaux plc., Sunderland, Tyne & Wear, England

We thank the helpful staff of the Richardson Printing Corporation, especially David E. Richardson, D. Thomas O'Connor and James S. Measell, for their understanding, advice and continued interest in this book. We also thank Deana Wynn for her patience during the long color photography sessions and Ronda Ludwig for the expert layout of this book.

Additional black & white and color photography by Mike Posgay.

Resource Centers
The Rakow Library, Corning Museum of Glass, Corning, New York, USA
Toronto Reference Library, Toronto, Ontario, Canada
The New York Public Library, Science & Technology Division, New York, NY, USA
Ohio State University, Columbus, Ohio, USA
The British Library, Newspaper Library, London, England
The Patent Office, Public Record Office, Richmond, England

8

# The World of Wade

# Book 2

# Development of the Wade Potteries

# DEVELOPMENT OF THE WADE POTTERIES.

The WADE GROUP OF POTTERIES, or WADE CERAMICS LTD., the name by which the company is known today, traces its origins back, via two potteries, to the early and mid eighteenth century.

GEORGE WADE & SON LTD. had its origin with the HENRY HALLEN pottery, established in 1810 and WADE, HEATH & CO. LTD., along with A. J. WADE & CO. LTD., previously WADE & CO., originated with WADE, COLCLOUGH AND LINGARD founded in 1867.

## HENRY HALLEN POTTERY.

In 1810, Henry Hallen established a small single bottle oven pottery and workshop near Chesterton, just west of Burslem. Through hard work and the understanding of the pottery trade, Hallen developed his pottery into a sizable business specializing in porcelain products for the textile industry, then growing rapidly in Northern England. In the mid-nineteenth century, due to an increased demand for his product, Hallen moved his business to a larger pottery located in Wellington Street. The pottery thrived and carried on trading through to the end of the century when it was eventually taken over by George Wade and thus ceased trading under the name of Hallen.

## WADE & CO.

The Wade family was first heard from in 1867 when John Wade, along with two partners, formed a pottery in Burslem, Staffordshire. The pottery was given the name of WADE, COLCLOUGH AND LINGARD. The company manufactured Jet and Rockingham ware, mainly teapots, but also a variety of other "occasional" tableware items.

In 1887, after twenty years of business, the partnership was dissolved. John Wade then carried on the business under the name of WADE & CO. In 1894, John Wade took over the Union Pottery, located in the High Street, (renamed Greenhead Street in 1954) Burslem. This pottery was previously owned by the firm of BUCKLEY, HEATH & CO. By this time, the 1890's, John Wade had been joined in partnership by two of his nephews, Albert Joseph Wade and William Wade.

## J. & W. WADE & CO.

William Wade joined his uncle in his pottery business and eventually formed the J. & W. WADE & CO., specializing in the manufacture of glazed wall and floor tiles. Finally, Albert Joseph Wade, who had started his business career as a schoolteacher, also joined his uncle at WADE & CO. By the early twentieth century, both WADE & CO. and J. & W. WADE & CO. had developed into two highly successful businesses.

## GEORGE WADE POTTERY.

In the latter part of the nineteenth century, the exact date is not known, George Wade (1863-1938), elder brother of A. J. and William Wade, formed his own pottery under the name of the GEORGE WADE POTTERY. The

*A. J. Wade (1866 - 1933).*

pottery was located at the top of Hall Street. The major product of this new endeavor was the manufacture of pottery fittings for the textile industry. George Wade soon became strong competition to the Henry Hallen pottery as both were producing similar items for the same industry.

In the early 1900's, George Wade finally bought out the Hallen pottery and combined the two businesses at a new works called the Manchester Pottery, also located in High Street, Burslem. (Ref. article by Sir George Wade in *The Jolly Potter*).

George Wade had a number of other business interests besides his pottery. One major interest was in the CHROMO TRANSFER COMPANY of Burslem, of which he was

*George Wade (1863 - 1938).*

Joint Managing Director. He also held the position of Secretary of the Earthenware Manufacturer's Association, a post he held for a number of years.

## GEORGE WADE & SON LTD.

In 1906, George Wade's son, George Albert Wade (better known as Sir George Wade 1891-1986) joined his father at the Manchester Pottery. With the outbreak of WWI in 1914, G.A. Wade enlisted and was commissioned in the South Staffordshire Regiment. He saw active service in both France and Egypt and was awarded the M.C. and Bar. In 1915, he married Miss Florrie Johnson, the daughter of a local area pottery manufacturer. They had two daughters, Cynthia Wade and Iris Wade (who later married Straker Carryer of Wade (Ulster) Ltd. fame) and a son, G. Anthony J. Wade (1925-1987), who also eventually joined the business.

On June 24, 1919, the original firm of GEORGE WADE was incorporated into GEORGE WADE & SON LTD. to carry on the business of pottery fittings for the textile industry, electrical porcelain insulators and other porcelain articles for industrial purposes. By the late 1920's, the company had also added decorative figurines of ladies and animals to their range of products which were produced until the outbreak of WWII.

## A. J. WADE & CO. AND WADE, HEATH & CO. LTD.

In the 1920's, the Wade pottery changed its name to the High Street Pottery but still housed the two businesses of WADE & CO. and J. & W. WADE & CO. In June 1927, J. & W. WADE & CO. was formed into a private company to be known as A. J. WADE & CO. In the following December of 1927, WADE & CO. was also formed into a private company taking the name WADE, HEATH & CO. LTD. Both companies were headed by A. J. Wade but for WADE, HEATH & CO. LTD., which had extended its range of teapots to include Russet, Samian and Mosaic and many styles of decorations, he had taken a partner, George Henry Heath. Heath had had many years of experience with the Wade

*Flaxman Tile Works circa 1949 from a painting by Robert Barlow.*

potteries, having worked for the family since he joined J. & W. WADE & CO. near the end of the nineteenth century.

From 1900 until 1911, Heath had worked as a travelling representative for the Wade pottery, thereafter turning his attention to the inside management of the company. George Heath was also from a long line of potters. His father, Daniel Heath, had been a member of the firm of BUCKLEY, HEATH & CO. which, in the early 1890's, was producing earthenware at the Union Pottery which was taken over by WADE & CO. in 1894.

*Flaxman Tile Works as it appears today from Greenhead Street.*

## WADE POTTERIES LIMITED.

Following the death of A. J. Wade in January 1933, G. A. Wade (then Col. George A. Wade MC), A. J. Wade's nephew, took over leadership of A. J. WADE & CO. and WADE, HEATH & CO. LTD. In October 1935, the two companies, along with the NORTH HILL ROAD MILL CO., combined forming WADE POTTERIES LIMITED.

On the death of his father, in 1938 Col. G. A. Wade inherited complete control of both WADE POTTERIES LIMITED and his father's business of GEORGE WADE & SON LTD. at the Manchester Pottery of which he had been a director since the 1920's and chairman since 1936. However, WADE POTTERIES LIMITED and GEORGE WADE & SON LTD. were still run as two completely separate businesses for quite some time.

## ROYAL VICTORIA POTTERY.

In 1938, WADE, HEATH & CO. LTD., moved its operations from the High Street Pottery, which was then renamed the Flaxman Tile Works, to the Royal Victoria Pottery on Liverpool Road, today known as Westport Road. This pottery had been built in 1814 by John and Richard Riley, and an oval plaque reading "Hill Works 1814" still appears above the old main entrance to the pottery. In 1830, the pottery was taken over by Samuel Alcock and Co. and then in 1888, by Dunn, Bennett and Co. until 1938 when it then passed into the hands of the Wade family.

PORCELAIN ANIMALS AND BIRDS

FIGURES OF DISTINCTION

# WADE PRODUCTIONS

Every article in the varied range of Wade products represents a long-established tradition of craftsmanship, allied to modern manufacturing methods and the use of the very finest raw materials. Write to-day for fuller details and prices of the Wade productions shown here. They mean profit for YOU.

**GEORGE WADE & SON**
LTD
*Manchester Pottery.*

**BURSLEM, STOKE-on-TRENT**

FLOWERS

PORCELAIN OVENPROOF COOKING WARE

*Advertisement from the February 1940 issue of The Pottery Gazette and Glass Trade Review.*

*An informal Sir George Wade (circa 1959).*

# WORLD WAR II.

After the outbreak of WWII in 1939, work at the various Wade potteries gradually slowed down with eventually all work coming to a halt at both the Flaxman Tile Works and the Manchester Pottery. The production of pottery continued throughout the war years at the Royal Victoria Pottery but with certain restrictions as directed by the Board of Trade under the Domestic Potters (Manufacture and Supply) Order. This order designated that all items manufactured for domestic consumption were to be plain, white, undecorated ware. However, items manufactured for the export market, which was still required to help finance the war effort, were given a license to be produced with full decoration.

Due to the concentration of the pottery industry during the war years, a number of potteries were forced to close down operations on their own premises for the duration of the war and carry on a more limited production with one of their pre-war competitors. This happened to THE STAFFS. TEAPOT CO. which, in 1941, closed its pottery and carried on business at the Royal Victoria Pottery. An announcement in the October 1941 issue of *The Pottery Gazette and Glass Trade Review* reads as follows: The Royal Victoria Pottery and the Staffs. Teapot Co. wish to inform the trade that their productions are being maintained at the above address. (The address given was that of the Royal Victoria Pottery).

Due to wartime restrictions, WADE, HEATH & CO. LTD. was forced to make the following announcement to its customers in the January 1943 issue of *The Pottery Gazette and Glass Trade Review:* "We regret - circumstances compel us to limit our supplies. In the meantime we are endeavoring to maintain a fair and equitable distribution to our many friends." Unfortunately, this announcement had to be made on a number of other occasions during the war.

# POST WAR PRODUCTION.

It wasn't until August 6, 1952, that the Board of Trade Order was rescinded and WADE, HEATH & CO. LTD. was allowed to manufacture and sell decorated ware for the home market. Mr. E. L. Nickels, then a director of WADE, HEATH & CO. LTD., wrote in *The Jolly Potter,* the Wade potteries in-house magazine, that "...it took only about five months before stores began taking on their pre-war look, the drabness of the plain white ware once again giving place to color and beauty."

GEORGE WADE & SON LTD. was back in business by 1946 but still unable to produce any items for decorative purposes. The pottery was being kept busy producing electrical porcelain insulators for use in the home-building program, a program desperately needed to help rebuild the major cities devastated by the bombing of WWII. It was to be some years before the Manchester Pottery got back into the field of decorative ware. In 1947, G. Anthony J. Wade joined the company and in 1948 became a Director and then a Joint Managing Director in 1949.

*G. Anthony J. Wade (circa mid 1950's)*

# WADE (ULSTER) LTD.

In 1946, Col. G. A. Wade, along with his son-in-law H. Straker Carryer, acquired and converted a linen mill in Portadown, Northern Ireland. This, on January 2, 1950, was incorporated into WADE (ULSTER) LTD. as a subsidiary of GEORGE WADE & SON LTD. to produce die-pressed insulators required for the rebuilding program. In 1953, when need for industrial ceramics lessened, the Irish pottery entered into the field of decorative giftware. Amongst its first products were goblets and tankards for use as souvenirs for the coronation of Queen Elizabeth II in June 1953.

In October 1956, a large portion of the WADE (ULSTER) LTD. pottery was destroyed by an early morning fire. Within six days of the fire, the Wade factory staff had cleared up the debris, installed one hundred yards of new roof, relit the kiln and had the power restored. Within another twenty-four hours, three quarters of the employees

*H. Straker Carryer (circa mid 1950's)*

## FLAXMAN TILE WORKS - LAST DAYS.

After the end of WWII, A. J. WADE & CO. resumed the manufacture of glazed tiles, mainly for use as fireplace surrounds. The building was also the base for the silk screen department which was used mainly for products manufactured by WADE, HEATH & CO. LTD. In the early 1960's, with the increasing popularity of gas fires and alternative fireplace surrounds such as marble or stone etc., the pottery began to falter. By 1969, the production of glazed tiles ceased altogether at the Flaxman Tile Works. Fireplaces were still sold by A. J. WADE & CO., but all materials were supplied by other sources.

The presses and kilns were no longer required and the A. J. WADE & CO. staff was drastically reduced. The smaller staff comprised mainly of sales and administrative personnel and the actual fireplace assemblers known as "slabbers." The works was finally closed down in November 1970. The building is still standing today and is gradually being restored to use after many years as a storage depot. As of date of publication, the old Flaxman Tile Works is housing the new WADE POTTERY STORE.

were back at their jobs. Quite a feat! Luckily the business and property were well insured and the company received £87,323 (including £10,000 for loss of profits) under Policies of Insurance. The pottery buildings were completely restored by early 1958. In November 1966, the Irish pottery changed its name to Wade (Ireland) Ltd.

## THE WADE GROUP OF POTTERIES.

On March 7, 1958, at a shareholders meeting of WADE POTTERIES LIMITED held at the Flaxman Tile Works, the Directors of the company announced they had entered into a contract to acquire the whole of the issued share capital of GEORGE WADE & SON LTD. and its subsidiary WADE (ULSTER) LTD. With the formation of a new Board

*Tuesday Morning.
October 30th 1956.*

*Tuesday Morning
October 30th 1956.*

*Wade (Ulster) Ltd. The fire of 1956.*

*November 4th 1956.*

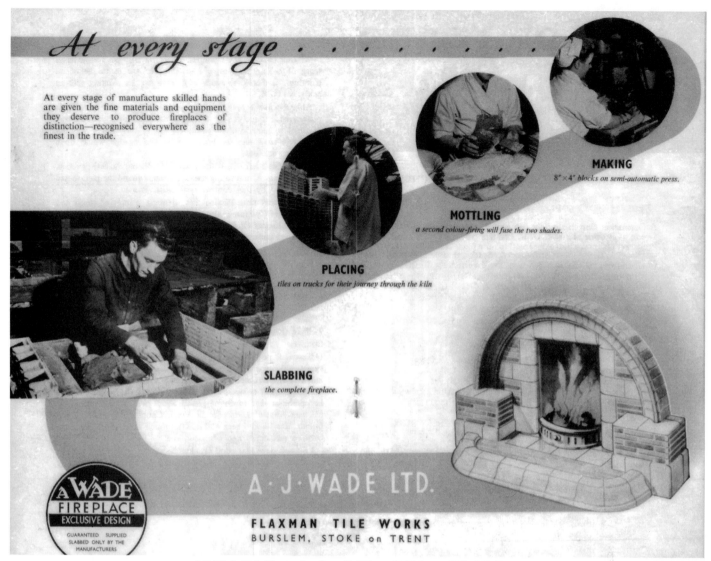

*A.J. Wade Ltd. Illustration from the Winter 1953 issue of The Jolly Potter.*

of Management, the Directors of both WADE POTTERIES LIMITED and the Directors of GEORGE WADE & SON LTD. were to remain unchanged but with the addition of Mr. Hubert Thurman Robinson, the technical Director of the Manchester Pottery and Mr. Henry Straker Carryer, Joint Managing Director of the Irish pottery.

At the time of the takeover, the Directors of WADE POTTERIES LIMITED were Sir George Albert Wade, M.C., J.P. (Chairman); Annie Florence Wade; Reginald Clive Birbeck; Ernest Boyce Hunt Shields; George Anthony Johnson Wade, M.C.; Frank Ernest Hulme; and John Maxwell Bryson McBratney. The Directors of GEORGE WADE & CO. LTD. were Sir George Albert Wade, M.C., J.P.; George Anthony Johnson Wade, M.C.; Hubert Thurman Robinson; and George Thomas Brett.

## WADE REGICOR AND
## WADE (PDM) LTD.

In the early 1950's, WADE, HEATH & CO. LTD. entered into an agreement with Reginald Corfield (Sales) Ltd. to produce advertising ware which was to be distributed by the Corfield company. This collaboration lasted for a number of years but ended in 1969 when WADE, HEATH

& CO. LTD. formed its own distribution arm to be known as WADE (PDM) LTD.

For many years, WADE REGICOR and later WADE (PDM) LTD., was based in Purley, Surrey. In 1989, the company was relocated to the Royal Victoria Pottery in Burslem thus giving closer co-ordination between the manufacture and distribution of the advertising ware. In 1991, WADE (PDM) LTD. ceased to be a separate arm of what is now WADE CERAMICS LIMITED and was absorbed into the parent company.

In January 1988, WADE POTTERIES LIMITED acquired AVON TIN which had been associated with Wade since 1970. AVON TIN manufactured a wide range of decorated tin and aluminum plate products including the wide range of "waiter trays" and pressed metal ashtrays distributed through WADE (PDM) LTD. This association was very short lived as Wade sold their acquisition the following year.

## WADE CERAMICS LIMITED.

With the death of G. Anthony J. Wade in 1987, the long run of the Wade Group of Potteries, with a family member at its helm, came to an end. In 1989, the company was taken over by Beauford PLC which gave the group of pot-

# WADE POTTERIES LIMITED

## Directors :

### COL. SIR GEORGE ALBERT WADE, M.C. (Chairman)

ANNIE FLORENCE WADE
ERNEST BOYCE HUNT SHIELDS
FRANK ERNEST HULME

REGINALD CLIVE BIRBECK
GEORGE ANTHONY JOHNSON WADE, M.C.
JOHN MAXWELL BRYSON McBRATNEY

Flaxman Tile Works,
Burslem, Stoke-on-Trent.
7th March, 1958.

1.    Your Directors are pleased to inform the Shareholders that they have entered into a conditional contract for the acquisition of the whole of the issued share capital of George Wade & Son Ltd. The contract is conditional (inter alia) on the approval of your Company in General Meeting.

2.    George Wade & Son Ltd. manufactures insulators and electrical porcelain and the well-known ornamental figures known as Whimsies. It has a subsidiary Wade (Ulster) Ltd. which carries on a similar business in Northern Ireland and also manufactures a range of ornamental ware known as Irish Porcelain. The products of George Wade & Son Ltd. and its subsidiary are not in competition with those of your Company, and your Directors consider that the business of those companies can be operated in conjunction with that of your Company and its existing subsidiaries to the great advantage of your Company.

**HISTORY AND BUSINESS:**—George Wade & Son Ltd. (in this appendix referred to as "the Company") was incorporated in England on the 24th June, 1919 as a Private Limited Company to acquire and take over as a going concern and carry on the business of manufacturers of pottery fittings for textile machinery, gas burners, bottle stoppers, electrical porcelain insulators and other porcelain articles for industrial purposes then carried on by the late George Wade at Manchester Pottery, High Street, Burslem in the County of Stafford under the style or firm of "GEORGE WADE". This business had been developed from the businesses of George Wade, established in 1867, and of Henry Hallen, established in 1810.

*Extract from a notice to the shareholders of Wade Potteries Ltd. on the takeover by that company, of George Wade & Son Ltd. March 1958.*

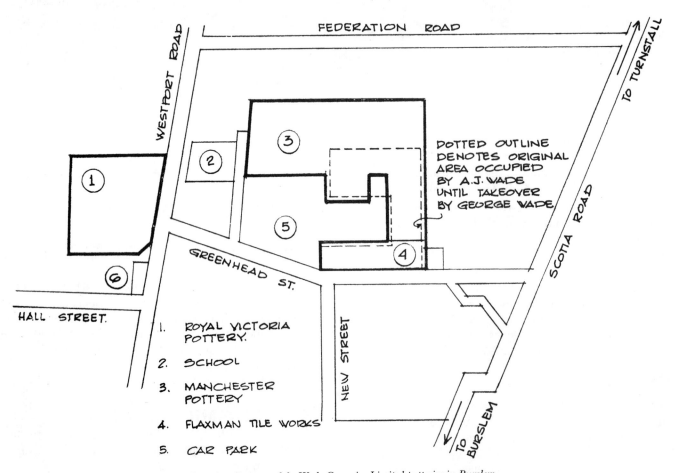

*Location diagram of the Wade Ceramics Limited potteries in Burslem.*

teries a new name - WADE CERAMICS LIMITED. At this time, the company names of GEORGE WADE & SON LTD. and WADE, HEATH & CO. LTD. ceased to exist. WADE (IRELAND) LTD. remained as such until 1990 when the company changed its name to Seagoe Ceramics and by 1992, although still a member of Beauford PLC, the Irish pottery was no longer connected directly to WADE CERAMICS LIMITED.

Today, WADE CERAMICS LIMITED consists of two potteries, both based in Burslem, the old Manchester Pottery on Greenhead Street and the Royal Victoria Pottery on Westport Road. The Flaxman Tile Works is now the Wade pottery outlet shop.

*Illustration of Wade Promotional Ceramics (note the rare 1979 Whitbread Train ashtray).*

*Casting Shop. Royal Victoria Pottery. Circa 1953.*

The World of Wade

Book 2

Backstamps

# BACKSTAMPS.

Since *The World of Wade* was published in 1988, a number of Wade Pottery backstamps have been uncovered. Also, further research has uncovered new information pertaining to backstamps and trade names that were shown in the first book.

The major additional marks are the three "owl" marks, two of which were used by George Wade & Son Ltd. and one by Wade (Ulster) Ltd., and the backstamps used by Wade, Heath & Co. Ltd. during the years of WWII. The registered trade name "scintillite," used by George Wade & Son Ltd., was also found to have been used earlier than previously thought.

The earliest ink or transfer type marks, found on Wade items sought after by collectors, are those used by Wade & Co. on teapots, vases, biscuit barrels etc., manufactured at the High Street Pottery (see Mark Types "O" and 1). In 1927, when the company changed its name to Wade, Heath & Co. Ltd., the mark was revised to include the new company name (Mark Type 2).

From 1927 through until the war years, Wade, Heath & Co. Ltd. used a variety of marks as illustrated in the following charts. With the onset of WWII, restrictions on the manufacture of pottery were brought in by the government, and the Wade backstamps were amended to reflect these new conditions. From 1941, when restrictions were first imposed, to 1952, when they were removed, a number of backstamp variations were used by Wade, Heath & Co. Ltd.

# THE WAR YEARS.

In the September 1942 issue of *The Pottery Gazette and Glass Trade Review,* an order from the Board of Trade, The Domestic Pottery (Manufacture and Supply) order 1942 (S.R. & O. 1038) listed the potteries licensed to manufacture undecorated utility ware for home consumption. The firms were listed in three categories; Group I, Group II and Group III. All wares were to be stamped with an indelible, under-the-glaze mark; A for Group I, B for Group II and C for Group III. Wade, Heath & Co. Ltd. were listed under Group II for jugs.

A new Board of Trade list was published under the title of The "A, B, C" Pottery Firms in the October 1945 issue of *The Pottery Gazette and Glass Trade Review.* The revised, second schedule of The Domestic Pottery (Manufacture and Supply) order 1945 (S.R. & O. 498) listed six groups. Items in Group I were to be marked with the letter C, items in Group II with the letter B, items in Group III with the letters BY, items in Group IV with the letter A, items in Group V with the letters CY (to be imprinted on jugs only) and items in Group VI with the letters CZ (to be imprinted on pudding bowls only). Wade, Heath & Co. Ltd. appeared in Group II and IV. At the time of publication, no reference had been found as to the origin of the Wade backstamp with the letter J (Mark Type 7B). It would appear that this stamp was used by Wade, as one of the used, original stamps was located at the Royal Victoria Pottery.

When wartime regulations were lifted, Wade, Heath & Co. Ltd. used a number of backstamps, eventually settling on Mark Type 19 around 1953. At this time, George Wade & Son Ltd. also adopted this backstamp, and both companies used it for quite a number of years.

# SCINTILLITE FIGURINES.

George Wade & Son Ltd. at the Manchester Pottery was, until the late 1920's, primarily a manufacturer of industrial porcelain ware which was usually either simply marked or stamped with a number. With the introduction of figurines to the line, a new decorative backstamp was used, i.e. Mark Type 20A, the first "owl mark." In 1931, this Mark Type, along with the word Scintillite, was eventually registered to George Wade & Son Ltd. as Registration No. 520, 878. (Ref. *The Pottery Gazette and Glass Trade Review, May 1931*).

Many of the cellulose-finished Van Hallen figurines are found with Mark Type 20A, and these figurines were usually referred to throughout the 1930's by both the pottery staff and trade magazines as "Scintillite figures." However, the underglaze versions of the Van Hallen figurines and the underglazed animal figures modelled by Faust Lang in the 1930's were usually marked by the blue, handpainted Mark Type 21A, often along with the year of issue.

# POSTWAR MARK TYPES.

After the war, George Wade & Son Ltd. mold-marked much of their figural giftware, and on those not marked, a paper label was applied to the underside of the base.

The second "owl" mark, Mark Type 23A, was used in the late 1940's by George Wade & Son Ltd. on many of their porcelain items manufactured for the industrial market. This Mark Type was used at the Manchester Pottery for items made for the "free market," in other words, items not made to a customer's own design but intended for the general market. Examples of Wade industrial ware using this mark are ceramic cleats, ceiling roses, insulators and electrical fire element holders.

In the late 1950's, George Wade & Son Ltd. resurrected their patented name "scintillite" to describe the then new sparkling glaze used for the tortoise line of giftware. This line was later extended to include many other giftware items such as aqua dishes, the covered shore-crab dish, pet-face dishes, etc.

Mark Type 19 was in general use by George Wade & Son Ltd. from the early 1950's until the company's takeover by Beauford PLC in 1989.

# WADE (ULSTER) LTD.

Wade (Ulster) Ltd., established in 1946, was incorporated in 1950 and used the third "owl" mark, Mark Type 27C, on its industrial ceramic ware. With the introduction of the Irish giftware, the pottery began using a number of molded mark types which often used the words Irish Porcelain along with a stylized shamrock leaf. In 1966, when the Irish pottery changed its name to Wade (Ireland) Ltd., no specific changes were made to the backstamps.

# RECENT MARK TYPES.

In more recent years, the Wade Potteries have used a

great number of special mark types. The majority of these include either the name of the client for whom the piece was manufactured or the name of the line of gift or tableware. Many examples of these marks are illustrated following the chart of regular Wade mark types.

In 1989, when the Wade Group of Potteries was taken over by Beauford PLC, the two major potteries, the Manchester Pottery (George Wade & Son Ltd.) and the Royal Victoria Pottery (Wade, Heath & Co. Ltd.), ceased to exist as such, and the new Wade Ceramics Limited mark, Mark Type 27B was introduced and is found on much of today's Wade gift and tableware.

For further notes on Wade mark types and dating products by use of such marks, see *The W of W pg. 5*.

## SPECIAL BACKSTAMPS.

Examples of the many "special backstamps" used by the Wade Group of Potteries and Wade Ceramics Ltd. on their lines of tableware and special orders.

S1   Ringtons Rose Bowl and Plant Trough.
S2   No record.
S3   Williamson & Magor Elephant Tea Caddy.
S4   Open Range (Various shapes).
S5   Open Range (Various shapes).
S6   Santa's Grotto Teapot (First produced Christmas 1989).

S7   Open Range (Various shapes).
S8   Myrna Coffee Pot.
S9   Small size Cider Mug (Taunton Cider).
S10 Small size Teapot - Royal Society for the Protection of Birds - 1988.
S11 Standard Fine Bone China Backstamp (Royal Victoria Pottery).
S12 Old Parr Flagons.
S13 No record.
S14 Open Range (Various shapes).
S15 No record.
S16 Irish Distillers Backstamp.
S17 Belfry Hotel Coaster Dish.
S18 Whyte & Mackay Flagon Backstamp.
S19 Open Range (Various shapes).
S20 No record.
S21 Gordon Highlander Backstamp for Highland Wildlife Decanter.
S22 Gordon Highlander Backstamp for Highland Wildlife Decanter.
S23 One Cup China Teapots. Open Range. ( 3x shapes).
S24 No record.
S25 Open Range (Various shapes).
S26 to S35  Taunton Cider Cider Mug Backstamps.
S36 Boston Tea Party Teapot, Sugar & Creamer Backstamp.
S37 Wilton Castle Dish.
S38 English Life Mug Backstamp.
S39 English Life Teapot Backstamp.
S40 Valor Teapot.

*Wade, Heath & Co. Ltd. advertisement as it appeared in the March 1935 issue of* The Pottery Gazette and Glass Trade Review. *(Note the Mickey Mouse figurine)*.

# WADE POTTERIES
# MARKS & BACKSTAMPS

**WADE & CO.**

Wades'

England.

*Mark Type O*
*Late 1900's - Mid 1920's*
*Ink Stamp*

WADES

ENGLAND

*Mark Type 1*
*Mid 1920's-1927*
*Ink Stamp*

WADES
ORCADIA
WARE
BRITISH MADE

*Mark Type 1A*
*Mid 1920's-1927*
*Ink Stamp*

**WADE HEATH & CO. LTD.**

WADEHEATH

ENGLAND

*Mark Type 2*
*1928-1937*
*Ink Stamp*

WADEHEATH
ORCADIA
WARE
BRITISH MADE

*Mark Type 2A*
*1928-1934*
*Ink Stamp*

WADEHEATH WARE
MADE IN ENGLAND
MANUFACTURED BY PERMISSION
WALT DISNEY MICKEY MOUSE LTD

*Mark Type 2B*
*1934 - Late 1930's*
*Ink Stamp*

---

WADEHEATH
BY PERMISSION
WALT DISNEY
ENGLAND

*Mark Type 2C*
*Mid 1930's - Late 1930's*
*Ink Stamp*

*Mark Type 2D*
*1934 - Late 1930's*
*Ink Stamp*

WADEHEATH
B
ENGLAND

*Mark Type 3*
*1939-1942*
*Ink Stamp*

Flaxman Ware
Hand Made Pottery
BY WADEHEATH
ENGLAND

*Mark Type 4*
*Circa 1936*
*Ink Stamp*

Wadeheath
Ware
England

*Mark Type 5*
*Circa 1937*
*Ink Stamp*

FLAXMAN
WADE
HEATH
ENGLAND

*Mark Type 6*
*Circa 1937-1938*
*Ink Stamp*

WADE
HEATH
ENGLAND

*Mark Type 7*
*Circa 1938-1950*
*Ink Stamp*

---

WADE
HEATH
ENGLAND

A

*Mark Type 7A*
*1942 - Mid 1940's*
*Ink Stamp*

WADE
HEATH
ENGLAND
J

*Mark Type 7B*
*Circa 1945(?)*
*Ink Stamp*

WADE
HEATH
ENGLAND

*Mark Type 8*
*Circa 1938-1950*
*Ink Stamp*

WADE
HEATH
ENGLAND
A

*Mark Type 8A*
*Circa 1942 - Late 1940's*
*Ink Stamp*

"GOTHIC"
WADE
HEATH
ENGLAND

*Mark Type 9*
*Circa Late 1930's-1950*
*Ink Stamp*

WADE
ENGLAND

*Mark Type 10*
*Circa Late 1940's*
*Ink Stamp*

WADE
MADE IN ENGLAND

*Mark Type 10A*
*Late 1940's*
*Ink Stamp*

WADE
ENGLAND

A

*Mark Type 10B*
*Circa 1945 - Late 1940's*
*Ink Stamp*

WADE
ENGLAND

"GOTHIC"

*Mark Type 11*
*Circa 1948-1954*
*Ink Stamp*

*Mark Type 11A*
*1947 - Mid 1950's*
*Transfer*

*Mark Type 12*
*Circa 1950-1955*
*Ink Stamp*

*Mark Type 12A*
*Circa Mid 1950's - Late 1950's*
*Ink Stamp*

*Mark Type 12B*
*Circa Mid 1950's - Late 1950's*
*Ink Stamp*

*Mark Type 12C*
*Circa Late 1950's*
*Ink Stamp*

*Mark Type 13*
*Circa 1947-Early 1950's*
*Ink Stamp*

WADE
ENGLAND

*Mark Type 14*
*Circa 1947-Early 1950's*
*Ink Stamp*

WADE
ENGLAND

*Mark Type 15*
*Circa 1947-1953*
*Ink Stamp*

*Mark Type 16*
*Circa 1953+*
*Transfer*

*Mark Type 17*
*Circa 1953+*
*Transfer*

*Mark Type 17A*
*1953 - Early 1960's*
*Ink Stamp*

*Mark Type 18*
*Circa 1953+*
*Transfer*

*Mark Type 18A*
*Circa Mid 1950's - 1960's*
*Transfer*

*Mark Type 18B*
*Circa Mid 1950's - 1960's*
*Transfer*

*Mark Type 18C*
*Circa Mid 1950's*
*Ink & Transfer*

WADE
ENGLAND

*Mark Type 19*
*Circa 1953+*
*Transfer*
*(George Wade & Son Ltd.*
*Also Used This Mark*
*From Circa 1953 On.)*

*Mark Type 19A*
*Late 1950's*
*Transfer*

*Mark Type 19B*
*1956 - Early 1960's*
*Transfer*

*Mark Type 19C*
*Circa 1956 - Early 1960's*
*Transfer*

*Mark Type 20*
*1985+*
*Transfer*

## GEORGE WADE & SON LTD.

*Mark Type 20A*
*1931 - Mid 1930's*
*Ink Stamp*

*Mark Type 21*
*Circa Early 1930's-Late 1930's*
*Ink Stamp*

*Mark Type 21A*
*Late 1930's*
*Ink Stamp*

WADE

MADE IN ENGLAND

*Mark Type 22*
*Circa Early 1930's-Late 1930's*
*Hand Painted Ink*

*Mark Type 23*
*Circa 1939*
*Ink Stamp*

*Mark Type 23A*
*1947+*
*Ink Stamp*

WADE

*Porcelain*
*Made in England*

*Mark Type 24*
*1958+*
*Molded*

WADE
PORCELAIN
MADE IN ENGLAND

*Mark Type 25*
*1957-1981*
*Molded*

WADE
MADE IN
ENGLAND

*Mark Type 26*
*1959+*
*Molded*

WADE
MADE IN ENGLAND

*Mark Type 27*
*1958+*
*Molded*

GENUINE
WADE
PORCELAIN

*Mark Type 27A*
*Mid 1980's*
*Transfer*

## WADE CERAMICS LTD.

*Mark Type 27B*
*1990+*
*Transfer*

## WADE (IRELAND) LTD.

*Mark Type 27C*
*Circa 1950+*
*Ink Stamp*

*Mark Type 28*
*1953+*
*Impressed*

*Mark Type 29*
*Mid 1954+*
*Impressed*

*Mark Type 30*
*Mid 1954*
*Transfer*

*Mark Type 31*
*Mid 1950's+*
*Molded*

*Mark Type 32*
*1955*
*Impressed*

*Mark Type 32A*
*Circa - Early 1960's - 1967*
*Transfer*

*Mark Type 32B*
*Circa Early 1960's - 1967*
*Transfer*

*Mark Type 33*
*1962*
*Molded*

*Mark Type 33A*
*1962*
*Moulded*

*Mark Type 34*
*Mid 1960's*
*Molded*

BY WADE
IRELAND

*Mark Type 35*
*1970*
*Impressed*

*Mark Type 36*
*1973*
*Impressed*

WADE
IRELAND

*Mark Type 37*
*1970+*
*Transfer*

MADE IN
IRELAND
BY
WADE

*Mark Type 38*
*Mid 1970's*
*Impressed*

*Mark Type 39*
*1965-1968*
*Impressed*

*Mark Type 40*
*1977+*
*Molded*

*Mark Type 41*
*1980+*
*Molded*
*&*
*Transfer*

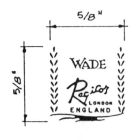

*Mark Type 41A*
*1991*
*Ink Stamp*

## WADE HEATH & CO. LTD.
## &
## REGINALD CORFIELD (SALES) LTD.

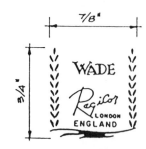

*Mark Type 42*
*1950-1957*
*Transfer*

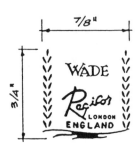

*Mark Type 43*
*1957-1966*
*Transfer*

(NOTE: MARK 43 SIMILAR TO
MARK 42 BUT HEAVIER
LETTERING.)

WADE
Regicor
HAND PAINTED
IN STAFFORDSHIRE
ENGLAND

*Mark Type 43A*
*Circa Early - Mid 1960's*
*Transfer*

*Mark Type 44*
*1962-1968*
*Transfer*

*Mark Type 45*
*1968-1970*
*Transfer*

## WADE (PDM) LTD.

*Mark Type 46*
*1970-1980*
*Transfer*

*Mark Type 47*
*1980+*
*Transfer*

*Mark Type 48*
*1980*
*Transfer*

*Mark Type 49*
*1990+*
*Transfer*

# SPECIAL BACKSTAMPS

*S 1*

*S 2*

*S 3*

*S 4*

*S 5*

*S 6*

S 7

ARABIA
DESIGN
*Myrna*
ENGLAND

S 8

A limited edition of this
Traditional Cider Mug
was reproduced for
Taunton Cider by
Wade Potteries - Staffordshire.

S 9

S 10

S 11

S 12

S 13

S 14

S 15

S 16

# The Belfry Hotel

**HANDFORTH, WILMSLOW**
**Tel . 061-437 0511/6**

# The Stanneylands Hotel

**Wilmslow, Cheshire**
**Tel . 0625 525225**

S 17

S 18

S 19

*Lady Clare*

S 20

S 21

S 22

S 23

S 24

S 25

S 26

S 27

*One of 65 mugs presented in recognition of outstanding devotion to duty at the 1982 TAUNTON CIDER WASSAIL*

S 32

**WADE**
ENGLAND

S 37

*A limited edition of 4000 produced for the TAUNTON CIDER COMPANY by Wade Heath Potteries, Staffordshire, in the year of 1981*

S 28

*500 pairs of these traditional Cider Mugs were reproduced in miniature by Wade Potteries for the TAUNTON CIDER COMPANY 1982*

S 33

*an English Life mug
Designs by Barry Smith and Barbara Wootton exclusively for*

**WADE**
ENGLAND

S 38

*500 of these traditional Cider Mugs were reproduced by Wade Potteries for the TAUNTON CIDER COMPANY 1989*

S 29

*One of 160 mugs presented in recognition of outstanding devotion to duty at Taunton Cider's first OPEN DAY 5th May 1986*

S 34

*ENGLISH LIFE
Designs by Barry Smith and Barbara Wootton exclusively for*

**WADE**
ENGLAND

S 39

S 30

*Valor*

A LIMITED EDITION OF 1000

S 35

by

**WADE**

S 40

*Produced exclusively for the Taunton Cider Company by Wade Potteries of Staffordshire*

S 31

S 36

**The World of Wade**

**Book 2**

**Designers and Modellers**

# DESIGNERS AND MODELLERS.

## JESSICA VAN HALLEN.

Jessica Van Hallen studied design at the Burslem School of Art and later at the Royal College of Art in London. Around 1930, Van Hallen, who was married to a descendant of Henry Hallen, the founder of the pottery that was eventually taken over by George Wade, joined George Wade & Son Ltd. to head a new department to produce decorative figurines. The intent of this new line, an idea of Col. George Wade and developed by Mrs. Van Hallen, was to supplement the then main product of the Manchester Pottery which was industrial porcelain, thereby adding diversity to the limited range of products manufactured at the pottery.

Most famous amongst the Van Hallen figurines are the pre-war, cellulose finished version of Snow White and the Seven Dwarfs. Her designs varied from the traditional crinoline dressed ladies to the then popular Art Deco figurines such as Ginger and Christina.

Van Hallen left George Wade & Son Ltd. shortly before WWII, and, after a short period at other potteries, she eventually became a freelance designer. For additional illustrations of Van Hallen designs for George Wade & Son Ltd. see *The W of W pgs. 10, 11 & 12, FIGS. 1, 2 & 3.*

## FAUST LANG.

Faust Lang, famous for his wood carvings for the Oberammergau Nativity Festival, was engaged by George Wade & Son Ltd. to model the special range of Wade animal and bird figurines presented at the British Industries Fairs from the mid to late 1930's.

Lang carved all his designs from wood which, when finished, were passed over to the mold makers where the master molds for slip-cast production were made. Amongst the many items designed by Faust Lang were the Parrot, Chamois Kid, Stag, Cockatoo, Ermine and Panther. For additional illustrations of Faust Lang designs for George Wade & Son Ltd. see *The W of W pgs. 15 & 16, FIGS. 7 & 8.*

## ROBERT BARLOW.

*Robert Barlow (circa early 1950's).*

After studying at the Burslem School of Art, Robert Barlow joined Wade, Heath & Co. Ltd. as a designer in the latter part of the 1930's. Due to a hearing disability, Barlow was able to carry on at the pottery for the duration of the war years. One of his first major designs was the Orb shape of tableware introduced to the line of tableware just before the start of the war.

In November 1938, for the opening of the new Royal Victoria Pottery showroom, Robert Barlow, in his spare time, had painted a huge mural based on Snow White and the Seven Dwarfs which was then a major selling item for Wade, Heath & Co. Ltd. The mural dominated the new showroom and was much admired by those attending the opening ceremony. Major (later Sir) George Wade presented Robert Barlow with a china posy bowl arrangement of anemones as a "thank you" gift.

After the war, ably assisted by modeller Frank Garbutt and decorator/designer Georgina Lawton, Barlow produced many shapes and decorations for the Wade, Heath lines of tableware. Robert Barlow finished his career at Wade, Heath & Co. Ltd. as Head Designer and Art Director. Amongst his designs were the Quack Quack Nursery Ware, the Peony Line and the Flair Line of Tableware. Barlow also designed a number of figurines for the pottery amongst which were the Quack Quack Family and the Tinker, Tailor, Soldier, Sailor series.

Over the years of publication of the in-house Wade magazine, *The Jolly Potter,* Barlow was a regular contributor

*An advertisement for Wade figures and flowers as it appeared in the February 1939 issue of The Pottery Gazette and Glass Trade Review.*

as designer for the cover pages along with the occasional article.

## NANCY GREAT-REX.

For a number of years after WWII, Nancy Great-Rex worked as a designer at Wade, Heath & Co. Ltd. Although her stay at the pottery was relatively short, she left behind a legacy of a frustratingly difficult set of figurines for today's Wade collectors to acquire. This set is the Butcher, Baker and Candlestick maker.

Great-Rex also contributed a number of highly amusing and decorative cover designs for *The Jolly Potter.*

## WILLIAM HARPER.

*William Harper (Spring 1990).*

William Harper, a prolific designer/modeller for George Wade & Son Ltd. between 1954 and 1962, was born in Newcastle-under-Lyme in 1923. Bill's early life was far from easy, and the tragic death of his mother when he was only two years old had a lasting effect on the little boy's life.

During his school days, Bill excelled at many subjects including art, a subject in which he regularly gained top marks. Toward the end of his school days, Bill also assisted in the production of the school magazine under the direction of the school art master, Mr. Podmore.

After leaving school at fourteen, Bill began working as an apprentice to a tinsmith where he learned to cut, bend and solder metal. This apprenticeship lasted only eighteen months, after which he attended The Elms Technical College in Shelton and private evening classes to learn typing, shorthand and bookkeeping.

After obtaining certificates for all three subjects, Bill gained employment, as a clerk, at Ind Coope's Brewery. By now WWII had started, and one of Bill's chores was to spend nights "fire watching." In 1942, Bill joined the Royal Air Force and became a wireless operator/air gunner. In 1944, Bill was posted overseas ending up in Foggia, Italy.

During his tour of duty in Italy, Bill often attended art classes at the King's Palace in Naples where he gained art experience studying the human form. At the end of the war, the twenty-three year old returned home with no job or real aim in life. Bill decided to enroll as a full time student at the Burslem School of Art where he studied oil painting and pottery.

In 1949, Bill married Jean Williamson, a nurse. With the birth of their first child, Bill and Jean moved to Tunstall where, after raising two more children, they still live.

In 1954, Bill joined George Wade & Son Ltd. where he designed numerous figurines and items of giftware, eventually becoming Head Designer and a junior director. After nine years with the pottery, Bill left to start up his own business in a small rented studio. He designed animal figurines which he sold to zoos and gift stores.

Unfortunately this operation was not a financial success, and Bill was forced to find work as a freelance designer with W.H. Bossons of Congleton, with whom he stayed until 1971. In 1972, Bill became a freelance designer with Royal Doulton, a position which he holds to this day.

William Harper's designs varied between 3/4" high miniatures to teapots designed for the Irish pottery. Amongst the great number of figurines and ornaments designed by Harper are the Early Whimsies, the Walt Disney Hat Box series, the Walt Disney "Blow-Ups," the Noddy series, the Minikins, the Drumbox series, the Flying Bird wall plaques, the T.T. Tray, Silhouette series, Tortoise family, the Treasure Chest box, the Hedgehog box, the Shore Crab box, the Seagull boat, the Bridge, Barge and Swallow posy bowls, the Irish Song Figures and many many more.

In a recent letter, Bill wrote "If I had a favorite piece, it would be the Tortoise, of which many hundreds of thousands were sold, and also displays the Wade techniques to perfection - high detail, simple coloring and translucent glazing."

Following are photographs of a number of pieces developed by William Harper for George Wade & Son Ltd. Not all of these pieces developed beyond the prototype stage but a number, often with changes, did develop into successful giftware lines.

**FIG.1. Prototype Designs by William Harper for George Wade & Son Ltd.**

**A.** **PAIR OF COCKATOOS** - 2-7/8" high by 2-3/4" across.

**B.** **OWLS.** The pair on the left measures 2-3/8" high, and the single owl on the right measures 2" high.

**C.** **DOLEFUL LION** - measures 2" high.

**D.** **THE BUTLIN BEAVER** - measures 2-1/2" high.

**E.** **LONG TAILED DOOR MOUSE** - measures 4-1/4" high. This item was intended to be used as a spirit container.

**F.** **CAT** - measures 2" high.

**G.** **BABYCHAM** - measures 2-7/8" high. This figurine is based on the well known Babycham beverage advertising character.

**H.** **MERMAID BOWL.** The prototype bowl on the left measures 6" high by 11" across. It is shown next to the production model.

**I.** **CARAVAN** - measures 2-1/4" long by 1-5/8" high by 1-1/2" wide.

**J.** **CONTEMPORARY BOWLS.** The bowl on the left measures 2" high by 4" in diameter. The bowl on the right measures 4" high by 3-3/4" in diameter.

K. WALL PLAQUE - measures 6" high by 4" across.
L. BOOK END - measures 6" high.
M. AUSTIN MINI ASHTRAY - measures 1-3/4" high by 4-3/4" long.
N. SCENT HOLDER - measures 3-3/4" high.
O. JACK OF DIAMOND ASHTRAY - measures 4" wide by 4-3/4" long. QUEEN OF SPADES ASHTRAY - measures 4" wide by 4-1/4" long.

FIG.1"A"

FIG.1"B"

FIG.1"C"

FIG.1"D"

FIG.1"E"

FIG.1"F"

FIG.1"G"

FIG.1"K"

FIG.1"H"

FIG.1"I"

FIG.1"L"

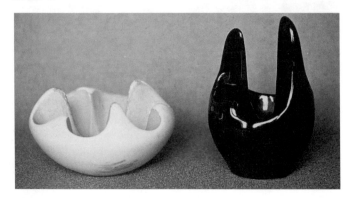

FIG.1"J"

FIG.1"M"

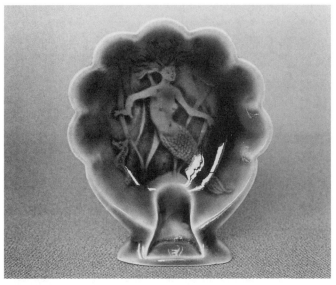

FIG.1"N"

FIG.1"O"

*Ken Holmes (Spring 1990).*

## PAUL ZALMAN.

Paul Zalman was a Hungarian refugee in his mid-thirties, when, in early 1957, he was introduced to Anthony Wade by Burslem studio potter Joseph Szeiler, also of Hungarian ancestry. Zalman stayed with the Wade potteries for only a short time, and his best known designs for the pottery are the Mabel Lucie Attwell figurines of Sam and Sarah and the Ascot bowl.

## LESLIE MCKINNON.

McKinnon was the granddaughter of one-time British prime minister Ramsay MacDonald. Her best known designs produced for George Wade & Son Ltd. during her short stay at the pottery were the Happy Family series and the London Characters set.

## KEN HOLMES.

Ken Holmes began his career as an apprentice mold maker with a Longton pottery. After experience with a number of local potteries, work became hard to find in the field of potting so Ken was forced to look elsewhere for employment. This new work took the form of employment in the coal mines and, after that, as a brick layer's laborer. When business at the potteries improved, Ken was able to resume his career as a mold maker, soon becoming the youngest head mold maker in the area.

After a number of years of experience, Ken eventually became a block maker with the Royal Doulton Pottery. It was here that he first came in contact with designer Alan Mazlankowski. In the mid 1970's, Mazlankowski left Doulton and went to work for Wade Potteries where he designed the Survival and Connoisseur series. It was soon after this that Ken left Doulton to take up a position as a block maker at George Wade & Son Ltd.

Part of Ken's job at Wade was to create and develop ideas that might appeal to potential customers. Many of the prototypes produced from these ideas were rarely used but, on occasion, some were resurrected for later use by clients of the pottery.

Ken was closely involved with the production of one of the Wade potteries' most adventurous items, the magnificent Thompson's Gazelle and Cheetah. This was sculpted by Mazlankowski but taken from the model stage through to the production stage by Ken Holmes. The care and knowledge needed for firing such a complicated piece of pottery was made somewhat easier by Ken's long and varied experience in potting.

In the mid 1980's, Ken became the head modeller for George Wade & Son Ltd. Amongst Ken's designs for the pottery are the Thornton's Van and later the Tetley Tea and Coffee Van money boxes; the Tetley Tea Brew Gaffer and Sidney salt and pepper shakers; the My Fair Ladies sets 1 & 2 and the Sophisticated Ladies; the new range of pressed Dinosaurs; and the new range of limited collectables Pets and Children.

Much of Ken's work is to bespoke customers for instance, the commemorative knight for the Order of the Knights Templer, a retriever for Debenham's Department Store, the bride and groom wedding cake decoration for Dunbar's of Scotland, London Taxi, Equestrian figure of Robert the Bruce for a whisky container, and the St. Bernard dog key ring for St. Bruno Tobacco, etc.

# BARBARA COOKSEY.

Designer Barbara Cooksey joined Wade Ceramics in 1985 at the Royal Victoria Pottery when it was still operating under the name of Wade, Heath & Co. Limited.

After studying art and ceramics in Birmingham and Stoke-on-Trent, Barbara obtained a BA in Three Dimensional Design at Birmingham Polytechnic, specializing in ceramics and glass and a Master of Arts Degree in

*Barbara Cooksey (Spring 1990).*

Ceramic Design from North Staffordshire Polytechnic in Stoke-on-Trent. In the early days of her career, Barbara gained some work experience in the design department at Royal Worcester and some experience demonstrating china painting at the Gladstone Pottery Museum.

Barbara Cooksey has exhibited examples of her work at the "Class of 82" exhibition of Coleridge of Highgate, London, the Summer Exhibition at Keele University and at the Young Blood Exhibition, the Barbican Centre in London.

Since joining Wade, Barbara has worked as a designer in Shape and Surface patterns for Earthenware, China and Tableware and also for promotions and incentives. Amongst Barbara's designs for tableware are "Summer Fruits," "Meadowland," "Tutti-Fruitti," both plain and decorated; "The Rose Trellis" and "Fuchsia" line of teapots, mugs, vases, planters, jugs and picture frames; "Floral Fayre" teapots and mugs along with various items in the "Herb Collection"; "Floral Rhapsody," "Charlotte" and "Rose" designs. Barbara also designed the "Kingsware" range, the "Wadeland Fire Engine Company" teapot and the "Potblack and Golf Bag" teapots made exclusively for Debenham's Department Store.

Recently, Barbara completed the designs for the new "Dinosaur" range which were then modelled by Ken Holmes. Barbara finds it hard to single out one item as her favorite; however, she is especially fond of her "Meadowland" pattern used on a line of tableware. The hand-painted "Tutti-Fruitti" is also a favorite of Barbara's as each piece was individually decorated and was reminiscent of the earlier hand-painted ware that Wade once made.

# JUDITH WOOTEN.

After spending most of her school days in the Stoke-on-Trent and Newcastle-under-Lyme areas, Judith graduated from the Newcastle College of Further Education and School of Art in Newcastle-under-Lyme in the subjects of Art History, Ceramic Design and Art. Between 1986 - 1988 Judith studied at the North Staffordshire Polytechnic in Stoke-on-Trent where she obtained a National Diploma in Industrial Ceramic Design and Technology.

Judith first came in contact with Wade Ceramics in late 1987 where, as part of her course with the North Staffordshire Polytechnic, she was required to complete a six-week placement at Wade Potteries PLC. After completing this assignment, Judith was offered the opportunity of working for Wade two to three days a week whilst finishing her studies, after which, she was to be offered a full time position with the pottery.

Judith has exhibited her work at a number of places including The New Designers (1989) Exhibition at the Business Design Centre in London. She assisted in the dressing of the stand at the International Spring Fairs at the NEC Birmingham in 1988, 1989, 1990 and 1991. Judith was invited to participate in the "Isetan British Fair" in Tokyo, Japan, in 1990.

In June 1988, Judith began work, on a full-time basis, at Wade Ceramics Ltd. as a ceramic designer. Judith's responsibilities include organizing and arranging local showcases, designing products for Wade's open range and spending much of her time between October and February developing new product lines with various stores for the next Christmas season.

Amongst Judith Wooten's designs for Wade Ceramics are the design and production of all artwork for the "English Life" range teapots and tea caddies taken from the original hand-built teapots by Barbara Wooten (no relation) and Barry Smith, the designs and illustrations for the "Cockleshell Cove" teapots, the "Wedding" teapot, the "Owl & Pussycat" teapots, the "Clown" teapots and the "Christmas" teapots.

Judith has designed many items for the Boots Department Store including the "Cat Burglar" range, the "House Mouse" range, the "Goose Fair" range and most recently the "Gymkhana," "Dressage," "White Rabbit" and "Drummer Boy" teapots.

# THE WADE EXPERIMENTAL POTTERY STUDIO.

In 1950, Sir George Wade, then Col. George Wade, quietly established an experimental pottery studio located at the Manchester Pottery, Burslem. At that time very little was known in the pottery business about this experiment, and it was not until around 1952 that it became a matter for public knowledge.

The aim of the studio was to develop, without the restrictions of market requirements and generally accepted ideas of design, unique pieces of ornamental pottery. In other words, it was to promote potting for personal pleasure rather than for economic considerations.

Col. Wade, himself a pioneer in the field of potting, gathered around him two creative talents to help develop his ideas. First brought in was designer/modeller Colin Melbourne, an exciting young designer, then in his early 20's, who had studied at the Royal College of Art in London and at the Stoke College of Art. Also recruited was H.T. Robinson, Technical Director of George Wade & Son Ltd., an expert in material and colors. Together, these three men went about creating and developing alternative designs and methods of pottery production to the then well established machine-made or mass-produced pottery of the period.

Subject matter for designs evolved through a procedure of discussions between Wade, Melbourne and Robinson which resulted in numerous sketches of the ideas eventually decided upon. The final ideas consisted mainly of the human form, birds or animals and abstract forms.

Most ideas and preliminary models were scrapped in the early stages of development, but one item that progressed through to fruition was "IVY" or, to give her her correct title, "Festival 51." For an illustration of "IVY" see the photograph below. This was a symbolic figure created by Col. Wade and Colin Melbourne to represent their ideas and feelings for the 1951 Festival of Britain. The figure was exhibited, to much astonishment and maybe horror by the establishment, at the "Festival of Britain" exhibition at

Kings Hall, Stoke-on-Trent. Today, "IVY" sits quietly on a tiled plinth in the main vestibule of the Manchester Pottery. She is a lasting reminder of the little-known George Wade Experimental Pottery.

*A series of models from the Experimental Pottery. From left to right. Back row. "The Business Man," "Spring Morning." Front row. "An Abstract Figure" designed by Robert Barlow and modelled by Colin Melbourne and one from a group of "Two Vegetable Forms."*

*George Wade (right) and Colin Melbourne (left) with "IVY."*

# FIGURINES.

By George Wade & Son Ltd.,

Wade, Heath & Co. Ltd. and

Wade Ceramics Ltd.

circa 1927 - 1993.

# "VAN HALLEN" FIGURINES

*circa 1927 - early 1950's.*

Between the late 1920's and the late 1930's, George Wade & Son Ltd., at their Manchester Pottery, produced a variety of Classic and Art Deco figurines designed by Jessica Van Hallen, a talented designer and modeller specially brought in by George Wade to head up a new department to produce figural giftware.

The "Van Hallen" figurines proved to be extremely popular with both the buying public and the trade. The figurines were colorful and inexpensive, a highly desirable combination during the dark years of the Depression Era. Exquisitely designed, they were expertly described in a 1938 trade magazine as "...examples of the beauty and grace, combined with virility and sense of action..."

The figurines first appeared at a major trade show at Kelvin Hall, Glasgow, in the early 1930's. Thereafter, they appeared regularly at the British Industries Fairs then held at Olympia, London, often displayed "en-masse." For example, one exhibit displayed rows of the "Ginger" figurine forming a china chorus line.

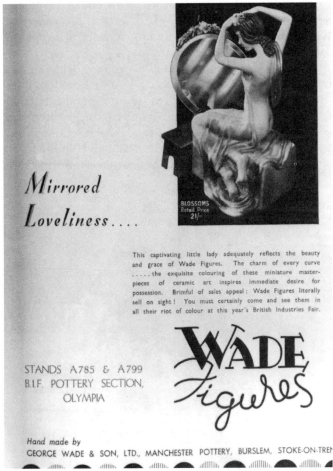

*An advertisement for Wade figures as it appeared in the February 1938 issue of The Pottery Gazette and Glass Trade Review.*

The "Scintillite" figurines were made in a similar manner as regular china until after the first firing. They were then decorated with the patented scintillite finish, which was described as "...a very full pallet of colorings, rich in their texture and delicacy." The finish was described as a "...cellulose spraying, claimed to be equal to the fine finish of a motor car body..." Unfortunately, this did not prove to be quite the case as, over the years, this finish often turned yellow and cracked leaving these figurines in a less than satisfactory condition. Today, Van Hallen figurines are highly prized by Wade collectors. However, collectors should be aware that only figures in a very good condition are worth the high prices asked.

In the late 1930's, a number of the Van Hallen figurines were issued in an underglaze version such as Juliette and Romance which are illustrated in the color section. In the early 1950's, a very small number of the Van Hallen figurines were produced and finished with an underglaze decoration and presented to Wade staff members on special occasions such as retirement, etc. See the photograph of Mrs. Alice Edge from the *Winter 1956 issue of The Jolly Potter.*

*Mrs. Alice Edge at her retirement in 1956, after twenty-one years of service as a figurine caster for Wade, Heath & Co. Ltd.*

In one of our conversations with the late Mrs. Georgina Lawton, she spoke of, and showed us, an underglaze version of Curtsey (*See The W of W. pg. 11*) that she herself had decorated in 1952. Another of these "special occasion" figures, also decorated by Mrs. Lawton is No.412 in the color section.

No. 1.   JOYCE - with cellulose type finish and Mark Type 21 (without the word figure) on the base. The figurine is 7-1/4" high.

No. 2.   PEGGY - with cellulose type finish and Mark Type 21 (without the word figure) on the base. The figurine is 6-3/4" high.

No. 3.   COLORADO - with cellulose type finish and Mark Type 21 on the base. The figurine is 10" high.

No. 4.   ZENA - (miniature version) with cellulose type finish and Mark Type 21 on the base. The figurine is 4" high.

No. 5.   CHRISTINA - with cellulose type finish and Mark Type 21 on the base. The figurine is 11" high.

No. 6.   MARIA THERESA - with cellulose type finish and Mark Type 21 on the base. The figurine is 8" high.

No. 7.   STRAWBERRY GIRL - with cellulose type finish and is marked Wade on the base. The figurine is 5-1/4" high.

No. 8.    CLAUDE - with cellulose type finish and Mark Type 20A on the base. The figurine is 7-3/4" high.

No. 9.    TESSA - with cellulose type finish and Mark Type 21 on the base. The figurine is 4-3/4" high.

No. 10.   ELF 2 - with cellulose type finish and Mark Type 21 on the base. The figurine is 3-3/4" high.

No. 11.   HIAWATHA - with cellulose type finish and Mark Type 21 on the base. The figurine is 3-3/4" high.

No. 12.   DELIGHT - with cellulose type finish and Mark Type 20A on the base. The figurine is 3" high.

FIG.2.

## SNOW WHITE AND THE SEVEN DWARFS *1938.*

Designed by Jessica Van Hallen, these figurines were advertised in trade magazines as "...these little gems of pottery cannot fail to capture the imagination..." The original price for the complete set was 21 shillings. Each of the cellulose type finished figurines has Mark Type 21 on the base but without the word "figures." The name of the character portrayed is also included on the base.

No. 13.   SNOW WHITE - measures  6-3/8" high.

No. 14.   SLEEPY - measures 4" high.

No. 15.   SNEEZY - measures 3-3/4" high.

No. 16.   BASHFUL - measures 3-3/4" high.

No. 17.   DOC -  measures 4" high.

No. 18.   DOPEY - measures 3-3/4" high.

No. 19.   HAPPY - measures 4" high.

No. 20.   GRUMPY -  measures 3-1/2" high.

## "VAN HALLEN" Figurines continued.

No. 21.   JULIETTE- with underglaze type finish and Mark Type 21A. The figurine is 9-1/2" high and has the following written on the base in blue ink: Norma Shearer, star of M.G.M. in the Production of "Romeo & Juliet" Made in England.

No. 22.   PAVLOVA-with cellulose type finish and Mark Type 21on the base. The figurine is 9" high.

No. 23.   CARMEN-with cellulose type finish and Mark Type 21 on the base. The figurine is 9-3/4" high.

No. 24.   SPRINGTIME-with cellulose type finish and Mark Type 21 on the base. This figurine is 9-1/4" high.

No. 25.   ROMANCE-with underglaze type finish and Mark Type 21A on the base. The figurine is 6-1/2" high.

No. 26.   PHYLLIS-with cellulose type finish and Mark Type 21 on the base. The figurine is 5-1/4" high.

FIG.2.     CURLS - with cellulose type finish and Mark Type 21 on the base. The figurine is 6" high.

## ASPREY & CO. DECANTER

*circa early 1930's.*

Asprey & Co. was established in Mitchum, a suburb of London, in 1781 by William Asprey. In 1847, the company relocated to 166 New Bond Street, London, where it remains to this day.

The company was, and still is, renowned for its high quality products such as gentlemen's and ladies' dressing cases, sterling silver flatware and tableware, jewelry and gold and silver ornaments.

The "Scotsman" whisky decanter was produced by

Wade for Asprey & Co. circa the early 1930's. This decanter had previously been produced for Asprey & Co. in the late 1920's by Royal Doulton along with a matching "Irishman" decanter containing Irish whisky. It is most probable that Wade also produced the matching "Irishman" decanter but to-date, an example has not surfaced.

The original design for the "Scotsman" decanter was registered at the Patent Office, Trade Mark Register under the No. 675853 and described as "The novelty claimed is in the shape or configuration and pattern of the earthenware bottle as shown." The date of registration was April 21, 1920 and the applicant was Arthur William Hilling of 166, New Bond Street, London. We assume from this that

FIG.3.

FIG.4.

Hilling was a designer employed by Asprey & Co. at that time.

On the same date, application was also made for registration under No. 675852, again described as for the decanter noted above. The design in the form of a line drawing represents a figural bottle of a male person in farm worker type clothing with a pipe stuck in the band of the hat and a kerchief tied around the neck.

FIG.3.    "SCOTSMAN" Decanter.

FIG.4.    "SCOTSMAN" Decanter Base.

# NURSERY RHYME FIGURINES

*circa 1948 - 1958.*

An illustrated article in the January 1948 issue of *The Pottery Gazette and Glass Trade Review,* shows the three earthenware figures, Wynken, Blynken and Nod from the Nursery Rhyme of that name along with the additional figure of "I've a Bear Behind" which was described as "...having a quaint humour all its own." These figurines were decorated with hand-made flowers on the base and were marked with the Wade, Heath & Co. Ltd. Mark Type 10.

These four figurines were produced at the Royal Victoria Pottery by Wade, Heath & Co. Ltd. over a number of years. They were produced in the early years for export only (1948 - 1952) and later for both the export and home markets. After 1952, the figurines, still produced at the Royal Victoria Pottery, were made without flowers around the base. These later versions were marked with Mark Type 19 on the underside of the base.

Two figurines made of plaster and decorated with a cellulose-type finish are believed, by the authors and Wade personnel, to be prototype versions of Blynken and Wynken and are illustrated in the color section as Nos. 85 and 86. A third figurine, Nod (2-5/8" high) has also surfaced but is not illustrated. Production versions of the figurines appeared on the market so soon after the end of the

WW II that it is more than likely the prototypes were made in the late 1930's when the cellulose-type finish was still being used.

No. 27.    WYNKEN (without flowers) - measures 2-3/4" high with Mark Type 19 on the base.

No. 28.    BLYNKEN (without flowers) - measures 2-1/8" high with Mark Type 19 on the base.

No. 29.    WYNKEN (with flowers) - measures 2-3/4" high with Mark Type 10 on the base.

No. 30.    BLYNKEN (with flowers) - measures 2-1/8" high with Mark Type 10 on the base.

No. 31.    NOD (with flowers) - measures 2-1/2" high with Mark Type 10 on the base.

No. 32.    I'VE A BEAR BEHIND (with flowers) - measures 2-1/2" high with Mark Type 10 on the base.

The Butcher, Baker and Candlestick Maker figurines were designed by Nancy Great-Rex and produced between the early and mid-1950's. Nancy Great-Rex also designed a number of other figures for Wade as well as many covers for the company magazine, *The Jolly Potter*. Of the three figurines, the Candlestick Maker is the most difficult to find with the Butcher turning up more frequently. These figurines have been found with both Mark Types 15 and 19.

No. 33.    CANDLESTICK MAKER - measures 4" high with Mark Type 19 on the base.

FIG.5.    A. BUTCHER - measures 3-1/4" high with Mark Type 19 on the base.
B. BAKER - measures 3-7/8" high with Mark Type 19 on the base.
C. CANDLESTICK MAKER (See No. 33).

FIG.5.

No. 34.    MOMMA BEAR - measures 3-3/4" high with Mark Type 19 on the base.

No. 35.    BABY BEAR - measures 1-3/4" high with Mark Type 19 on the base.

No. 36.    POPPA BEAR - measures 3-1/2" high with Mark Type 19 on the base. *(For Goldilocks, see The W of W No.6, pg.33).*

*Nursery Rhyme Figurines by Wade, Heath & Co. Ltd. An advertisement from the January 1953 issue of the Pottery Gazette and Glass Trade Review.*

**No. 37.   SOLDIER** - measures 3" high with Mark Type 15 on the **base.** *(For Tinker, Tailor, Sailor, Rich Man, Poor Man, Beggar Man and Thief, see The W of W Nos. 10 - 16 pg.33).*

# THE NODDY SET *1958 - 1960.*

When the NODDY series was introduced in 1958 by George Wade & Son Ltd., the company described the series as "Enid Blyton's famous Noddy characters, from the screen to your counter. Packed to attract. The four Noddy characters are individually packed in presentation boxes - they each have their own distinguishing color. They're so well made...by Wade of England."

*THE NODDY SERIES from the September 1958 issue of The Pottery Gazette and Glass Trade Review.*

No. 38. **BIG EARS** - measures 2-3/4" high and is unmarked, although it originally would have had a paper label.

No. 39. **MR. PLOD** - measures 2-1/2" high and is unmarked. As with Big Ears, originally it would also have had a paper label.

Other figurines in the set were: Miss. Fluffy Cat *(See The W of W No.49 pg.34)* and Noddy *(See The W of W FIG.27 pg.29)*. The Noddy Set "© Darrell Waters Ltd."

## SNIPPETS *1956 - 1958.*

A series of porcelain figures and ships made by George Wade & Son Ltd. modelled in the form of paper "cut-out"

type of figures. Set One consisted of three figures from the Hansel and Gretel children story. Set two comprised of models of the three ships which sailed with Christopher Columbus in search for the Americas in 1492. See also Nos. 91-96 in the color section.

No. 40. **GRETEL** - measures 2-1/4" high and has a transfer mark "WADE 'SNIPPET' No.5 'GRETEL' REAL PORCELAIN MADE IN ENGLAND."

## MABEL LUCIE ATTWELL CHARACTERS *1959.*

A set of two porcelain figurines produced by George Wade & Son Ltd. based on the popular Mabel Lucie Attwell illustrations. These two figurines were designed by Paul Zalman, a Hungarian refugee who worked at the Wade Potteries for a very short time in the late 1950's.

Copyright of the Mabel Lucie Attwell illustrations is owned by the "Mabel Lucie Attwell Estate."

No. 41. **SAM** - measures 3-1/8" high by 3" long and is mold - marked "WADE PORCELAIN-MABEL LUCIE ATTWELL © MADE IN ENGLAND."

No. 42. **SARAH** - measures 3" high by 4" long and is mold - marked "WADE PORCELAIN-MABEL LUCIE ATTWELL © MADE IN ENGLAND."

## ALPHABET TRAIN - *1958 - 1959.*

Trade literature describes this children's set, made by George Wade & Son Ltd. as "Educational and Ornamental." The multicolored engine and cars are decorated with letters of the alphabet on the sides and either letters or numbers on the roof of the cars. Sets were also made with illustrations of famous London scenes on the sides of the cars. The engine is approx. 1" high by 2" long and the cars, 3/4" high by 1" long.

FIG.6. **THE ALPHABET TRAIN** - consisting of six cars and the engine.

FIG.7. **ALPHABET TRAIN ENGINE AND CAR** - single glaze, undecorated version.

## BISTO-KIDS *circa mid 1970's.*

These two figures were designed by George Wade & Son Ltd. in Burslem, England, but were actually made in the Irish pottery, Wade (Ireland) Ltd. The figures, in the

**FIG.6.**

**FIG.7.**

form of salt and pepper shakers, were based on advertising characters for "BISTO" made by the Rank, Hovis McDougall Foods Company.

No. 43.   **BISTO-KID SALT SHAKER (GIRL)** - measures 4-3/8" high and is marked "©RHM FOODS LTD. & Applied Creativity - WADE Staffordshire."

No. 44.   **BISTO-KID PEPPER SHAKER (BOY)** - measures 4" high and is marked "©RHM FOODS LTD. & Applied Creativity - WADE Staffordshire."

# NURSERY FAVORITES *1990 - 1991.*

A limited re-issue of five of the popular Nursery Favorite figurines was made by Wade for a U.S. based customer. These figurines, although from the same molds as the original George Wade & Son Ltd. issue, are all marked with the year of manufacture, thus enabling collectors to differentiate between the originals and the re-issues. See also section on Reproductions and Re-issues.

No. 45.   **MARY MARY** - measures 2-7/8" high and is mold-marked WADE ENGLAND 90.

No. 46.   **POLLY KETTLE** - measures 2-7/8" high and is mold-marked WADE ENGLAND 90.

No. 47.   **TOM PIPER** - measures 2-3/4" high by 2" long and is mold-marked WADE ENGLAND 90.

No. 48.   **GOOSEY GANDER** measures 2-5/8" high and is mold-marked WADE ENGLAND 91.

No. 49.   **OLD WOMAN IN THE SHOE** - measures 2-1/2" high by 2-1/8" long and is mold-marked WADE ENGLAND 91.

# TETLEY TEA SALT & PEPPER SHAKERS *1990 - 1992.*

The Brew Gaffer & Sidney Teafolk salt & pepper pots produced by Wade Ceramics Ltd. were offered as promotional items by Lyons Tetley between October 14, 1990 and December 31, 1992. These items were obtained by submitting three tokens from the catering packs of Lyons Tetley Tea Bags.

No. 50.   **BREW GAFFER SALT** - measures 3-1/2" high with Mark Type 27B on the base.

No. 51.   **SYDNEY PEPPER** - measures 3-3/4" high with Mark Type 27B on the base.

# SOPHISTICATED LADIES *1991 - 1992.*

This set of four hand-decorated figurines by Wade Ceramics Ltd. had a very short life. Wade named this set, Sophisticated Ladies; however, collectors will note that the figurines are marked My Fair Ladies on the base. A number of these figurines have been found with the backstamp along with the figure name omitted. This set has also been found, undecorated, with an all-over white glaze.

No. 52.   **FELICITY** - measures 6" high with Mark Type 27B on the base.

No. 53.   **SUSANNAH** - measures 6" high with Mark Type 27B on the base.

No. 54.   **EMILY** - measures 5-3/4" high with Mark Type 27B on the base.

No. 55.   **ROXANNE** - measures 5-3/4" high with Mark Type 27B on the base.

**FIG.8.**

**FIG.9.**

**FIG.8.**   **SOPHISTICATED LADIES** with all over White Glaze. Emily and Susannah. Both figurines have Mark Type 27B on the base.

**FIG.9.**   **SOPHISTICATED LADIES** with all over White Glaze. Felicity and Roxanne. Both figurines have Mark Type 27B on the base.

## MY FAIR LADIES SET ONE *1990 - 1992.*

Slip cast figurines under the name My Fair Ladies, were reintroduced in 1990 by Wade Ceramics Ltd. There were four designs, each design decorated in two different colorways, for a total of eight figurines in the set. The figurines are marked with a grey transfer type mark on the base reading My Fair Ladies Fine Porcelain Wade Made in England, along with the name of the figurine.

No. 56.  KATE - measures 3-7/8" high with Mark Type 27B (modified) on the base.

No. 57.  RACHEL - measures 3-7/8" high with Mark Type 27B (modified) on the base.

No. 58.  MARIE - measures 3-3/4" high with Mark Type 27B (modified) on the base.

No. 59.  SARAH - measures 3-3/4" high with Mark Type 27B (modified) on the base.

No. 60.  LISA - measures 3-3/4" high with Mark Type 27B (modified) on the base.

No. 61.  HANNAH - measures 3-3/4" high with Mark Type 27B (modified) on the base.

No. 62.  CAROLINE - measures 3-7/8" high with Mark Type 27B (modified) on the base.

No. 63.  REBECCA - measures 3-7/8" high with Mark Type 27B (modified) on the base.

## MY FAIR LADIES SET TWO *1991 - 1992.*

This second set of the My Fair Ladies series had four designs, each design decorated in two different colorways, for a total of eight figurines in the set. The transfer type mark on the base is similar to that of set one but in a bright red color.

No. 64.  BELINDA - measures 3-3/4" high with Mark Type 27B (modified) on the base.

No. 65.  ANITA - measures 3-3/4" high with Mark Type 27B (modified) on the base.

No. 66.  EMMA - measures 4" high with Mark Type 27B (modified) on the base.

No. 67.  NATALIE - measures 4" high with Mark Type 27B (modified) on the base.

No. 68.  MELISSA - measures 4" high with Mark Type 27B (modified) on the base.

No. 69.  AMANDA - measures 4" high with Mark Type 27B (modified) on the base.

No. 70.  LUCY - measures 3-3/4" high with Mark Type 27B (modified) on the base.

No. 71.  DIANE - measures 3-3/4" high with Mark Type 27B (modified) on the base.

## MY FAIR LADIES LIQUOR CONTAINERS *1992.*

A number of each figurine from Sets One and Two of The My Fair Ladies figurines were purchased by Hebrides Scotch Whisky and used as whisky containers and distributed in the U.S. through a mail order catalogue company. Each figure had an applied label on the back reading:

Hebrides Scotch Whisky Glasgow 3cl 40% vol. 30 ml (04896)-549. The hole in the base, left from the slip casting process, was corked and sealed with a silicon type compound.

FIG.10.

FIG.10.  SARAH (set 1) and MELISSA (set 2) showing the applied whisky label.

## ICI MAN *circa late 1960's.*

This figurine was produced by George Wade & Son Ltd. to promote the drug Atromid-S in the UK and Regelan, its counterpart marketed in Germany. This antihyperlipidemic agent is used as an adjunct to diet for the reduction of severely elevated plasma lipids in patients who do not respond to diet for weight loss.

No. 72.  ICI MAN - measures 3-1/8" high and is mold-marked on the back ATROMIDIN WADE ENGLAND along with the ICI trade mark. A larger, 8-1/2" high figurine with an all-over blue glaze was also produced. This larger figurine is mold marked Wade England on the back along with a rectangle, presumably to display the name of the advertised product.

## SHERWOOD FOREST SERIES *1989 - 1990.*

These limited edition figurines were produced by George Wade & Son Ltd. and Wade Ceramics Ltd. for POS-NER Associates of Canada in quantities of 5,000 figurines per model. Each of these die-cast figurines is mold-marked MIANCO®, the registered trade mark of POS-NER Associates, followed by the year of issue.

No. 73.  ROBIN HOOD (1989) - measures 2-3/4" high and is mold-marked MIANCO'89 WADE ENGLAND around the base.

No. 74.  MAID MARIAN (1990) - measures 2-5/8" high and is mold-marked MIANCO'90 WADE ENGLAND around the base.

No. 75.  FRIAR TUCK - measures 1-3/4" high. The figurine illustrated is a prototype model.

## AQUARIUM SET *circa 1976 - 1980.*

A set of six die-cast figurines were produced by George Wade & Son Ltd. for King British Aquarium Accessories Ltd. The Lighthouse, Seahorse, Mermaid and Bridge were purchased in September 1976 and the Diver and Snail in February 1977. Equal quantities of each model were produced over a period of 3-4 years. The company also purchased, from Wade, a number of the Crocodile, Turtle, Frog and Seal miniature figurines which had been used for the Red Rose Tea promotions. Of the six figurines specifically made for King British Aquarium Accessories Ltd., the Seahorse and Snail (in this order) are the most difficult to find. *(For the Diver and Mermaid see The W of W Nos.23 and 24 pg.33).* See also Nos. 311, 312, 313, 314 and 315, in this book, for further prototype models of the Seahorse.

No. 76.   LIGHTHOUSE - measures 3" high with 1-1/4" dia. meter base. The figurine is mold-marked, around the edge of the base, WADE ENGLAND.

No. 77.   SNAIL - measures 1-1/4" high. The figurine is mold-marked around the base, WADE ENGLAND.

No. 78.   SEAHORSE - measures 3-1/4" high. This is a prototype figurine.

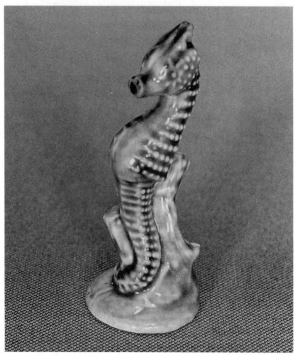

FIG.11.

FIG.11.   SEAHORSE - measures 3" high and is mold-marked WADE ENGLAND around the base. This is an illustration of the production model.

No. 79.   BRIDGE - measures 2-3/4" high by 3-5/8" across the span. The figurine is mold-marked, WADE ENGLAND with WADE appearing on one side of the bridge and ENGLAND on the other.

## HARRODS DOOR MAN *1991.*

This hollow, slip cast, figurine manufactured by Wade Ceramics Ltd. is described by the company as an "egg cup" but it could easily pass as a pencil holder for desktop use.

No. 80.   HARRODS DOOR MAN - measures 4" high and is marked with a transfer type mark, Harrods KNIGHTS-BRIDGE.

## MISCELLANEOUS FIGURINES
*early 1930's - 1993.*

No. 81.   DAISETTE - with cellulose type finish and Mark Type 21 on the base. The figurine measures 9-3/4" high.

No. 82.   "WELSH LADY" HANDLE - measures 3-1/2" high and has a mark type similar to Mark Type 22 around the inside of the base (see Fig. 12). This figurine was originally used as a handle for a pin cushion in the shape of a lady's skirt.

FIG.12.

FIG.12.   "WELSH LADY" HANDLE illustrating the mark type.

No. 83.   KING HENRY VIII - with cellulose type finish and marked: Henry VIII Wade England, on the underside of the base. The figurine is 4-1/2" high.

No. 84.   QUEEN ELIZABETH - with cellulose type finish and marked: Queen Elizabeth Pageant Made in England, on the underside of the base. The figurine is 4-3/8" high.

FIG.13.   KING HENRY VIII AND QUEEN ELIZABETH illustrating the mark type.

No. 85.   BLYNKEN - with cellulose type finish. This prototype figurine measures 2-1/8" high and is unmarked.

No. 86.   WYNKEN - with cellulose type finish. This prototype figurine measures 2-3/4" high and is unmarked.

No. 87.   "SPANISH LADY" HANDLE - measures 3-7/8" high and has a mark type similar to Mark Type 22 around the inside of the base. This figurine was originally used as a handle for a pin cushion in the shape of a lady's skirt.

No. 88.   FAIRY CANDLEHOLDER - measures 3" high and is marked Made in Ireland by Wade Co. Armagh. See also FIGS. 172 and 173 in the section on Wade (Ireland) Ltd. in this book.

FIG.13.

FIG.14.

No. 89.  "FAT CONTROLLER" - measures 2" high. This was a prototype proposed for the Thomas the Tank Engine series. At least three variations of the "Fat Controller" were made at the prototype stage. These variations were different in both size and decoration.

No. 90.  BURGLAR (1993) - measures 3-1/4" high and is mold marked Wade on the underside of the base. This slip cast figurine was made by Wade Ceramics Ltd. in a limited edition of 2,000 for Elaine and Adrian Crumpton. Other figurines proposed for the set are a Policeman (see FIG.14) a High Court Judge and a Prisoner.

FIG.14.  POLICE MAN (1993) - measures 3-5/8" high and is mold-marked Wade on the underside of the base. This slip-cast which has dark blue uniform and black boots was made for Elaine and Adrian Crumpton in a limited edition of 2,000 pieces. See also FIG. 219.

No. 91.  GINGY - measures 1-3/8" high and has a transfer mark "WADE 'SNIPPET' No.6 'GINGY' REAL PORCELAIN MADE IN ENGLAND".

No. 92.  GRETEL - measures 2-1/4" high and has a transfer mark "WADE 'SNIPPET' No.5 'GRETEL' REAL PORCELAIN MADE IN ENGLAND". See also No. 40 in the color section.

No. 93.  HANSEL - measures 2-1/2" high and has a transfer mark "WADE 'SNIPPET' No.4 'HANSEL' REAL PORCELAIN MADE IN ENGLAND."

No. 94.  REVENGE - measures 1-1/2" high by 1-3/4" wide and has a transfer mark "WADE 'SNIPPET' No.3 'REVENGE' REAL PORCELAIN MADE IN ENGLAND."

No. 95.  SANTA MARIA - measures 1-3/4" high by 2" wide and has a transfer mark "WADE 'SNIPPET' No.2 'SANTA MARIA' REAL PORCELAIN MADE IN ENGLAND."

No. 96.  MAYFLOWER - measure 2-3/8" high by 2-1/2" wide and has a transfer mark "WADE 'SNIPPET' No.1 'MAYFLOWER' REAL PORCELAIN MADE IN ENGLAND." For further information on the Wade Snippets, see page 41.

## KNIGHT TEMPLAR *1991.*

The original design for this figurine was a special order to commemorate 200 years of The Great Priory of England and Wales. The original figurine was mounted on a wooden base and had the following inscription on the face of the porcelain base: 1791 - CHRISTI ET TEMPLI SALOMORIS + RAVPERES COMMILITONES 1991. The following inscription appeared on the underside of the base: Made Exclusively for The Great Priory of England and Wales and its Provinces Overseas by Wade Ceramics to Commemorate 1791 - The Bicentenary - 1991.

In 1991, permission was given to Wade Ceramics Ltd. to produce a limited edition of one hundred figurines for the Potteries Centre for members of their Wade Collectors Club.

This slip cast figurine is marked with the issue number out of one hundred e.g. the figure illustrated is marked 25 of 100. There is some variation on the decoration used on the original and special order figurines. See FIG.15.

No. 97. KNIGHT TEMPLAR (1991) - measures 9-5/8" high and has Mark Type 27A on the base along with the wording Limited Edition No.25 of 100 Issued December 1991.

FIG.15.

FIG.15.   KNIGHT TEMPLAR (1991). The original figurine presented to members of the order.

## ROBERTSON'S GOLLIES *early to mid 1960's.*

A set of eight porcelain figurines by George Wade & Son Ltd. feature the Robertson's marmalade trade mark "Golliwog" playing various musical instruments. Each figurine has "Robertson" mold-marked on the front of the base. Later, less expensive versions of the Robertson's "Gollies" were produced in Europe. These can be differentiated from the Wade figurines by the color of the base. The Wade figurines have a white porcelain base. The two figurines not shown are believed to be a DRUMMER and a BAND SINGER.

No. 98.   SAXOPHONE PLAYER - measures 2-5/8" high with an unmarked ribbed base.

No. 99.   TRUMPET PLAYER - measures 2-5/8" high with an unmarked ribbed base.

No. 100.   ACCORDION PLAYER - measures 2-5/8" high with an unmarked ribbed base.

No. 101.   CLARINET PLAYER - measures 2-5/8" high with an unmarked ribbed base.

No. 102.   DOUBLE BASE PLAYER - measures 2-5/8" high with an unmarked ribbed base.

## WEE WILLIE WINKIE WALL PLAQUES
*late 1950's-early 1960's.*

A set of four wall plaques produced by George Wade & Son Ltd. as wall decorations for children's bedrooms. Each plaque features scenes based on the Wee Willie Winkie Nursery Rhyme and is mold-marked Made in England on the back of the plaque.

No. 103.   "TAPPING AT THE WINDOWS, PEEPING THROUGH THE LOCKS" WALL PLAQUE - measures 4-1/4" high by 5-3/8" across.

## MISCELLANEOUS PROTOTYPES FOR GEORGE WADE & SON LTD.

The following prototypes were produced for Wade by William Harper in the 1950's. We feel it is important to show illustrations of prototypes as it is always possible that more than one of each was produced and occasionally they find their way in to the collectors market.

No. 104.   MISS. FLUFFY CAT - measures 2-1/2" high and is slip-cast and unmarked.

No. 105.   NODDY - measures approx. 2-1/2" high and is slip-cast and unmarked.

No. 106.   NODDY - measures approx. 2-1/2" high and is slip-cast and unmarked.

No. 107.   MR. PLOD - measures 2-3/8" high and is slip-cast and unmarked.

No. 108.   BIG EARS - measures 2-3/4" high and is slip-cast and unmarked.

No. 109.   BIG EARS AND NODDY MONEY BOX - measures 4-3/4" high by 4-1/2" long and is unmarked.

No. 110.   GIRL ON MOTOR SCOOTER - measures 3" high by 2-3/4" long and is unmarked.

No. 111.   "I'M HEP" - measures 1-1/2" high and is slip-cast and unmarked.

No. 112.   IRISH LEPRECHAUN - measures 1-1/2" high by 1-5/8" long and is unmarked.

No. 113.   BIG EARS AND NODDY IN A MOTOR CAR - measures 3" high and is unmarked.

No. 114.   AIRLINE PILOT - measures 2-1/2" high and is slip-cast and unmarked.

No. 115.   POGO - measures 2-3/4" high and is slip-cast and unmarked.

No. 116.   CARTOON BOY - measures 2-3/4" high and is slip-cast and unmarked.

No. 117.   FLOOK - measures 2" high, and is slip-cast and unmarked. This figurine was based on a popular British cartoon series. The BOY figurine in No. 116 was from the same cartoon series.

No. 118.   SHIP BOWL - measures 4" in diameter and is unmarked.

No. 119.   BABY ZEBRA - measures 1-1/4" high and is slip-cast and unmarked.

No. 120.   BABY ZEBRA - measures 1-1/4" high and is slip-cast and unmarked.

No. 121.   ADULT ZEBRA - measures 1-1/2" high by 2" long and is slip-cast and unmarked.

No. 122.   YACHT - measures 5-1/4" high and is unmarked.

No. 123.   CANTERBURY TALES "THE REEVE" - measures 3-1/2" high and is unmarked.

No. 124.   CANTERBURY TALES "THE SQUIRE" - measures 3-1/2" high and is unmarked.

No. 125.   CANTERBURY TALES "THE NUN'S PRIEST" - measures 3-1/2" high and is unmarked.

No. 126.   CANTERBURY TALES "THE PRIORESS" - measures 3-1/2" high and is unmarked.

# BRIDE AND GROOM *1992.*

The all-over white glazed figurine of a bridal couple was designed and modelled by Ken Holmes as a special order for Dunbar Cake Decorations. According to records, only a few thousand of these figurines were produced.

FIG.16.

FIG.16.   BRIDE AND GROOM - measures 4-1/4" high and is mold-marked Wade England on the base.

# "WELCOME HOME" *1993.*

This is the first limited edition issue by Wade Ceramics Ltd. in a series based on a theme of children and pets. The first of these figurines, designed and modelled by Ken Holmes, was released in June - July of 1993. Each model in the series is limited to 2,500 numbered pieces, each of which sits on a wooden plinth.

FIG. 17.

FIG. 17.   "WELCOME HOME." The figurine is 3-3/4" high by 4-3/4" long and is marked: Wade Limited Editions "Welcome Home" Modelled by Ken Holmes. This fugurine is the first in a series of Wade collectables Limited edition of 2,500. The wooden base measures 6-3/8" long by 4-1/2" wide. The proposed second model in the series (Fireside Friend) is seen in the background.

# The World of Wade Book 2
# Color Plates.

**PRE-WORLD WAR 2 FIGURINES**
**(1 - 26)**

1

2

3

4

5

6

7

8

9

10

11

12

**SNOW WHITE AND THE SEVEN DWARFS**
**(13-20)**

13

14

15

16

17

18

19

20

(DISNEY CHARACTERS ©THE WALT DISNEY COMPANY)

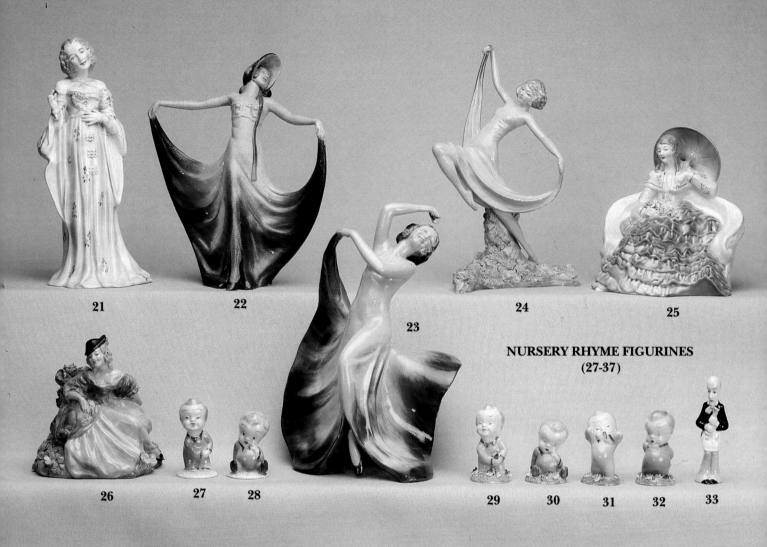

**21**

**22**

**23**

**24**

**25**

**NURSERY RHYME FIGURINES**
**(27-37)**

**26**

**27**

**28**

**29**

**30**

**31**

**32**

**33**

**MABEL LUCIE ATTWELL CHARACTERS**
**(41-42)**

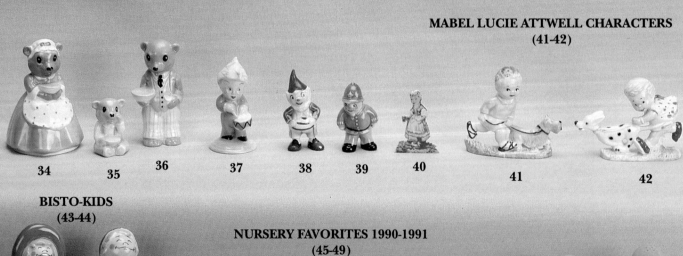

**34**

**35**

**36**

**37**

**38**

**39**

**40**

**41**

**42**

**BISTO-KIDS**
**(43-44)**

**NURSERY FAVORITES 1990-1991**
**(45-49)**

**43**

**44**

**45**

**46**

**47**

**48**

**49**

**50**

**51**

# SOPHISTICATED LADIES
## (52-55)

52     53     54     55

# MY FAIR LADIES   SET ONE
## (56-63)

56   57   58   59   60   61   62   63

# MY FAIR LADIES   SET TWO
## (64-71)

64   65   66   67   68   69   70   71

# ICI MAN    SHERWOOD FOREST SERIES
## (72)      (73-75)

72   73   74   75   76   77   78   79   80

81

82

83    84

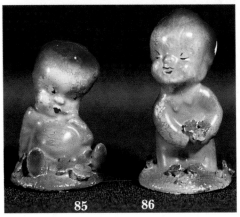

85    86

87    88

89    90

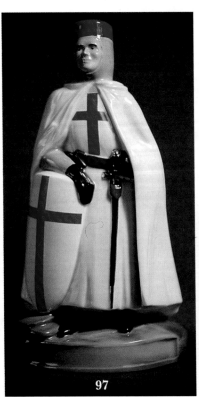

97

**SNIPPETS**
**(91-96)**

91    92    93

94    95    96

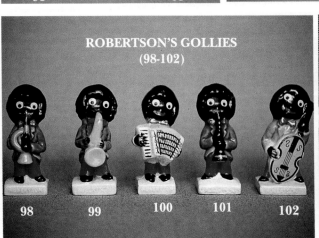

**ROBERTSON'S GOLLIES**
**(98-102)**

98    99    100    101    102

103

52

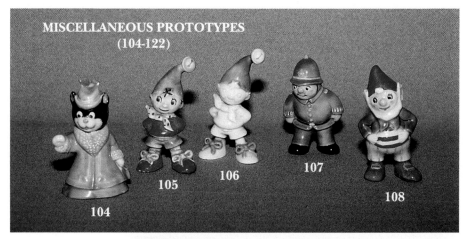

**MISCELLANEOUS PROTOTYPES**
**(104-122)**

104 105 106 107 108

109

110 111 112 113 114 115

116 117 118 119 120 121 122

**CANTERBURY TALES PROTOTYPES**
**(123-126)**

123 124 125 126

127  128  129  130  131  132  133  134  135  136

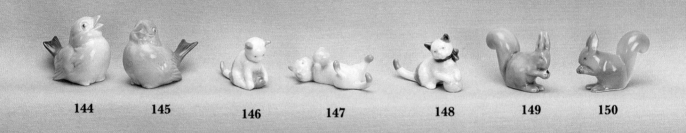

137  138  139  140  141  142  143

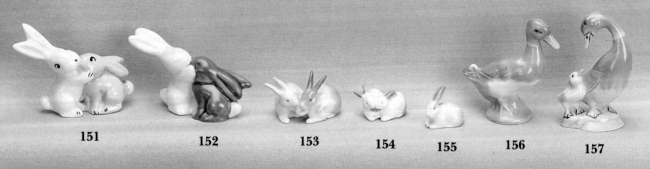

144  145  146  147  148  149  150

151  152  153  154  155  156  157

158  159  160  161  162  163  164  165

54

## "DISNEYS"
### (166-170)
#### (DISNEY CHARACTERS ©THE WALT DISNEY COMPANY)

166     167     168     169     170

## TV PETS
### (171-174)

## DISNEY "HAT BOX"
### (175-177)

## HANNA-BARBERA CARTOON
### CHARACTERS (178-180)

171   172   173   174   175   176   177   178   179   180

©1994 HANNA BARBERA PRODUCTIONS INC.

181   182   183   184   185   186   187   188   189   190

191   192   193   194   195   196   198

197

## WHIMSIE-LAND SERIES 1984-1988
### (199-1 - 199-5)

199-1   199-2

199-3   199-4   199-5

200   201   202

# ANIMAL AND BIRD FIGURINES
## (203-239)

203

204

205

206

207

208

209

210

211

212

213

214

215

216

217

218

219

220

221

222

223

224

225

226

227

228

229

230

231    232    233

234

235    236

(DISNEY CHARACTERS ©THE WALT DISNEY COMPANY)

237    238    239

57

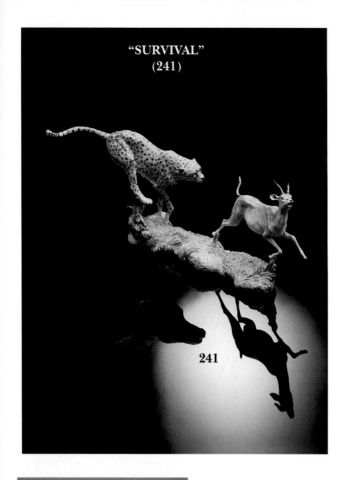

"SURVIVAL"
(241)

241

240

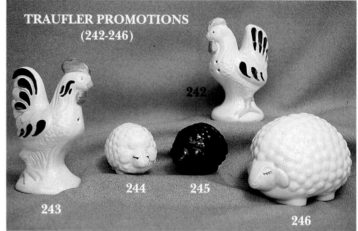

TRAUFLER PROMOTIONS
(242-246)

242

243    244    245    246

247

248

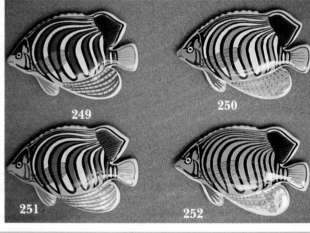

249    250

251    252

253    254

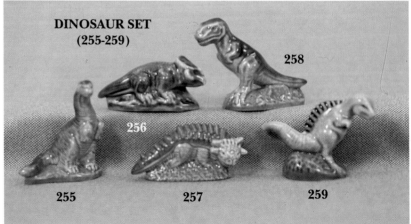

DINOSAUR SET
(255-259)

258

256

255    257    259

260

261

262

263

264

265

266

267

268

269

270

271

272

273

274

275

281

## CORONATION STREET
### (282-1 – 282-3)

## BRIGHTON PAVILION
### (283-285)

## WHIMSIE-ON-WHY
## VILLAGE SET
### (286-33 – 286-36)

282-1    282-2    282-3    283    284    285    286-33   286-34   286-35   286-36

287-1   287-2    287-3    287-4    287-5    287-6    287-7    287-8    288-1    288-2    288-3    288-4    288-5

## PARTY CRACKER FIGURINES
### (287-1 – 290-8)

289-1    289-2    289-3    289-4    289-5    289-6    289-7    289-8      291

290-1    290-2    290-3    290-4    290-5    290-6    290-7    290-8     292

293         294         295

## U.S.A. RED ROSE TEA FIGURINES
### (298-16 – 298-19)

298-16    298-17    298-18    298-19    298-19

296                   297

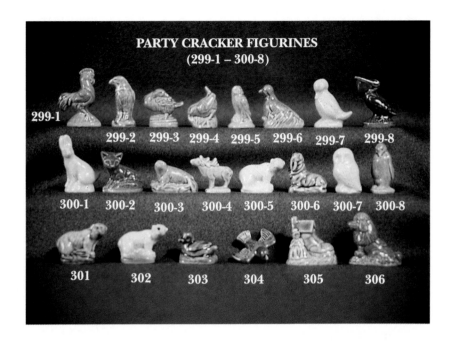

**PARTY CRACKER FIGURINES**
(299-1 – 300-8)

299-1 · 299-2 · 299-3 · 299-4 · 299-5 · 299-6 · 299-7 · 299-8

300-1 · 300-2 · 300-3 · 300-4 · 300-5 · 300-6 · 300-7 · 300-8

301 · 302 · 303 · 304 · 305 · 306

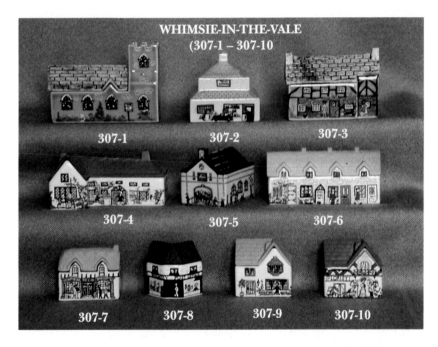

**WHIMSIE-IN-THE-VALE**
(307-1 – 307-10)

307-1 · 307-2 · 307-3

307-4 · 307-5 · 307-6

307-7 · 307-8 · 307-9 · 307-10

308 · 309 · 310
(DISNEY CHARACTERS ©THE WALT DISNEY COMPANY)

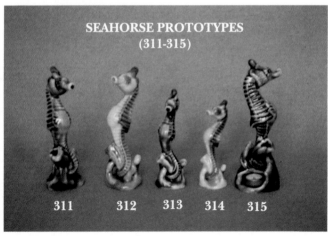

**SEAHORSE PROTOTYPES**
(311-315)

311 · 312 · 313 · 314 · 315

316
317
318
319
320
321
322
323
324
325
326
327
328
329
330
331
332
333
334
335
336
337
338

# WHIMTRAYS 1987-1988
### (339-343)

339     340     341     342     343

## ZOO LIGHTS
### (345-354)

## DOG PIPE REST
### (344)

344

345     346     347     348     349     350     351     352

353     354     355     356     357     358     359     360

## WHIMTRAYS 1958-1965
### (359-360 & 363-365)

361     362     363     364     365     366

## TEENAGE POTTERY
### (367-369)

367     368     369     370

# MISCELLANEOUS GIFTWARE ITEMS
## (371-389)

371    372    373    374    375    376

377    378    379    380

381    382    383

384    385    386    387    388    389

## MONEY BOXES
### (390-399)

390    391    392    393    394    395

396    397    398    399

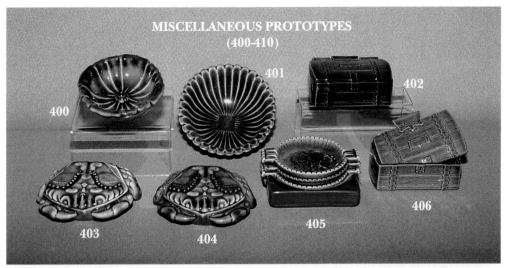

**MISCELLANEOUS PROTOTYPES**
(400-410)

400
401
402
403
404
405
406

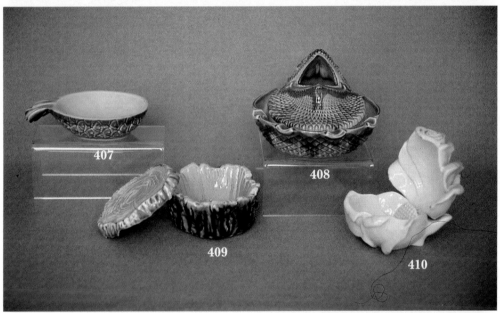

407
408
409
410

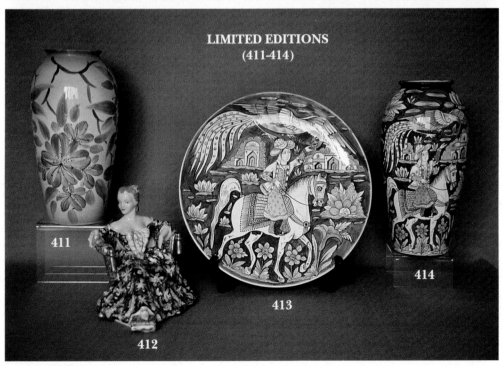

**LIMITED EDITIONS**
(411-414)

411
412
413
414

# WALL PLATES, TANKARDS AND POTTERY TRAYS
## (415-441)

415

416

417

418

419

420

421

422

423

424

425

426

427

428

429

430

431

432

433

434

435

436

437

438

439

440

441

442    443    444    445    446

447    448    449    450    451    452

453    454    455    456    457    458

459    460    461    462    463    464    465    466    467    468    469    470

471    472    473    474    475

# MISCELLANEOUS GIFTWARE ITEMS
## (476-513)

476      477      478      479      480      481

482      483      484      485      486      487      488      489      490

491      492      493      494      495

496      497      498      499      500

501      502      503      504      505      506      507

508      509      510      511      512      513

514          515          516          517

518          519          520          521

522          523          524          525

526       527       528

529       530       531

532       533       534

535

536       537       538       539

540       541       542       543

544       545       546       547

548          549          550          551

552          553          554          555

556          557          558          559          560

561          562          563

564      565      566      567

568      569      570      571

572       573       574       575

576       577       578       579

580       581       582       583

# MISCELLANEOUS VASES AND FLOWER JUGS
## (584-612)

584 585 586 587 588 589 590 591 592 593

594 595 596 597 598 599 600 601 602

603 604 605 606 607 608 609 610 611 612

613

614

615

616

617

618

619

620

621

622

623

624

625

627

628

629

630

631

632

626

633

634

635

636

637

638

639

640

76

**TEAPOTS, COFFEE POTS AND COOKIE JARS**
(641-655)

641  642  643  644

645  646  647

648

649

650  651  652  653  654  655

(DISNEY CHARACTERS ©THE WALT DISNEY COMPANY)

# TEAPOTS, HOT WATER POTS AND COFFEE POTS
## (656-672)

656

657

658

659

660

661

662

663

664

665

666

667

668

669

670

671

672

## TEAPOTS, CREAM AND SUGARS
### (673-689)

673

674    675    676    677    678    679

680    681    682    683    684

685    686    687    688    689

## TEA CADDIES
### (690-694)

690    691    692    693    694

# TEAPOTS
## (695-711)

695

696

697

698

699

700

701

702

703

704

705

706

707

708

709

710

711

80

712   713   714

715   716   717   718   719   720

721   722   723   724

725   726   727

# TEAPOTS, MUGS AND TEA CADDIES
## (728-761)

728  729  730  731  732  733

734  735  736  737  738

739  740  741  742

743　　　　744　　　　745　　　　746　　　　747　　　　748

749　　　　750　　　　751　　　　752　　　　753　　　　754

755　　　　756　　　　757　　　　758

759　　　　760　　　　761

# TEAPOTS, MUGS, COOKIE JARS AND TEA CADDIES
## (762-789)

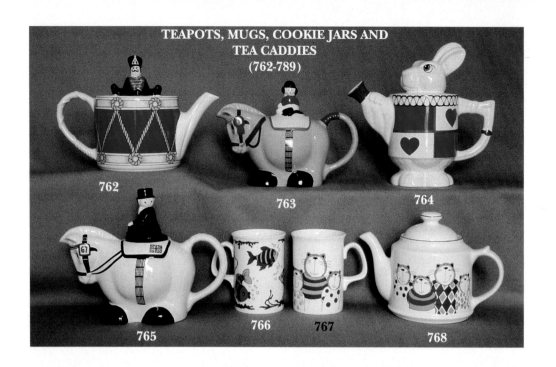

762     763     764

765     766     767     768

769     770

771     772

773     774     775

776     777     778

779

780

781

782

783

784

Cookies

785

786

787

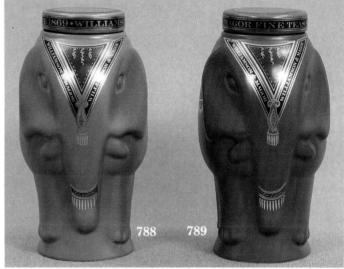

788 789

**MISCELLANEOUS TABLEWARE**
(790-811)

790

791

792

793

FRIED GREEN TOMATOES
AT THE WHISTLE STOP CAFE

794      795      796

797      798      799      800      801

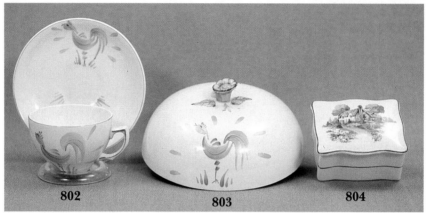

802      803      804

805      806

807

808      809

810

811

# MISCELLANEOUS TABLEWARE
## (812-829, 846-851)

812    813    814    815    816    817

818    819    820    821    822    823    824

825    826    827    828    829    830

## WALT DISNEY CHILDREN'S DISHES (830-845)

833    835    841    843

831    832    834    836    837    839    840    842    844    845

(DISNEY CHARACTERS ©THE WALT DISNEY COMPANY)

838

846    847    848    849    850    851

# MISCELLANEOUS TABLEWARE
### (852-897)

852      853      854      855      856

857      858      859      860      861

865

862      863      864      866      867      868

869      870      871      872      873      874

875

876

877

878

879

880

881

882

883

884

885

886

887

888

889

890

891

892

893

894

895

896

897

898    899    900    901    902

903    904    905    906    907

908    909

910    911    912

**"MODE" TABLEWARE**
**(913-923, 934)**

913     914     915     916     917     918

919     920     921     922     923

**"ORB" TABLEWARE**
**(924-933)**

924     925     926     927     928     929

930     931     932     933     934

935          936          938          937          939          940

941          942          943

944          945          946          947

948          949          950          951          952          953

954        955        956

957        958        959

960      962      965      967

961      963      964      966      968

969      970      971      972      973

# "TUTTI-FRUITTI" TABLEWARE
## (974-988)

974

975

976

977

978

979

980

981

982

983

984

985

986

987

988

## "CLASSIC LINEN" TABLEWARE
### (989-997)

989
990
991
992
993
994

## "MUSIC" TABLEWARE
### (998-1001)

995
996
997
998
999
1000
1001

## "MEADOWLAND" TABLEWARE
### (1003-1004)

## "SUMMER FRUITS" TABLEWARE
### (1005-1006)

1002
1003
1004
1005
1006

## "INDIAN TREE" TABLEWARE
### (1007-1012)

1007
1008
1009
1010
1011
1012

1013       1014       1015       1016

1017       1018       1019       1020

1021       1022       1023       1024       1025

1026       1027       1028       1029       1030

1031       1032

1033      1034      1035

**IRISH PORCELAIN**
**(1036-1040)**

1036      1037

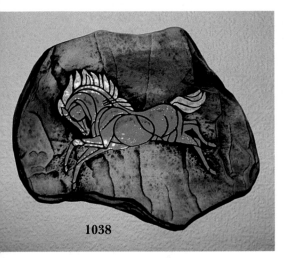

1038

1039

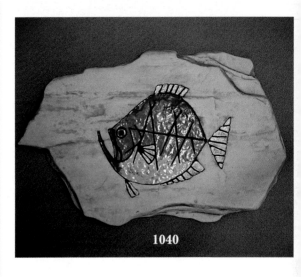

1040

1041

1042

97

1043    1044    1045    1046    1047    1048    1049

1050    1051    1052    1053    1054    1055

## MOURNE RANGE
### (1056-1062)

1056    1057    1058    1059    1060

1061    1062

1063    1064

98

1069     1065     1066     1067     1070

1071     1072     1068     1073     1074

## RAINDROPS GIFTWARE
### (1075-1080)

1075     1076     1077     1078     1079     1080

1081     1082

1083     1084     1085     1086     1087     1088

## IRISH CHARACTER FIGURES EARLY 1990'S
### (1089-1097)

1089     1090     1091     1092     1093     1094     1095     1096     1097

1098  1099  1100  1101  1102

1103  1104

1105  1106  1107  1108  1109

1110  1111  1112  1113  1114

1115  1116  1117  1118  1119  1114  1120

1121  1122  1123  1124  1125  1126  1127  1128  1129

1130   1131   1132   1133   1134

1135   1136   1137   1138   1139

1140   1141

1142   1143   1144

1145   1146

1147   1148   1149   1150

1151     1152     1153     1154     1155

1156     1157     1158

1159     1160

1161     1162     1163

## THE THISTLE AND THE ROSE CHESS SET
### (1164-1175)

1164   1165   1166   1167   1168   1169   1170   1171   1172   1173   1174   1175

# LIQUOR BOTTLES
## (1177-1183)

1176

1177     1178                  1182    1183    1184

## GILBEY'S WINE BARRELS
### (1185-1186)

1179     1180      1181

1185                        1186

## ADVERTISING ITEMS
### (1187-1307)

1187    1188    1189    1190    1191

1192    1193    1194    1195

103

1196

1197

1198

1199

1200

1201

1202

1203

1204

1205

1206

1207

1208

1209

1210

1211

1212

1213

1214

1215

1216  1217  1218  1219  1220

1221  1222  1223  1224  1225  1226

1227  1228  1229  1230  1231

1232  1233  1234  1235  1236  1237  1238

**1239**

**1240**

**1241**

**1242**

**1243**

**1244**

**1245**

**1246**

**1247**

**1248**

**1249**

**1250**

**1251**

**1252**

**1253**

**1254**

**1255**

**1256**

**1257**

**1258**

**1259**

**1260**

1261
1262
1263
1264

1265
1266
1267
1268
1269

1270
1271
1272
1273
1274

1275
1276
1277
1278
1279
1280
1281

1282
1283
1284

1285    1286    1287    1288

1289    1290    1291    1292    1294    1293    1295

1296    1297    1298    1299    1300    1301

1302    1303    1304    1305    1306    1307

108

**VAUX BREWERIES TANKARDS (1308)**

**TAUNTON CIDER MUGS (1309)**

1310

1311

1312

1313

# ADVERTISING ITEMS
## (1314-1333)

1314　1315　1316　1317

1318

1319　1320　1321

1322　1323　1324　1325

1326

1327　1328

1329　1330

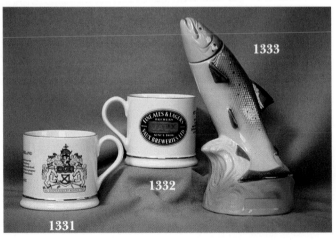

1331　1332　1333

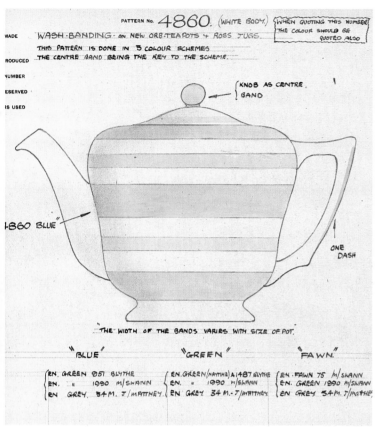

PATTERN No. 4860. (WHITE BODY.)

WHEN QUOTING THIS NUMBER THE COLOUR SHOULD BE QUOTED ALSO

MADE — WASH-BANDING on NEW ORB-TEAPOTS 4 ROSS JUGS.

THIS PATTERN IS DONE IN 3 COLOUR SCHEMES
THE CENTRE BAND BEING THE KEY TO THE SCHEME.

KNOB AS CENTRE BAND

4860 BLUE

ONE DASH

"THE WIDTH OF THE BANDS VARIES WITH SIZE OF POT."

"BLUE"
EN. GREEN 951 BLYTHE
EN. " 1990 M/SWANN
EN. GREY. 34 M. J/MATTHEY.

"GREEN"
EN. GREEN (MAYTIME) A/487 BLYTHE
EN. " 1990 M/SWANN
EN. GREY. 34 M. J/MATTHEY.

"FAWN."
EN. FAWN 75 M/SWANN
EN. GREEN 1990 M/SWANN
EN. GREY 34M. J/MATTHEY

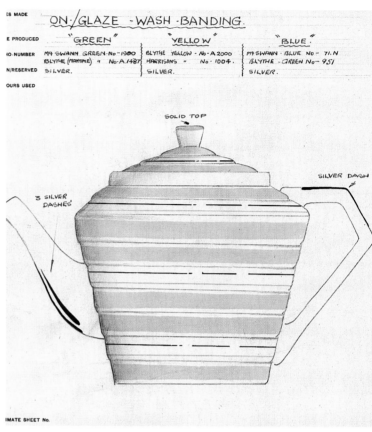

IS MADE

## ON/GLAZE -WASH-BANDING.

| | "GREEN" | "YELLOW" | "BLUE" |
|---|---|---|---|
| IO-NUMBER | Mª SWANN GREEN No 1990 | BLYTHE YELLOW - No A 2000 | Mª SWANN BLUE No - 71.N |
| | BLYTHE (MAYTIME) " No A 1487 | HARRISONS " No 1004. | BLYTHE - GREEN No - 951 |
| N/RESERVED | SILVER. | SILVER. | SILVER. |

OURS USED

SOLID TOP

3 SILVER DASHES

SILVER DASH

IMATE SHEET No.

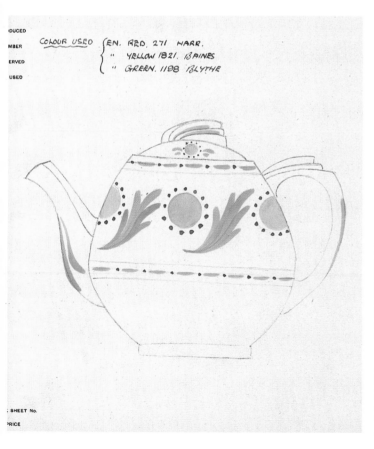

COLOUR USED
EN. RED. 271 HARR.
" YELLOW 1821. BAINES
" GREEN. 1198 BLYTHE

: SHEET No.
PRICE

DATE PRODUCED

## UNDER/GLAZE ENAMELLING.

LITHO NUMBER

OPEN/RESERVED

COLOURS USED

COLOURS USED
IN WATER.

U/G YELLOW - No 15117 - BLYTHE
U/G PINK. - No 1133 - HARRISONS
U/G MAUVE - No 116 - HARRISONS
U/G GREEN - No 2164 - M.º SWANN.

"COLOURED GLAZES."
GREEN - MAYERS No 4683
PINK. - MAYERS No 3007.B.
YELLOW - "OUR OWN MIXED IVORY."

ESTIMATE SHEET No.
SELLING PRICE

COLOURS USED :—

BROWN. N⁰372. E.W.T.MAYER.
TERRA COTTA. 172.A.
DRAKENECK GREEN 4653 .
OLD GOLD. 265 .

(WHITE BODY.)
DIPPED YELLOW GLAZE.

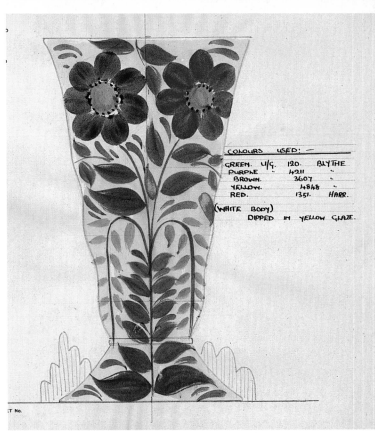

COLOURS USED :—

GREEN. U/G. 120. BLYTHE.
PURPLE. 4211 "
BROWN. 3607 "
YELLOW. 4848 "
RED. 1351. HARR.

(WHITE BODY)
DIPPED IN YELLOW GLAZE.

T No.

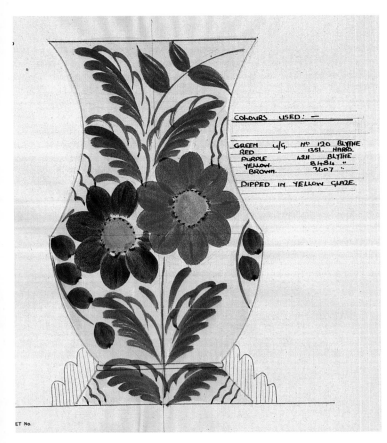

COLOURS USED :—

GREEN U/G. N⁰ 120 BLYTHE
RED. 1351. HARR.
PURPLE. 4211 BLYTHE
YELLOW. 8484 "
BROWN. 3607 "

DIPPED IN YELLOW GLAZE.

ET No.

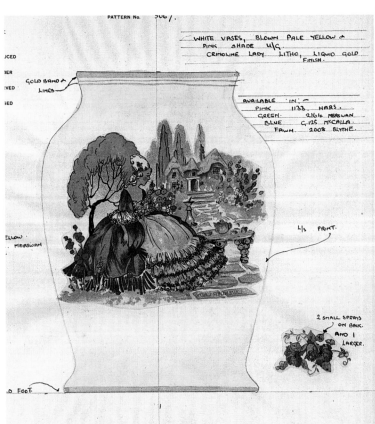

PATTERN No. 3067.

WHITE VASES, BLOWN PALE YELLOW &
PINK SHADE U/G.
CRINOLINE LADY LITHO, LIQUID GOLD
FINISH.

GOLD BAND &
LINES

AVAILABLE IN :—
PINK 1133. HARS.
GREEN. 2164 MERSWAN
BLUE G.125 McCALLA.
FAWN. 2008 BLYTHE.

L/S PRINT.

2 SMALL SPRAYS
ON BACK.
AND 1
LARGER.

112

ANIMALS FIGURES, CARTOON,

WHIMSIES and NOVELTY FIGURES.

By

George Wade & Son Ltd.

and

Wade, Heath & Co. Ltd.

circa mid 1930's - mid 1980's.

# ANIMAL FIGURES.

*By George Wade & Son Ltd. and Wade, Heath & Co. Ltd. circa mid 1930's - mid 1980's.*

Although George Wade & Son Ltd. was primarily a manufacturer of industrial ceramic ware and Wade, Heath & Co. Ltd. a producer of teapots and tableware, the two potteries often ventured into the field of figural giftware.

The following items are some typical examples of slip-cast figurines produced by the two potteries in the 1930's, late 1940's and 1950's. No figurines were produced by either pottery during the years of WWII.

## GIANT PANDA *1939.*

In the late 1930's a Giant Panda took up residence at the London Zoo. This event was greeted by many articles in the press and increased attendance at the Zoo. Wade, Heath's contribution to help celebrate this event was the introduction of a 7-1/2" high Giant Panda figure along with children's Panda Nursery Ware. For an illustration of this figurine and the Panda Nursery Ware, see the advertisement on pg. 192.

## THE PENGUIN FAMILY *late 1940's - mid 1950's.*

The Penguin family was produced by Wade, Heath & Co. Ltd. circa late 1940's through to the mid 1950's. The figurines were marked in a number of ways. The most frequently found backstamps are either Made in England or Mark Type 15. The figurines can also be found unmarked. During the years of production, variations occurred in the style of decoration from relatively light coloring to a dark glaze.

No. 127.  MRS. PENGUIN - measures 3" high with Mark Type 15 on the base.

No. 128.  BENNY - measures 2-1/8" high with Mark Type 15 on the base.

No. 129.  PENNY - measures 2" high and is unmarked.

No. 130.  MR. PENGUIN - measures 3-1/2" high and is unmarked.

FIG.18.  MR. PENGUIN - pepper shaker, measures 3-1/2" high and has Mark Type 15 on the base.

## MISCELLANEOUS ANIMALS.

In the 1930's, George Wade & Son Ltd. introduced quite a large range of miniature, slip-cast figurines with an underglaze finish. For trade literature illustrating some of this range see *The W of W pg. 14 FIG.5.*

No. 131.  STANDING RABBIT - measures 2-3/8" high. This slip-cast figurine is unmarked but can be found with Mark Type 15 or ink-stamped Made in England. This figurine was originally produced in the mid 1930's by George Wade. A number of molds were made thus variations in size exist.

FIG.18.

No. 132.  MINIATURE DEER - measures 1-1/8" high by 1-1/4" long and is unmarked. This is a George Wade mold and the figurine was produced circa late 1930's.

## THE RABBIT FAMILY *late 1940's - mid 1950's.*

The Rabbit family was produced by Wade, Heath & Co. Ltd. circa the late 1940's through to the mid 1950's. The figurines can be found unmarked or marked either Made in England or with Mark Type 15.

No. 133.  PUFF - measures 2" high and is unmarked.

No. 134.  MR. RABBIT - measures 3-1/2" high and is unmarked. *(For the two other members of the Rabbit family, Mrs. Rabbit and Fluff, See The W of W FIG.15 pg.23).*

## MISCELLANEOUS ANIMALS.

No. 135.  DOG - measures 3-1/8" high with Mark Type 15 on the base.

No. 136.  DOG - measures 3-1/8" high with Mark Type 15 on the base. These slip-cast figurines are sometimes referred to as Begging Puppy. Nos. 135 and 136 are George Wade molds and the figurines were produced circa mid to late 1930's.

No. 137.  CALF - measures 1-3/4" high by 1-1/4" long and is marked Made in England. This was a George Wade mold and the figurine was produced circa late 1930's. After WW II, the mold was used by Wade Heath who re-issued the figure between the late 1940's and the mid 1950's.

No. 138.  MINIATURE LAMB - measures 1-1/2" high by 1-1/4" long. This is a George Wade mold.

No. 139.  LARGE LAMB - measures 2-1/4" high and is unmarked. This is a George Wade mold.

No. 140. MINIATURE FOAL - measures 1-1/2" high by 1-1/4" long and is unmarked. This is a George Wade mold.

No. 141. MOUNTAIN GOAT - measures 2-7/8" high by 3" long. This slip-cast figure was made by George Wade in the late 1930's and has Mark Type 22 on the base.

No. 142. ELEPHANT - measures 2" high by 2-1/2" long. This slip-cast figure was made by George Wade in the late 1930's and was re-issued by Wade Heath in the 1950's.

No. 143. ENGLISH SETTER - measures 2-1/4" high by 3-3/8" long with Mark Type 15 on the base. This figure, although issued by Wade Heath between the late 1940's and mid 1950's, is from a George Wade mold first issued in the late 1930's.

No. 144. CHICK - measures 1-3/4" high by 2-1/4" long. This slip-cast figurine is unmarked but dates from early to late 1930's.

No. 145. CHICK - similar to No. 144 but with a slight color variation. These birds usually surface in pairs which leans toward the belief that they were originally sold in pairs.

No. 146. KITTEN WITH BALL - measures 1-1/4" high by 2" long with Mark Type 15 on the base.

No. 147. KITTEN ON BACK - measures 1" high by 2-7/8" long with Mark Type 15 on the base.

No. 148. KITTEN WITH BALL AND BOW - measures 1-5/8" high by 2-1/4" long with Mark Type 14 on the base.

No. 149. SQUIRREL - measures 1-5/8" high and is unmarked.

No. 150. SQUIRREL - similar to No.149. These slip-cast "squirrel figurines" were made from George Wade molds in the mid to late 1930's and by Wade Heath from the late 1940's to circa 1960. They were made in a number of color glazes with the grey glaze being the most frequently found.

No. 151. KISSING RABBITS - measures 2-1/2" high and has Mark Type 15 and Mark Type 19 on the base.

No. 152. KISSING RABBITS (NOT MADE BY WADE) - measures 2-1/4" high. See section on Reproductions.

No. 153. LARGE DOUBLE BUNNIES - measures 1-1/4" high by 1-3/4" long and has Mark Type 22 on the base.

No. 154. SMALL DOUBLE BUNNIES - measures 3/4" high by 1-1/4" long and is unmarked.

No. 155. MINIATURE BUNNY - measures 7/8" high by 1-1/8" long and has Mark Type 22 on the base.

No. 156. DRAKE - measures 3" high by 3" across and has Mark Type 22 on the base.

No. 157. DRAKE AND DADDY - measures 3" high and is unmarked.

No. 158. DRAKE - measures 3" high by 3" across and is marked: Wade England in ink.

No. 159. DUCK - measures 3" high by 3" long and has Mark Type 22 on the base.

No. 160. DUCK - measures 2-3/4" high by 2" across and is marked: Wade England in ink.

No. 161. DRAKE - measures 1-3/4" high by 1-7/8" long and has Mark Type 19 on the base. This slip-cast figurine was made from George Wade molds in the mid to late 1930's and by Wade Heath from the late 1940's to circa late 1950's.

# THE QUACK QUACK FAMILY
*circa 1952 - late 1950's.*

This set of duck figurines produced by Wade, Heath & Co. Ltd., was designed by Robert Barlow to compliment the popular line of children's dishes marketed under the name of Quack Quack Nursery Ware. This line of nursery ware and figurines were produced between 1952 and late 1950's. Records show that this range was still in production in 1956. Originally it was believed that the Quack Quack line was first introduced in the 1930's; however, further research has not been able to substantiate this assumption. For the range of children's dishes, see also *The W of WFIG's* 93 and 94 pg.136.

No. 162. MR. DUCK - measures 2-1/2" high and is ink stamped England.

No. 163. DILLY - measures 1-1/2" high and is ink stamped England.

No. 164. DACK - measures 1-1/2" high and is ink stamped England.

No. 165. MRS. DUCK - measures 2-1/2" high and is ink stamped England.

# CARTOON, WHIMSIES and NOVELTY FIGURES.
*By George Wade & Son Ltd. and Wade, Heath & Co. Ltd. 1935 - 1988.*
## MICKEY MOUSE *1934.*

An article in the September 1934 issue of *The Pottery Gazette and Glass Trade Review* announced the introduction of Mickey Mouse by Wade, Heath & Co. Ltd. The company secured the sole selling rights for the British Empire (excluding Canada) to reproduce earthenware versions of the popular "Mickey Mouse" characters.

It was reported that the pictures for the models were to be drawn personally by Walt Disney. The four characters to appear were "Mickey," "Minnie," "Pluto," and "Horsecollar." (For an illustration of the Mickey Mouse figurine, see the advertisement below as it appeared in the April 1935 issue of *The Pottery Gazette and Glass Trade Review*). At the same time, a series of children's Nursery Ware was introduced. For illustrations of the Mickey Mouse Nursery Ware see the advertisement in the section on Tableware.

## "DISNEYS" *1961 - 1965.*

These larger, slip-cast models of the famous HAT BOX series were introduced in 1961 featuring LADY, TRAMP, SCAMP and BAMBI to be followed by JOCK and DACHIE in 1962 and then SI, AM, THUMPER and TRUSTY.

None of these "Blow-Up" Disneys, as these slip-cast figurines are often referred to by Wade collectors, are easily found Thumper, Tramp and Jock are proving hard-to-find with Dachie being the most elusive of the series.

No. 166. THUMPER - measures 5-1/4" high and is marked "Wade Porcelain, copyright Walt Disney Productions, Made in England."

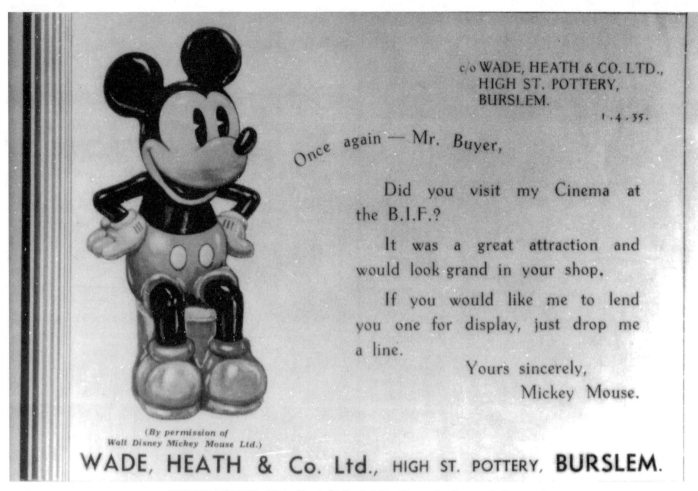

*MICKEY MOUSE by Wade, Heath & Co. Ltd.(An illustration from trade literature).*

No. 167. BAMBI - measures 4-1/2" high and is marked "Wade Porcelain, copyright Walt Disney Productions, Made in England."

No. 168. LADY - measures 4-1/4" high and is marked "Wade Porcelain, copyright Walt Disney Productions, Made in England."

No. 169. TRAMP - measures 6" high and is marked "Wade Porcelain, England."

No. 170. TRUSTY - measures 5-7/8" high and is marked "Wade Porcelain, England."

## TV PETS *1959 - 1965.*

A series of ten animal figurines made by George Wade & Son Ltd. based on the adventures of TIM'S television characters of the 1950's and 1960's. Each figurine was packaged in a different colored gift box shaped to resemble a TV set.

The first set, issued in July/August 1959 consisted of Fifi the Poodle, Bengo the Boxer, Pepi the Chichuahua and Simon the Dalmation. Two further figures, Mitzi and Chee Chee were issued in November 1959, followed by Bruno Jnr. and Droopy Jnr. in 1961 and finally Percy and Whisky in 1965. None of the figurines are mold marked but originally all had the black and gold "Wade Genuine Porcelain" paper label on the base.

No. 171. CHEE-CHEE - measures 2-1/4" high. Issued in November 1959.

No. 172. BENGO - measures 2-3/8" high. Issued in July 1959.

No. 173. SIMON - measures 2-3/8" high. Issued in July 1959.

No. 174. MITZI - measures 2" high. Issued in November 1959.

## DISNEY "HAT BOX" SERIES *1956 - 1965.*

These porcelain figurines produced by George Wade & Son Ltd. were based on characters from the extremely popular Walt Disney animated feature films. Each figurine was presented in its own round, cardboard box similar in shape to a hat box, thus the name of the series. For further information see *The W of W pgs. 82 and 83.*

No. 175. ARCHIMEDES - measures 2" high and is unmarked; however, it would originally have had the black & gold Wade paper label on the base. This figurine is from the Walt Disney movie, *The Sword in the Stone.*

No. 176. SI - measures 1-3/4" high and is unmarked; however, it would originally have had the black & gold Wade paper label on the base. This figurine is from the Walt Disney movie, *Lady and the Tramp.*

No. 177. THE GIRL SQUIRREL - measures 2" high and is unmarked; however, it would originally have had the black & gold Wade paper label on the base. This figurine is from the Walt Disney movie, *The Sword in the Stone.*

*An advertisement for the original characters from Lady and the Tramp as it appeared in the Summer 1956 issue of The Jolly Potter.*

## HANNA-BARBERA CARTOON CHARACTERS *circa 1962.*

The figurines in this set were originally thought to have been issued by George Wade & Son Ltd. between 1959 - 1960; however, an advertisement reproduced here which appeared in the *October 1962 issue of Pottery and Glass* shows the set to have been introduced in the Fall of 1962.

**No. 178. YOGI BEAR** - measures 2-1/2" high on a 1-1/8" diameter base.

**No. 179. HUCKLEBERRY HOUND** - measures 2-3/8" high on 1-1/8" diameter base.

**No. 180. MR. JINKS** - measures 2-3/8" high on a 1-1/8" diameter base.

## DRUM BOX SERIES *1956 - 1959.*

A set of five animal figurines designed by William Harper and made by George Wade & Son Ltd. None of these figurines were mold-marked but originally had the black and gold "Wade Genuine Porcelain" paper label on the base. Each figurine was marketed in a round decorative box in the form of a drum.

**FIG.19.**

**FIG.19.** An illustration of Jem, the 2" high tuba playing bulldog along with the carton that gave the series its name. See also *The W of W FIG.26 pg.29.*

**No. 181. HARPY** - measures 2" high and is unmarked.

**No. 182. TRUNKY** - measures 2-1/8" high and is unmarked.

*Advertisement for YOGI AND HIS FRIENDS from Pottery and Glass, October 1962.*

## NOVELTY ANIMAL FIGURES *1955 - 1960.*

A set of five die-pressed, comic animal figurines all of which are unmarked but were produced by George Wade & Son Ltd. When issued, however, these figurines would have had the black and gold "Wade Genuine Porcelain" paper label on the base. See also *The W of W FIG. 25 pg. 28.*

No. 183.  JUMBO JIM - measures 1-3/4" high.
No. 184.  BERNIE AND POO - measures 2" high.

## MINIKINS *1956 - 1959.*

After the success of the Whimsies, the name of George Wade & Son Ltd. had become synonymous with miniature porcelain figurines. Due to the increased demand for porcelain miniatures, Wade devised a low-priced item comprising mini rabbits, dogs, penguins, donkeys, bulls and cats to meet this demand and gave the series the name Minikins.

Due to the 3/4" or less overall height of the Minikins, a new style of glazing machine had to be developed. Fettlers and decorators sat by a large turntable each doing their appointed tasks. The miniatures were carried by a belt through the glazing machine and then fired at a temperature of 1300 degrees Celsius in batches of 12,000 animals.

These miniature animal figurines, designed by William Harper, were issued in three series. Series "A" issued in 1956, Series "B" in 1957 and Series "C" in 1958. See also *The W of W FIGS. 28 and 29 pg. 30.*

No. 185.  RABBIT (series A) - measures approx. 1" high and is unmarked.
No. 186.  RABBIT (series A) - measures approx. 1" high and is unmarked.
No. 187.  KITTEN (series A) - measures approx. 1" high and is unmarked.

## HAPPY FAMILIES *1962 - 1965.*

Of the Happy Families series, designed by Leslie McKinnon, the Tiger family was the only set not re-issued when George Wade & Son Ltd. re-issued the Happy Families series in 1978. It is for this reason that the Tiger family is the most difficult to find. For prototype figurines of the "Zebra Family", which never went into production see Nos. 119, 120 and 121 in the color section. For other sets in this series see *The W of W Nos. 117-1 to 126-3 pg. 37.*

No. 188.  TIGER (Baby) - measures 1/2" high by 1-1/8" long and is unmarked.
No. 189.  TIGER (Baby) - measures 1/2" high by 1-1/8" long and is unmarked.
No. 190.  TIGER (Parent) - measures 1-3/4" high by 2" long and is unmarked.

## WHIMSIES *1971 - 1984.*

With the success of the miniature figurines made by George Wade & Son Ltd. for use as premiums, Wade decided to introduce a retail line based on the premium figurines using the well-established name of Whimsies. This line was produced using the same method of manufacture as the original Whimsies of 1953 - 1959. See *The W of W pg. 91.*

Over the years of production a number of variations occurred both in size and color. Nos. 191, 192 and 193 show "all - over" black glazed variations of three of the Whimsies. These will be of interest to collectors of "variations" of regular Wade issues. Each figurine is mold-marked WADE ENGLAND.

No. 191.  LAMB - measures 1-3/8" high by 1-1/8" overall.
No. 192.  RAM - measures 1-3/16" high by 1-3/8" overall.
No. 193.  GORILLA - measures 1-1/2" high by 1-1/4" overall.

There are also variations in size affecting at least three of the figurines in this series. These figurines are Hippo, Pig and the Bison. These changes in size occurred when molds had to be remade due to production problems caused by the bulky shape of the animals. It was found that the seams were splitting when the figurines were in the clay state and the only way to resolve this problem was to reduce the bulk. This entailed the making of new steel tools, slightly smaller in size. Due to the excellent workmanship of the toolmakers, the difference between the various sizes of figurines was minimal. See FIG.20, FIG.21, and FIG.22 for illustrations of these variations.

**FIG.20.**

FIG.21.

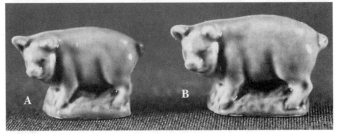

FIG.22.

| FIG.20. | A. HIPPO - measures 15/16" high by 1-1/2" long. |
| | B. HIPPO - measures 1"high by 1-5/8" long. |
| | C. HIPPO - measures 1-1/16" high by 1-3/4" long. |
| FIG.21. | A. BISON - measures 1-1/8" high by 1-5/8" long. |
| | B. BISON - measures 1-3/8" high by 1-3/4" long. |
| FIG.22. | A. PIG - measures 13/16" high by 1-1/2" long. |
| | B. PIG - measures 1" high by 1-3/4" long. |

# WHIMSIES *1953 - 1959.*

Planning for set one of the early Whimsies began in early 1953. Each figurine, designed by William Harper, was required by Wade to appear "alive" either by expression or posture, an effect made easier by the use of true porcelain as the body, thus enabling the designer to use a high degree of detail.

After the detailed modelling of the figures, the next stage of production was the "forming" of the item. Forming was done by a then revolutionary process using hardened steel forming tools which were part cast and part hand engraved, and using "wet-pressed" porcelain dust that was pressed in a machine, under considerable pressure, to form the figurine. Using this forming process, it was possible to make up to 30,000 figurines per day, a much cheaper and speedier method of manufacture than using the more usual slip-cast system of forming.

The miniature figurines were then dried and "hand fettled" by operatives sitting on either side of a slow-moving conveyer belt. The fettling process involved the delicate use of a sharp tool used to remove all rough edges and surplus pieces of clay left from the forming process. Next came the decorating, also done by operatives sitting on each side of the belt. Each person had one particular job to do such as applying the eyes or one small area of decoration. The piece then went on to the next operative for further decoration.

After decorating, the pieces, again on a slow-moving conveyer belt, went through a glaze spraying machine. The individual pieces were then placed on a trolley on batts set twelve tiers high. The trolleys, holding around 12,000 miniatures were then rolled into the tunnel oven where they were fired at around 1250 degrees Celsius.

The firing temperature imposed some limitations on the type of colors available. The single firing process, where the glaze was applied directly to the clay article, was less expensive than traditional potting which separates bisque and glost firings. Finally, each item was inspected and boxed.

It was by this method of manufacture that George Wade & Son Ltd. was able to develop a profitable business in the lean years after the war. Later, the company was able to use the same method of manufacture for many other lines of miniatures such as the Minikins.

No. 194. SHIRE HORSE - measures 2" high by 2-1/8" overall and is unmarked. This rare, brown-glazed model, is a variation from the more frequently found white-glazed model.

No. 195. SHIRE HORSE - measures 2" high by 2-1/8" overall and is unmarked.

No. 196. POLAR BEAR - measures 1-3/4" high by 1-3/4" overall and is unmarked. This figure is shown to illustrate the size difference between it and the "Blow-up" Polar Bear.

No. 197. POLAR BEAR "BLOW-UP" (circa 1962) - measures 6" high and is unmarked but originally had the "Wade Genuine Porcelain" paper label on the base.

FIG.23. BABY POLAR BEAR "BLOW-UP" (circa 1962) - measures 3-3/4" high by 4" overall and is unmarked. The figurine is shown here with the miniature Polar Bear from set 6 of the Polar set of Whimsies issued in 1956.

FIG.23.

FIG.24. BABY SEAL "BLOW-UP" (circa 1962) - measures 4-3/4" high by 5" overall and has the black and gold Wade paper label on the base. This figurine is shown here with the miniature Baby Seal from set 6 of the Polar set of Whimsies issued in 1956.

No. 198. GIANT PANDA - measures 1-1/4" high and is unmarked. The Panda shown in *The W of W No. 152-37 pg.39* is actually from the Wade range of premiums (See FIG.28). The figurine illustrated here is the correct figure for Set No. 8 - Zoo Set of the Early Whimsies.

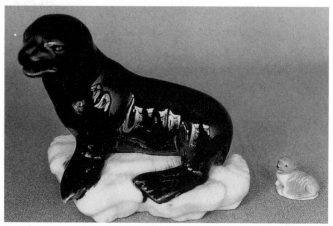

**FIG.24.**

**FIG.25.**

**FIG.25.** **PROTOTYPE OF THE MONKEY AND BABY.**

    A. This 3-1/2" high Monkey and Baby, modelled by Wm. Harper approx. 1953, was the forerunner of the early Whimsies series. The large figurine never went into production and was not part of the later "Blow-up" Whimsies.

    B. The 1-7/8" high production version of Monkey and Baby. This was part of the 1955, Set 4 of the early Whimsies.

# WHIMSIE - LAND SERIES *1984 - 1988.*

The Whimsie-Land series was introduced by George Wade & Son Ltd. in 1984 to replace the discontinued second Whimsies series. The complete Whimsie-Land range was dropped when Wade temporarily went out of the giftware market. The last five figurines in the Wildlife set were in production for a short time only and are therefore proving to be much harder to find than the other figurines in the series.

**WHIMSIE - LAND BRITISH WILDLIFE SET 1987.**

No. 199-1. PHEASANT - measures 1-1/4" high by 2" long and is mold-marked WADE ENGLAND.

No. 199-2. FIELD MOUSE -measures 1-1/4" high by 1-1/2" long and is mold-marked WADE ENGLAND.

No. 199-3. GOLDEN EAGLE - measures 1-1/8" high by 1-3/4" long and is mold-marked WADE ENGLAND.

No. 199-4. OTTER - measures 1-1/2" high by 1-5/8" long and is mold-marked WADE ENGLAND.

No. 199-5. PARTRIDGE - measures 1-1/2" high by 1-3/4" long and is mold-marked WADE ENGLAND.

# WHIMSIE - LAND KEY RINGS *1988.*

When Wade discontinued production of the Whimsie - Land series a number of remaining stock was made available as key ring specialties. The following illustration shows the duck, puppy, kitten, panda bear and badger in the key ring format.

*Illustration of Whimsie-Land key rings.*

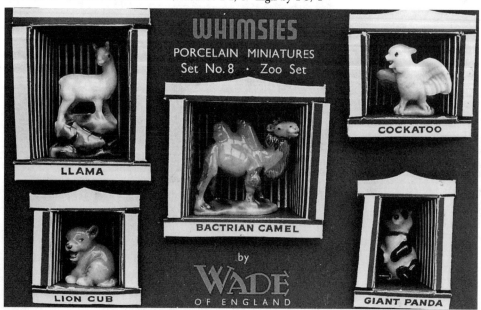

*An illustration of the packaging used for Set No.8 Zoo Set. Note the Giant Panda in the bottom right hand corner.*

BIRDS, ANIMALS and PREMIUMS.

By Wade Heath & Co. Ltd.

and

George Wade & Son Ltd.

circa late 1930's - 1991.

## THE TORTOISE FAMILY - *1958 - 1988.*

The tortoise family was a very popular seller in the George Wade & Son Ltd. retail line. The thirty-year production was the longest uninterrupted run of any Wade retail item. When first introduced, the new sparkling glaze was given the name "Scintillite," a resurrection of the old registered trade name first used by Wade in the early 1930's for the cellulose finish on the Van Hallen figures.

Circa 1969, two variations to the baby tortoise were made for a pharmaceutical company. One was marked on the top of the shell: "Slow Fe" and the other, "Slow Ke." For further information on the tortoise family see *The W of W pgs. 31 and 35.*

No. 200. **BABY TORTOISE - measures 1-1/4" high by 3" long and 2-1/8" across and is mold-marked WADE PORCE-LAIN MADE IN ENGLAND. This figurine is similar to the regular tortoise (*See The W of W No.58 pg.35*) but with the addition of an extra piece in the top tool to emboss the words "Devil's Hole Bermuda."**

No. 201. **MINI TORTOISE (circa 1964-1965) - measures 7/8" high by 2" long by 1-1/2" across and is mold-marked WADE PORCELAIN MADE IN ENGLAND. This hard to find, green tortoise was issued, by Wade, in a very limited quantity. This experimental color version of the popular tortoise range did not sell well and was soon withdrawn from production.**

No. 202. **BABY TORTOISE (circa 1964-1965) - measures 1-1/4" high by 3" long and 2-1/8" across and is mold-marked WADE PORCELAIN MADE IN ENGLAND. This is the larger, green version of No.201.**

FIG.26.

FIG.26. **TORTOISE ASHBOWL - measures 1-1/4" high by 6" long and 4-1/4" across. This unusual, rectangular shaped ashbowl is unmarked.**

## ANIMAL and BIRD FIGURINES.

In the mid to late 1930's, a series of beautifully modeled birds and animals were designed by Faust Lang. These underglazed figurines were produced by George Wade & Son Ltd. After WWII, the molds were taken over by Wade, Heath & Co. Ltd. and produced from the late 1940's through to the mid 1950's. For trade literature illustrating a number of these figurines see *The W of W pgs. 16 & 17, FIGS. 8 & 9.*

No. 203. **SINGLE BUDGERIGAR - measures 7-1/2" high and has Mark Type 10 on the base. This figurine was in production as late as the mid 1950's.**

No. 204. **FLICKA - measures 4-1/2" high and has Mark Type 21A on the base. This figurine dates from the late 1930's.**

No. 205. **BIRD - measures 3-1/2" high on a 2-1/2" diameter slip-cast base. The figurine is ink marked L Wade England No.124.**

No. 206. **PELICAN - measures 6-1/4" to the top of beak by 7-1/4" overall and has Mark Type 10 on the base. This figurine was in production as late as the mid 1950's.**

FIG.27.

FIG.27. **BIRD VASES (1936 - 1939).**
**A. Small bird vase measures 3-1/2" high and has Mark Type 5 on the base.**
**B. Large bird vase measures 6-3/4" high and has Mark Type 4 on the base.**

## POSY BOWLS.

To use up surplus figurines originally made by George Wade & Son Ltd., Wade, Heath & Co. Ltd. took over the figurines and applied them to new custom-made bases. These bases also held mustard pots from lines such as the Bramble and Basket Ware series. The pots were ideally suited for use as "posy bowls," and when decorated with china flowers, became a quite unique and innovative method for using up surplus stock.

No. 207. **SQUIRREL POSY BOWL - measures 2-3/4" high by 3-1/2" overall and has Mark Type 10 on the base.**

No. 208. **STANDING RABBIT POSY BOWL - measures 2-3/4" high by 3-1/2" overall and has Mark Type 10 on the base.**

## PREMIUMS and PROMOTIONAL ITEMS.

It had been thought that there were two sizes of Pandas in the Zoo Set (Set No.8 Early Whimsies). We have since learned that this was not the case. The large Panda shown in *The W of W No.152-37 pg.39* was not from the Early Whimsies set but in actual fact was from a later range of "stock premi-

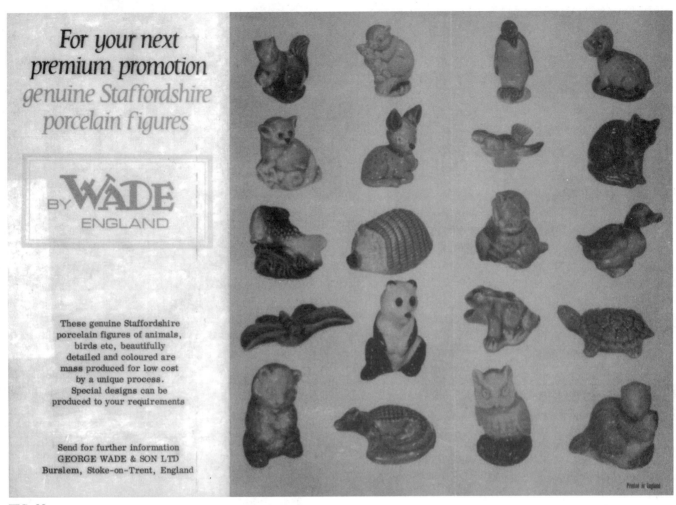

FIG. 28.

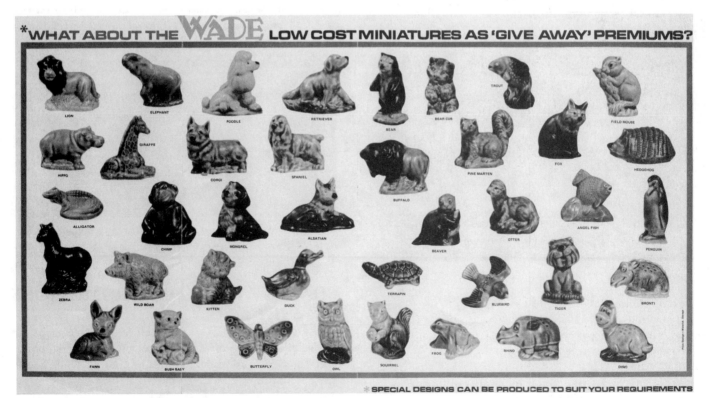

FIG.29.

123

ums" made by George Wade & Son Ltd. in the early 1960's. (See FIG.28). For the Zoo Set Giant Panda see No.198.

**FIG. 28.** An illustration from early 1960's trade literature showing the "early range" of George Wade & Son Ltd. premiums. Note the hard to find Panda in the second row from the bottom.

**FIG.29.** An illustration from the Spring 1969 trade literature showing the "extended range" of George Wade & Son Ltd. premiums. Note that the Panda has been dropped from the range. Notable additions to the range were Bronti, Tiger, Rhino, Standing Bear and the Black Zebra. The black Zebra was used for Brooke Bond Foods Ltd. but the color was changed in 1976, when the figurine was included in Whimsies Set 7. Wade considered the black color to be unattractive for young collectors.

**No. 209.** PANDA - measures 1-1/2" high and is unmarked.(See also FIG.28).

**No. 210.** SPILLER'S DOG 1991 - measures 1-1/8" high by 2-1/8" long and is mold-marked WADE ENGLAND. This figurine was issued as a promotional item for Spillers Foods Ltd. (pet food suppliers).

## ARTHUR PRICE OF ENGLAND - PROMOTIONAL FIGURINES.
*circa late 1970'S - early 1980'S.*

Arthur Price of England, distributors of silver plated-ware, offered a number of items, gift-packed, along with porcelain figurines taken from the 1971 - 1984 line of Whimsies.

**FIG.30.**

**FIG.30.** **ON THE FARM.** This set included items from the 1975 Set 6 and the 1977 Set 8 of the Whimsies.

**FIG.31.** **JUNGLE BABIES.** This set included items from the 1971 Set 1, the 1973 Set 4, the 1975 Set 5 and the 1979 Set 10 of the Whimsies.

**FIG.31.**

## ANIMAL and BIRD FIGURINES and POSY BOWLS *continued*

**No. 211.** LAUGHING RABBIT - measures 7" high and has Mark Type 6 on the base. This figurine was issued in three sizes in the late 1930's.

**No. 212.** DUCK POSY BOWL - measures 2-3/4" high by 3-1/2" overall and has Mark Type 10 on the base.

**No. 213.** KISSING BUNNIES POSY BOWL - measures 2-3/4" high by 3-1/2" overall and has Mark Type 10 on the base.

**No. 214.** HERON - measures 7-1/2" high and has Mark Type 10 on the base. This slip-cast figurine was in production as late as the mid 1950's. See also illustraton from the Dec. 1951 issue of *The Jolly Potter.*

*An illustration of figure caster Mrs. Joan Beckett from the December 1951 issue of The Jolly Potter. Note the Heron figurines on the left of the picture.*

## SHARPS EASTER EGG PROMOTIONS
*1970 & 1971.*

Between March 27 and March 30, 1970, Sharps, an English manufacturer of candies and sweets, used a porcelain Easter Bunny, manufactured by George Wade & Son Ltd., as a promotional item (see No. 216). Between April 9 and April 12, 1971, the company used a porcelain figure of Bo-Peep, as a promotional item. This was also made by George Wade & Son Ltd. (see No. 215).

WADE POTTERY
'Bo-Peep'
MILK CHOCOLATE EGG
With Milk Chocolate
Buttons in the Carton

**40p**

[8/–]
RECOMMENDED PRICE
Packed **6** PER OUTER

*Sharp's advertisement for the 1971 Easter Egg promotion featuring Bo-Peep.*

Sharps was founded in 1880 and became a successful manufacturer of toffee and fudge. The company gained Royal Patronage and was awarded Warrants in 1947 and 1955. Sharps was an independent company until 1981 when it became part of Trebor, a major manufacturer of mints and sugar confectionery. Trebor was founded in 1907 as Robertson & Woodcock but later acquired its name Trebor from the name of the building housing the company's headquarters. This name also spelt founder Robert Robertson's first name backwards and was looked upon as lucky omen.

In 1990, Trebor became part of Trebor Bassett Ltd. The Bassett portion of the company was founded in 1842 by George Bassett who, quite accidentally in 1899, discovered Liquorice Allsorts. The story is, that whilst showing a customer a tray of samples, a salesman knocked the tray over and the customer was so impressed with the resulting mixed up confectioneries, he immediately placed an order. Thus Liquorice Allsorts was born.

**No. 215.** **BO-PEEP** - measures 2-5/8" high and is mold-marked **WADE ENGLAND** around the base.

**No. 216.** **LARGE EASTER BUNNY** - measures 2-1/2" high and is unmarked.

**No. 217.** **SMALL EASTER BUNNY** - measures 2" high and is unmarked. This is an unauthorized reproduction of the Wade Easter Bunny. For further information see the section on Reproductions.

## ANIMAL FIGURINES *continued*

Rabbits and various species of dogs and puppies have been a favourite subject for potteries in their giftware lines for many years. In the 1930's, 1940's and again in the 1950's, the Wade potteries produced a number of these animal figures many of which are similar and sometimes almost identical to those made by other potteries. Some of the most difficult figurines to identify by Wade collectors are the sitting rabbits (items No.219 - 223 in the color section) which are very similar to those made by Sylvac and Price Bros. *See also The W of W FIG. 14 pg. 22.*

In most cases the larger figures were marked by the potteries using their established backstamp. However, the smaller rabbits were often either unmarked or simply stamped Made in England. It is these smaller, vaguely marked, rabbits that cause the confusion.

Careful comparison of item Nos.219, 220 and 221 (which are either marked Made in England or unmarked) with examples of rabbits bearing Wade backstamps would indicate that these are indeed Wade products.

**No. 218.** **ALSATIAN** - measures 7-1/2" long by 5-1/4" high and has Mark Type 4 on the base. Note the glass eyes, an unusual feature for a Wade figurine.

**FIG. 32.** **SITTING PUP** - measures 4-1/4" high with shape No.329 and has Mark Type 6 on the base. This slip-cast figurine is all-over blue with brown eyes and nose.

*Sharp's advertisements for the 1970 Easter Egg promotion featuring the Easter Bunny.*

FIG. 32.

No. 219. RABBIT - measures 3" high and is unmarked.

No. 220. RABBIT - measures 4-3/4" high and is ink stamped Made in England.

No. 221. RABBIT - measures 4-3/4" high and is ink stamped Made in England.

No. 222. RABBIT - measures 5-5/8" high and has Mark Type 6 on the base.

No. 223. RABBIT - measures 6" high and has Mark Type 6 on the base.

No. 224. ERMINE - with underglaze finish and has Mark Type 21A on the base. The figurine is 9-1/4" high. Date of issue, 1939, is also marked on the base. This figurine was designed by Faust Lang.

No. 225. CHAMOIS KID - with underglaze finish and has Mark Type 21A on the base. The figurine is 5-3/8" high. This figurine was designed by Faust Lang.

No. 226. PANTHER - with underglaze finish and has Mark Type 21A on the base. The figurine is 8-1/2" high. Date of issue, 1939, is also marked on the base. This figurine was designed by Faust Lang.

No. 227. BROWN BEAR - with underglaze finish and has Mark Type 21A on the base. The figurine is 9-1/2" high. Date of issue, 1939, is also marked on the base. This figurine was designed by Faust Lang.

No. 228. HIPPOPOTAMUS - with underglaze finish and has Mark Type 22 on the base. The figurine measures 4-1/2" long by 1-3/8" high. See also FIG.33.

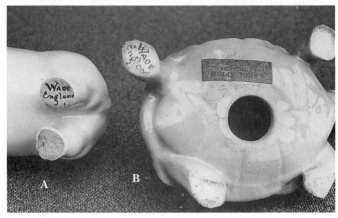

FIG. 33.

No. 229. TORTOISE - with underglaze finish and has Mark Type 22 on the base. The figurine measures 3" long by 1-1/4" high at the head. See also FIG.33.

FIG. 33. A. HIPPOPOTAMUS (BASE) showing variation of Mark Type 22.
B. TORTOISE (BASE) showing variation of Mark Type 22. The applied paper label reads: Carol Speir, 5 Bridge St., Richmond, Surrey.

No. 230. PUP IN BASKET - with underglaze finish and has Mark Type 6 on the base. The figurine is 6" high.

No. 231. CHEEKY DUCKLING - with underglaze finish and has Mark Type 4 on the base. The figurine is 7" high.

No. 232. DACHSHUND - with underglaze finish and has Mark Type 5 on the base. The figurine measures 6-1/2" long by 3-1/2" high.

No. 233. "SALTY" THE SEAL - with underglaze finish and is marked: WADEHEATH ENGLAND BY PERMISSION WALT DISNEY on the base. The figurine measure 6-1/4" long by 6-1/2" high by 6" wide.

*Wade, Heath & Co. Ltd. advertisement as it appeared in the August 1937 issue of the Pottery Gazette and Glass Trade Review.*

No. 234. PLUTO - with underglaze finish and has Mark Type 4 on the base. The figurine is 4-1/2" high.

No. 235. PLUTO'S PUP No.1 - with underglaze finish and has Mark Type 6 on the base. The figurine is 2-1/2" high.

No. 236. PLUTO'S PUP No.2 - with underglaze finish and is marked: WADEHEATH BY PERMISSION WALT DISNEY ENGLAND on the base. The figurine is 4" high.

No. 237. OPEN-MOUTHED BIRD - with underglaze finish and has Mark Type 4 on the base. The figurine is 6-3/4" high.

127

No. 238. PLUTO'S PUP No.1 - similar to No.235 but in a different colorway.

No. 239. TERRIER PUP - with underglaze finish and has Mark Type 4 on the base. The figurine is 6-3/8" high. Note the glass eyes on this figurine.

No. 240. RAZORBACK - measures 5" high by 8" overall and is unmarked. The red example illustrated was photographed at the Royal Victoria Pottery but Wade Razorbacks with a black glaze have been seen in private collections.

No. 241. "SURVIVAL." This hand-cast sculpture is from a very limited edition of 50 pieces and was first made available in early 1991. The sculpture was modelled by Alan Maslankowski and features a Cheetah chasing a Grants Gazelle. Each piece is individually numbered and comes with a framed certificate of authenticity signed by the artist and the Chairman of Wade Ceramics Limited.

## TRAUFLER PROMOTIONAL ITEMS
*1992.*

Traufler is a British import company specializing in the distribution of tableware. A number of designs distributed by the company featured farmyard scenes. To help promote these lines, Wade Ceramics Ltd. produced four animal figurines to compliment the imported ware. All the figurines were unmarked.

No. 242. HEN PEPPER SHAKER - measures 3-5/8" high.
No. 243. ROOSTER SALT SHAKER - measures 4-5/8" high.
No. 244. WHITE SHEEP (SMALL) - measures 1-5/8" high.

FIG. 34.

No. 245. BLACK SHEEP (SMALL) - measures 1-5/8" high.
No. 246. WHITE SHEEP (LARGE) - measures approx. 2-3/4" high.

## MISCELLANEOUS GIFTWARE.

No. 247. BENGO MONEY BOX - measures 6" high and is unmarked. This money box was based on the character from the TV Pet series. Production date circa mid 1960's.

No. 248. PIG FAMILY CRUET SET. Mr. Pig (salt shaker) measures 3-3/4" high and is ink stamped Wade England. Mrs. Pig (pepper shaker) measures 3-1/8" high and is ink stamped Wade England. The tray measures 5-1/4" long by 3-1/2" wide and is unmarked.

No. 249. EXOTIC FISH WALL PLAQUE - measures 3-3/4" long by 2-1/2" wide and is mold-marked Wade Porcelain Made in England.

No. 250. EXOTIC FISH WALL PLAQUE - measures 3-3/4" long by 2-1/2" wide and is mold-marked Wade Porcelain Made in England.

No. 251. EXOTIC FISH WALL PLAQUE - measures 3-3/4" long by 2-1/2" wide and is mold-marked Wade Porcelain Made in England.

No. 252. EXOTIC FISH WALL PLAQUE - measures 3-3/4" long by 2-1/2" wide and is mold-marked Wade Porcelain Made in England.

No. 253. FROG - measures 1-1/2" high and is marked Wade England.

No. 254. RUDDY DUCK - measures 1-3/8" high by 2-1/4" long. The duck is hollow and unmarked and was made in a limited number of 3,400 pieces in the late 1970's.

FIG. 34. ST. JOHNS AMBULANCE BADGER (1990). This slip-cast figurine measures 4" high and is unmarked.

## DINOSAUR SET *1993.*

A set of five die-pressed figurines produced by Wade Ceramics Ltd. designed by Barbara Cooksey and modelled by Ken Holmes. This set was released in the Summer of 1993. All figurines are mold-marked WADE ENGLAND.

No. 255. CAMARASAURUS - measures 2" high by 1-3/4" long.
No. 256. PROTOCERATOPS - measures 1-1/8" high by 2-3/8" long.
No. 257. EUOPLOCEPHALUS - measures 1" high by 2-1/4" long.
No. 258. TYRANNOSAURUS REX - measures 1-3/4" high by 2-3/8" long.
No. 259. SPINOSAURUS - measures 1-5/8" high by 2-3/8" long.

*A Wade Ceramics Ltd. advertisement for the dinosaur collection.*

**FLOWERS.**

**By George Wade & Son Ltd.**

**circa 1930 - 1939.**

# FLOWERS.
*By George Wade & Son Ltd.*
*circa 1930-1939.*

During the 1930's, George Wade & Son Ltd. produced a wide variety of both earthenware and china flower table arrangements. The designs varied in both size and appearance, from small place name holders and menu holders to large centre pieces.

The bowls, vases, centres, jugs and posy pots embellished with modelled and painted flowers were greatly admired by both the public and the trade when the items were exhibited, alongside the Van Hallen figurines and the Faust Lang animals, at the various British Industries Fairs in the 1930's. One visitor in particular to the 1938 B.I.F. was very taken with the centre pieces displayed. This visitor was none other than H.M. Queen Mary who purchased a particularly pretty flower centre piece for her own use. *(Ref. April 1938 Pottery Gazette and Glass Trade Review).*

Popular British flowers most often used as decorations for the Wade posy arrangements included, the wild rose, tulips, pansies, poppies, anemones and general arrangements of assorted flowers. Most Wade flowers were marked on the base with the handwritten Mark Type 22 often accompanied by the number of the model in the range and the name of the flower. Some pieces were also imprinted with the molded mark British Made. For further illustrations of Wade Flowers, see *The W of W pgs. 18, 19, 20 and 21.*

No. 260. ANEMONES - measures 6" high and is marked Wade England No.48 E (handwritten in ink).

No. 261. PANSY - measures 3-5/8" high and is marked No.29 Made in England (handwritten in ink).

No. 262. PANSY - measures 3-3/4" high and is marked Wade England (ink stamp) and No.30 (handwritten in ink).

No. 263. PANSIES - measures 6" high and is marked Wade England No.64, Pansy (handwritten in ink).

No. 264. TRIANGULAR TABLE DECORATION - measures 5" across and is ink stamped Wade England.

No. 265. SMALL ARCH - measures 5" high and is marked Wade England (ink stamp) and No.57 (handwritten in ink).

No. 266. SMALL SATURN - measures 5" high and is marked Wade England No.60 (handwritten in ink).

No. 267. POSY BASKET - measures 3-1/2" high and is marked Wade England (ink stamp) and No.54 (handwritten in ink).

No. 268. POSY POT - measures 3" high and is marked Wade Made in England No.27 (handwritten in ink).

No. 269. POSY POT ASSORTED - measures 3" high and is mold-marked BRITISH MADE.

No. 270. POSY POT - measures 2-3/4" high and is marked Wade Made in England No.28 (handwritten in ink).

No. 271. JUG FLOWER ARRANGEMENT - measures 3" high and is marked Wade England B Jug (handwritten in ink).

No. 272. BASKET ARRANGEMENT - measures 4-1/2" long and is marked Wade Made in England (handwritten in ink).

*George Wade & Son Ltd. advertisement from the April 1939 issue of The Pottery Gazette and Glass Trade Review.*

No. 273. **PRIMROSES** - measures 1-5/8" high and is marked Wade Made in England (handwritten in ink).

No. 274. **BASKET ARRANGEMENT** - measures 2-1/2" high and is marked Wade Made in England No. 6 (handwritten in ink).

No. 275. **JUG FLOWER ARRANGEMENT** - measures 3" high and is marked Wade Made in England No.10 (handwritten in ink).

No. 276. **POSY POT** - measures 2-1/2" high and is mold-marked British Made along with No.18 Wade England (handwritten in ink).

No. 277. **POSY POT ASSORTED** - measures 1-1/2" high and is mold-marked British Made along with Wade England (handwritten in ink).

No. 278. **WILD ROSE** - measures 1-1/8" high and is marked Wade England No.1 W. Rose (handwritten in ink) and BRITISH MADE (molded).

No. 279. **POSY POT** - measures 1-1/2" high and is marked Wade England No.2 (handwritten in ink) and BRITISH MADE (molded).

No. 280. **TULIP POSY** - measures 1-1/4" high and in marked Wade England No.2 Tulip (handwritten in ink) and BRITISH MADE (molded).

No. 281. **WILD ROSE POSY POT** - measures 2" high and is mold-marked British Made along with W. Rose Wade England (handwritten in ink).

*Glost Tunnel Oven.*
*Royal Victoria Pottery. Early 1950's.*

# MISCELLANEOUS ITEMS.

## By

## George Wade & Son Ltd.,

## Wade, Heath & Co. Ltd. and

## Wade Ceramics Ltd.

## circa early 1950's - 1993.

## CORONATION STREET *1988 - 1989.*

Three miniature houses based on the popular and long-running British television series Coronation Street were commissioned by Granada Television to advertise the series. They were available for sale at the TV studio. These die-pressed models were made by George Wade & Son Ltd.

No. 282-1. **THE ROVER'S RETURN** - measures 1-7/8" high and is mold-marked Wade England. This is a model of the local pub frequented by the characters appearing in the series.

No. 282-2. **NO. 9 the DUCKWORTHS** - measures 1-5/8" high and is mold-marked Wade England. This model is the home of the Duckworth family.

No. 282-3. **THE CORNER SHOP** - measures 1-5/8" high and is mold-marked Wade England. Alf's local store is where much of the action of the series takes place.

## BRIGHTON PAVILION *1988.*

The famous pavilion in Brighton, the popular south coast resort in England, was recreated in delicate slip-cast porcelain models. This pavilion was originally built for the Prince Regent, later King George IV, in the late 18th century. There are two models to the set, a single, large dome and a smaller two-domed building. These were sold separately in the pavilion Gift Shop. Collectors usually acquire the single dome and two of the smaller buildings forming a set of three to more resemble the actual Brighton Pavilion.

No. 283. **SMALL TWO-DOMED BUILDING** - measures 1-7/8" high by 2" long and is unmarked.

No. 284. **LARGE SINGLE DOMED BUILDING** - measures 2-7/8" high by 2" in diameter and is unmarked.

No. 285. **SMALL TWO-DOMED BUILDING** - similar to No.283.

## WHIMSEY-ON-WHY VILLAGE SET *1987.*

These were the last four models added to Set 5 of the popular miniature Village series designed by Richard Wade. Each model is mold-marked Wade England on the underside of the base. These die-pressed models were made by George Wade & Son Ltd. For the first thirty-two models in this series, see *The W of W pgs. 43 and 106.*

No. 286-33. **SCHOOLTEACHER'S HOUSE** - No.33 in the series. This model measures 1-3/4" high.

No. 286-34. **FISHMONGER'S SHOP** - No.34 in the series. This model measures 1-5/8" high.

No. 286-35. **POLICE STATION** - No.35 in the series. This model measures 1-5/8" high.

No. 286-36. **LIBRARY** - No.36 in the series. This model measures 2" high.

## TOM SMITH & CO. LTD. PARTY CRACKERS *1986 - 1992.*

The Tom Smith Group Limited was founded in 1847 by Tom Smith who, at that time, was a manufacturer of wedding cake ornaments and confectionery operating under the name of Thomas Smith & Company, later revised to Tom Smith & Co. Ltd.

Smith originally thought of the Christmas Cracker idea after a visit to France where he saw a French confectioner selling Bon Bons, small candies or sweets wrapped in tissue paper. Smith redesigned the Bon Bon for the English market and included a small "love note" inside the wrapping alongside the sugared almonds. The idea was slow to take off in England but eventually caught on when Smith decided to replace the sugared almonds with a small gift.

In 1953, Tom Smith & Co. Ltd. merged with Caley Crackers. Further merges took place in the following years with Mead and Field, Neilson Festive Crackers and Mason and Church. In 1985, the company was taken over by Hovells of Maidstone and was subsequently subject to a management buy-out in 1989. Despite these numerous mergers and takeovers, the company still operates under the name of Tom Smith. The company has been granted Royal Warrants in 1906, 1909, 1910, 1911, 1964, 1975 and 1987.

Since 1976, George Wade & Son Ltd. and later Wade Ceramics Ltd., have supplied the Tom Smith Group Limited with miniature porcelain figurines for use as the party favors in certain lines of their Christmas crackers. It has been a custom for Tom Smith to have the exclusive right for use of the miniatures for a period of two years.

## WILD LIFE SET *1986 - 1987.*

A set of eight miniature animals first used by George Wade & Son Ltd. in their 1971-1984 retail line of Whimsies. The models used for the Tom Smith promotion were all single glazed, unlike the Whimsies which were multicolored.

No. 287-1. **DOLPHIN** - measures 1-1/8" high (same mold as the original Whimsie No.4 ).

No. 287-2. **PENGUIN** - measures 1-5/8" high (same mold as the original Whimsie No.56 ).

No. 287-3. **WILD BOAR** - measures 1-1/8" high (same mold as the original Whimsie No.54 ).

No. 287-4. **KOALA BEAR** - measures 1-3/8" high (same mold as the original Whimsie No.49 ).

No. 287-5. **ORANG-UTAN** - measures 1-1/4" high (same mold as the original Whimsie No.47 ).

No. 287-6. **RHINO** - measures 7/8" high (same mold as the original Whimsie No.31 ).

No. 287-7. **KANGAROO** - measures 1-5/8" high (same mold as the original Whimsie No.46 ).

No. 287-8. **LEOPARD** - measures 7/8" high (same mold as the original Whimsie No.32 ).

## NURSERY RHYME SET *1987.*

For one year only, a limited number of party crackers were issued by Tom Smith using six models from the Nursery Rhyme series of miniature figurines originally used as Red Rose Tea premiums between 1971-1979. Each model used for the Tom Smith promotion has a single, all-over glaze as opposed to the more colorful Red Rose Tea premiums.

FIG. 35.

FIG. 35.  TOM SMITH NURSERY RHYMES 1987.
  A. WEE WILLIE WINKY - measures 1-3/4" high.
  B. LITTLE BO-PEEP - measures 1-3/4" high.
  C. OLD KING COLE - measures 1-1/2" high.
  D. HICKORY DICKORY DOCK - measures 1-3/4" high.
  E. HUMPTY-DUMPTY - measures 1-1/2" high.
  F. OLD WOMAN IN A SHOE - measures 1-3/8" high and has an all-over honey glaze.

## MINIATURE HOUSES SET *1988.*

A short-lived series issued between January 1988 and March 1988. Originally, there were to have been two sets in this series but due to high costs, the second set was never produced. The model houses were based upon existing shapes from the Whimsey-on-Why Village series.

No.288-1.  VILLAGE STORE - measures 1-3/8" high and is mold-marked WADE ENGLAND on the base. This is the same shape as Whimsey-on-Why No. 9.

No.288-2.  ROSE COTTAGE - measures 1-1/8" high and is mold-marked WADE ENGLAND on the base. This is the same shape as Whimsey-on-Why No. 1.

No.288-3.  THE COACH HOUSE GARAGE - measures 1-1/2" high and is mold-marked WADE ENGLAND on the base. This is the same shape as Whimsey-on-Why No. 18.

No.288-4.  PINK HOUSE - measures 1-5/8" high and is mold-marked WADE ENGLAND on the base. This is the same shape as Whimsey-on-Why No.22.

No.288-5.  THE CHAPEL - measures 1-3/4" high and is mold-marked WADE ENGLAND on the base. This is the same shape as Whimsey-on-Why No. 13.

## FAMILY PETS SET *1988 - 1989.*

This set of eight party cracker miniature birds and animals was designed exclusively for Tom Smith by George Wade & Son Ltd. In 1990, after the exclusivity lapsed, five of the figurines (Parrot, Kitten, Rabbit, Puppy and Pony) were released for use as premiums for the U.S. Red Rose Tea promotion.

No.289-1.  PARROT - measures 1-3/8" high and is mold-marked WADE ENG on the base.

No.289-2.  KITTEN - measures 1" high and is mold-marked WADE ENGLAND on the base.

No.289-3.  RABBIT - measures 1-1/8" high and is mold-marked WADE ENG on the base.

No.289-4.  PUPPY - measures 1" high and is mold-marked WADE ENGLAND on the base.

No.289-5.  PONY - measures 1" high and is mold-marked WADE ENG on the base.

No.289-6.  MOUSE - measures 1/2" high and is mold-marked WADE ENGLAND on the base.

No.289-7.  FISH - measures 1" high and is mold-marked WADE ENGLAND on the base.

No.289-8.  GUINEA PIG - measures 3/4" high and is mold-marked WADE ENG on the base.

## WORLD OF DOGS SET *1990 - 1991.*

A set of eight miniature figurines, six from the original 1971-1984 retail Whimsies line and two especially designed by George Wade & Son Ltd. for Tom Smith were used in this series.

No.290-1.  POODLE - measures 1-1/2" high and is mold-marked WADE ENGLAND on the base. This model is from the George Wade & Co. Ltd. standard range of premiums. It was also used in the 1967-1973 Canadian Red Rose Tea promotion.

No.290-2.  ALSATIAN - measures 1-1/4" high and is mold-marked WADE ENGLAND on the base. Same mold as No. 25 in the 1971-1984 Whimsies.

No.290-3.  CORGI - measures 1-1/2" high and is mold-marked WADE ENGLAND on the base. Same mold as No. 7 in the 1971-1984 Whimsies.

No.290-4.  WEST HIGHLAND TERRIER - measures 1-1/4" high and is mold-marked WADE ENGLAND on the base. Original design for Tom Smith.

No.290-5.  BULLDOG - measures 1" high and is mold-marked WADE ENGLAND on the base. Original design for Tom Smith.

No.290-6.  HUSKY - measures 1-3/8" high and is mold-marked WADE ENGLAND on the base. Same mold as No. 58 in the 1971-1984 Whimsies.

No.290-7.  MONGREL - measures 1-1/4" high and is mold-marked WADE ENGLAND on the base. Same mold as No. 3 in the 1971-1984 Whimsies.

No.290-8.  SPANIEL - measures 1-3/8" high and is mold-marked WADE ENGLAND on the base. Same mold as No.5 in the 1971-1984 Whimsies.

## POSY BOWLS *1950's.*

The posy logs, as they were described in Wade advertising, were first introduced to the market in December 1953. The early versions were rather plain, undecorated pieces. Later, however, rabbits and squirrels were added to the logs, thus giving them more appeal to the buying public.

**No.291.** BARGE POSY BOWL (1954). This posy bowl, which is found in green or beige glazes, measures 8" long by 2-1/2" high. It is mold-marked WADE ENGLAND REG.IN GT.BRITAIN NO.871886.

**No.292.** STRAIGHT LOG POSY BOWL (1954 - 1959). This posy bowl measures 4-3/4" long by 1-1/4" high and is mold-marked WADE ENGLAND. This unusual blue glaze finish is more difficult to find than the more usual brown and green glazes.

**No.293.** "S" SHAPED LOG POSY BOWL (1954 - 1959). This posy bowl measures 6-1/2" long by 1-1/2" high and is mold-marked WADE ENGLAND. This blue glaze finish is more difficult to find than the more usual brown and green glazes.

**No.294.** STRAIGHT LOG POSY BOWL (1954 - 1959). This posy bowl measures 4-3/4" long by 1-1/4" high and is mold-marked WADE ENGLAND. This white glaze finish is more difficult to find than the more usual brown and green glazes.

**No.295.** "S" SHAPED LOG POSY BOWL (1954 - 1959). Similar to No.293 but in the hard to find light green glaze finish.

**No.296.** "C" SHAPED LOG POSY BOWL (1954 - 1959). This posy bowl measures 6" across by 2-5/8" high and is mold-marked WADE ENGLAND.The posy bowl which is found with or without the Rabbit or Squirrel, can also be found in other glazes.

**No.297.** "C" SHAPED LOG POSY BOWL (1954 - 1959). The posy bowl measures 6" across by 1-3/8" high and is mold-marked WADE ENGLAND. This bowl is usually found in the more common brown or green glazes.

## ASCOT BOWL *late 1950's.*

This blue bowl with a white horse decoration standing on a pedestal was designed by Paul Zalman circa 1957. The bowl measures 2-1/4" high by 3-1/4" in diameter and has Mark Type 25 molded on the underside of the base. See FIG. 36.

FIG. 36. ASCOT BOWL.

## U.S.A. RED ROSE TEA PROMOTION-AL FIGURINES *1990.*

Five figurines were added to the continuing U.S. Red Rose Tea promotion which started in 1985. The original fifteen figurines are described in *The W of W pg.102*. The additional five figurines were chosen from the Tom Smith's party crackers Family Pets Set after the set was discontinued in 1989.

**No.298-16.** PUPPY - measures 1" high and is mold-marked WADE ENGLAND.

**No.298-17.** COCK-A-TEEL - measures 1-3/8" high and is mold-marked WADE ENG. This figurine is from the same mold as the Tom Smith Family Pets "Parrot" but renamed for the Red Rose Tea promotion.

**No.298-18.** KITTEN - measures 1" high and is mold-marked WADE ENGLAND.

**No.298-19.** PONY - measures 1" high and is mold-marked WADE ENG.

**No.298-20.** RABBIT - measures 1-1/8" high and is mold-marked WADE ENG.

*Cover of Red Rose Tea packaging containing the above series*

## TOM SMITH & CO. LTD. PARTY CRACKERS *1992-1993.*

In the 1992 and 1993 Christmas seasons, Tom Smith issued two sets of party cracker figurines titled "Birds" and "Snow Animals."

### BIRD SET *1992-1993.*

**No. 299-1.** ROOSTER - same model as Whimsie-Land No.143-11 in *The W of W pg.39.*

**No. 299-2.** EAGLE - same model as Survival series No.267-7 in *The W of W pg.43.*

**No. 299-3.** GOOSE - same model as Farmyard series No.266-2 in *The W of W pg.43.*

**No. 299-4.** WREN - measures 1-1/2" high and is mold marked WADE ENG. This is a new model designed especially for the series.

**No. 299-5.** BARN OWL - same model as Whimsie No.162-37 in *The W of W pg.40.*

**No. 299-6.** PARTRIDGE - same model as Whimsie-Land FIG.40.C in *The W of W pg.88.*

No. 299-7. DUCK - same model as Whimsie-Land No.143-12 in *The W of W pg.39.*

No. 299-8. PELICAN - same model as Whimsie No.163-42 in *The W of W pg.40.*

## SNOW ANIMAL SET *1992-1993.*

No. 300-1. HARE - same model as Farmyard set No.265-5 in *The W of W pg.43.*

No. 300-2. FOX - same model as Whimsie-Land No.144-17 in *The W of W pg.39.*

No. 300-3. SEAL PUP - same model as Whimsie No.166-57 in *The W of W pg.40.*

No. 300-4. REINDEER - measures 1-1/4" high and is mold-marked WADE ENG. This is a new model designed especially for the series.

No. 300-5. POLAR BEAR - same model as Whimsie No.166-60 in *The W of W pg.40.*

No. 300-6. WALRUS - same model as Whimsie No.166-59 in *The W of W pg.40.*

No. 300-7. OWL - same model as Whimsie-Land No.144-20 in *The W of W pg.39.*

No. 300-8. PENGUIN - same model as Whimsie No.165-56 in *The W of W pg.40.*

## MISCELLANEOUS PREMIUMS BY GEORGE WADE & SON LTD.

The following figurines are examples of color variations of standard George Wade premium figurines unless noted otherwise.

No. 301. POLAR BEAR - measures 1-1/8" high and is mold-marked WADE ENGLAND. This is the correct color for the figurine of the Tom Smith Safari set 1976-1977. This figure replaces No.263-7 in *The W of W pg.43.*

No. 302. POLAR BEAR - measures 1-1/8" high and is mold-marked WADE ENGLAND. This is the Whimsie Polar Bear No.166-60. This figure was shown in error as the Tom Smith Polar Bear in *The W of W pg.43* and is shown here to help collectors differentiate between the two figurines.

No. 303. DUCK - same model as Farmyard set No.266-3 in *The W of W pg.43.* The origin of this all-over blue duck is not known at the time of writing.

No. 304. BLUE BIRD - same model as Whimsie No.165-52 in *The W of W pg.40.* This figurine is from a miscellaneous set of Tom Smith Party Crackers issued in 1992-1993.

No. 305. OLD WOMAN IN A SHOE - same model as No.213 in *The W of W pg.42.* This figurine is from the Tom Smith Nursery Rhyme set issued in 1987.

No. 306. POODLE - same model as No.197 in *The W of W pg.42.* The origin of this all-over orange/brown poodle is not known at the time of writing.

An article in the April 1993 issue of *The Wade Watch Newsletter* noted some research conducted between the editors and Sally Ball of Tom Smith Ltd. on some of the occasionally found figurines from Tom Smith Crackers. A variety of Wade figurines were found illustrated and noted in Tom Smith catalogues issued between 1985-1993. The figurines noted are listed below.

1987

Beige Hickory Dickory Dock; Beige Old Woman in a Shoe; Bright Blue Wee Willie Winkie; Bright Blue Old King Cole; Honey colored Bo-Peep; Dark Brown Humpty-Dumpty; Honey colored Hare; Dark Brown Gorilla, same model as Survival series No.267-2 in *The W of W pg.43.*

1988

Honey colored Hare.

1989

Beige Koala Bear; Honey colored Kangaroo; Little Bo-Peep, similar color to the Red Rose Tea issue No.216 in *The W of W pg.42;* Wee Willie Winkie, similar color to the Red Rose Tea issue No.215 in *The W of W pg. 42;* Hickory Dickory Dock, similar color to the Red Rose Tea issue No.223 in *The W of W pg.42.*

1990

Old King Cole, similar color to the Red Rose Tea issue No.202 in *The W of W pg.42;* Blue Squirrel, same model as Wildlife series No.265-6 in *The W of W pg.43;* Brown Hare.

1992

Bright Blue Blue Bird, same model as Whimsie No.165-52 in *The W of W pg.40;* Honey colored Koala Bear.

1993

Bright Blue Blue Bird, same model as Whimsie No. 165-52 in *The W of W pg.40;* Honey colored Koala Bear; Blue Mongrel.

The same issue of the newsletter reported that a number of Wade figurines had been made for a proposed General Foods Coffee promotion. Although this promotion did not proceed, it is possible a number of the figurines found their way onto the collectors market. These figurines are listed below.

White Owl with black eyes, orange beak on a green base; black Zebra on a green base; Penguin with black head, wings and back, orange beak and feet; white and tan Rabbit with pink nose and black eye; Whimsie-Land Panda, black and white; Tom Smith Badger with light grey body, white head with black stripes over the eyes, black nose on a green base; Red Riding Hood, Miss Muffett and Queen of Hearts, all pale pink; Cat 'n Fiddle, pale blue; Jack, Jill, Old Woman in a Shoe, Little Jack Horner, House that Jack Built and Mother Goose, all beige; Old King Cole, pale blue; Little Bo-Peep, Dr. Foster and Pied Piper, all green; Wee Willie Winkie, House that Jack Built, Tom Piper and Little Boy Blue, all blue; Hickory Dickory Dock and Puss' in Boots, both brown.

## "SIGNAL" TOOTHPASTE PROMOTION *circa late 1960's - early 1970's.*

In the late 1960's, Lever Rexona New Zealand Limited offered Wade Nursery Rhyme figurines free in cartons of "Signal 2" toothpaste which, at the time, was a leading toothpaste brand on the New Zealand market. The promotion had a run of less than a year and was comprised of the twenty-four figurines also used for the 1971 - 1979 Canadian Red Rose Tea promotion.

*Illustration of the Signal toothpaste carton featuring the Wade Nursery Rhyme Figurines promotion.*

## WHIMSEY-IN-THE-VALE *1993.*

In February 1993, Wade Ceramics Ltd. introduced a new line of miniature houses. The new models utilized the same molds as those used for some of the Whimsey-on-Why Village Houses. The applied decals were newly designed by Judith Wooten. Unlike the Whimsey-on-Why Village Houses, the Whimsey-in-the-Vale Houses are not numbered.

No. 307-1.   ST. LAWRENCE CHURCH - same model as No.268-7 in *The W of W pg.43.*

No. 307-2.   TOWN GARAGE - same model as No.271-32 in *The W of W pg.43.*

No. 307-3.   VALE FARM - same model as No.269-15 in *The W of W pg.43.*

No. 307-4.   BOAR'S HEAD PUB - same model as No.268-8 in *The W of W pg.43.*

No. 307-5.   ST. JOHN'S SCHOOL - same model as No.271-31 in *The W of W pg.43.*

No. 307-6.   JUBILEE TERRACE - same model as No.270-23 in *The W of W pg.43.*

No. 307-7.   ANTIQUE SHOP - same model as No.268-5 in *The W of W pg.43.*

No. 307-8.   WHIMSEY POST OFFICE - same model as No.269-9 in *The W of W pg.43.*

No. 307-9.   ROSE COTTAGE - same model as No.269-11 in *The W of W pg.43.*

No. 307-10.  FLORIST SHOP - same model as No.269-11 in *The W of W pg.43.*

## MISCELLANEOUS ITEMS

*early 1950's - mid 1960's.*

Soon after wartime restrictions were lifted on the manufacture of pottery fancies, George Wade & Son Ltd. was quick to enter the giftware retail market. The early Wade line of giftware consisted mainly of such items as the single-glazed posy logs, egg cups and barbecue tankards. As more glazes became available to the potteries, Wade extended their giftware lines to include items such as the Disney Hat Box series, various Whimsies, the Blue Bird posy bowl, the Sealion Corkscrew and the T.T. Tray etc.

No. 308.   DUMBO - measures 1-3/8" high by 1-5/8" overall and is unmarked. This is a prototype model.

No. 309.   DUMBO - measures 1-3/8" high by 1-5/8" overall and is unmarked. This is a production model.

No. 310.   THUMPER CANDLE HOLDER - measures 2" along each side of the triangular shaped base and is mold-marked WADE on the underside of the base.

No. 311.   SEAHORSE. This prototype model measures 3-3/4" high. This and the following four Seahorses were modeled by William Harper in the late 1950's.

No. 312.   SEAHORSE. This prototype model measures 4" high.

No. 313.   SEAHORSE. This prototype model measures 3" high.

No. 314.   SEAHORSE. This prototype model measures 2-3/4" high.

No. 315.   SEAHORSE. This prototype model measures 4-1/4" high. Note the compass embedded in the base.

No. 316.   SEA LION CORKSCREW (1960). The Sea Lion Corkscrew measures 5-3/4" high to the top of the removable ball handle of the corkscrew. This figural item originally had the black and gold Wade paper label attached to the body.

No. 317.   PEGASUS POSY BOWL (1958 - 1959). This bowl measures 4-3/8" high by 5-5/8" long and is mold-marked with Mark Type 24 on the underside of the base.

No. 318.   PALERMO POSY BOWL (1957 - 1959). The posy bowl measures 3-1/4" high by 6" across and is mold-marked with Mark Type 25 on the base. This bowl, also found in a smaller size, can also be found with green or white glazes.

No. 319.   BARBECUE TANKARD (early 1950's). The 1/2 pint tankard measures 4-1/2" high and is ink stamped with Mark Type 10 on the base. This tankard is also found with a brown glaze.

**FIG. 37.**

**FIG. 37.** "BUNNY" NIGHT LIGHT - measures 4-1/2" high by 5-1/2" long and has Mark Type 5 on the base. The night light has a green base with a green candle cover decorated with a yellow and brown daisy and a brown bunny.

**FIG. 38.** TWO PART "BUNNY" NIGHT LIGHT. See FIG.37 for details.

FIG. 38.

# SILHOUETTE SERIES *1961 - 1962.*

This series of trays and vases, produced in the early 1960's, featured giraffes, zebras and Viking ships as themes for the decoration. See also item Nos.328 and 329. Items in this series can be found in either single glazes or multicolored. The trays were made in at least three different shapes/sizes.

No. 320.    SILHOUETTE GIRAFFE VASE. The vase measures 4-1/8" high and is mold-marked with Mark Type 25 on the base.

# MISCELLANEOUS ITEMS
*early 1950's - mid 1960's continued*

No. 321.    BLUE BIRD TREE TRUNK POSY VASE (1957 - 1959). This posy vase measures 4" high with a 2-3/4" diameter base and is mold-marked with Mark Type 25.

FIG. 39.

**FIG. 39.** TREE TRUNK COVERED DISH. This 2" high by 3" diameter covered dish was modelled by Wm. Harper but never went into production.

**FIG. 40.** "BIRD BATH" BOWL (circa mid 1950's)- measures 3-1/8" high by 4-1/2" in diameter and is mold-

FIG. 40.

marked Wade on the underside of the base. This bowl can be found with or without holes around the rim and in a variety of colors. The bowl illustrated is solid green.

# TREE TRUNK CONDIMENT SET
*circa late 1950's.*

A set of shakers and mustard pot made as a "reserved line" in green, brown and possibly other glazes. Each piece has an impressed mark R97/1 on the underside of the base.

No. 322.    TREE TRUNK SALT - measures 2-1/8" high with 1-5/8" diameter base.

No. 323.    TREE TRUNK PEPPER - measures 2-1/8" high with 1-5/8" diameter base.

No. 324.    TREE TRUNK MUSTARD - measures 1-1/2" high with 1-5/8" diameter base.

No. 325.    TREE TRUNK SALT - measures 2-1/8" high with 1-5/8" diameter base.

No. 326.    TREE TRUNK PEPPER - measures 2-1/8" high with 1-5/8" diameter base.

# MISCELLANEOUS ITEMS
*early 1950's - mid 1960's continued.*

No. 327.    BLUE BIRD TREE TRUNK P0SY VASE (1957 - 1959). This posy vase measures 4" high with a 2-3/4" diameter base and is mold-marked with Mark Type 25.

No. 328.    SILHOUETTE VIKING SHIP TRAY. The tray measures 4-3/4" long by 3-3/8" wide and is mold-marked with Mark Type 25.

No. 329.    SILHOUETTE ZEBRA TRAY. The tray measures 4-1/2" long by 3-1/4" wide and is mold-marked with Mark Type 25.

No. 330.    T.T. TRAY (1959 - 1960). The tray measures 2-3/4" high and is marked with Mark Type 19 on the underside of the base.

No. 331.    SEA - GULL BOAT (1961). The boat is 6-1/4" long by 2-1/4" high and is mold-marked with Mark Type 25 on the underside of the base.

No. 332.    BRIDGE POSY BOWL (1954 - 1958). The bowl is 6"

long by 1-3/8" high and is mold-marked WADE ENG-LAND REGD. IN GT. BRITAIN NO.871653. This bowl was also made in a brown glaze.

No. 333.  SWAN EGG CUP - (circa mid 1950's). The egg cup measures 2-1/4" high by 3-1/2" long and is mold-marked MADE IN ENGLAND.

No. 334.  SWAN EGG CUP - (circa mid 1950's). The egg cup measures 2-1/4" high by 3-1/2" long and is mold-marked MADE IN ENGLAND. The Egg Cup has also been reported in a yellow glaze.

No. 335.  ARCHED BRIDGE POSY BOWL (mid 1950's). The bowl measures 6" long by 1-3/4" high and is mold marked WADE ENGLAND REGD. IN GT. BRITAIN NO.871653. Although similar to No.332 this multi-colored version of the bowl has a pronounced arch, a flying bird above one of the arches and keystones in both of the arches.

No. 336.  VIKING SHIP POSY BOWL (1976 - 1982). The posy bowl measures 7-3/8" long by 3-3/4" high and is mold marked with Mark Type 25 on the underside of the base. The Viking Ship Posy Bowl was originally issued in 1959 with a lighter blue brown finish. See *The W of W No.306 pg.44.*

No. 337.  POPPY BOWL - (late 1950's). The Poppy Bowl is 1-3/4" high by 3-1/4" in diameter and is unmarked. This bowl is also found with a red glaze.

No. 338.  LARGE TRADITIONAL POSY BOWL (1955 - 1959). Measures 3" high by 6-1/4" overall by 2-1/4" wide. The recessed base is mold-marked WADE ENGLAND.

## WHIMTRAYS *1987 - 1988.*

The new Whimtrays, introduced in 1987, replaced the long running shape of trays first introduced in 1958. Whimtrays were first introduced to use up remaining stock of the early Whimsies. In 1971 the early Whimsies were replaced by three of the 1971 - 1984 series of Whimsies. These, in turn, were replaced by a new shaped tray holding one each of five of the Whimsie-Land series of figurines. The new trays measure 4-1/2" long by 3-1/2" wide and are mold-marked WADE ENGLAND. For additional information on Whimtrays see *The W of W pgs.114 and 115.*

No. 339.  PUPPY - from the 1984 Whimsie-Land Pets series.
No. 340.  PONY - from the 1984 Whimsie-Land Pets series.
No. 341.  SQUIRREL - from the 1986 Whimsie-Land Hedgerow series.
No. 342.  OWL - from the 1986 Whimsie-Land Hedgerow series.
No. 343.  DUCK - from the 1985 Whimsie-Land Farmyard series.

## DOG PIPE RESTS *1973 - 1981.*

A set of five pipe rests featuring the adult dogs from the 1969 -1982 Dogs and Puppies series. For additional Dog Pipe Rests see *The W of W pgs.38 and 87.*

No. 344.  YORKSHIRE TERRIER - measures 3-1/4" in diameter by 2-1/4" high and is mold-marked WADE ENGLAND. The Yorkshire Terrier pipe rest appears to be the most difficult to find of the Dog Pipe Rests Series.

## ZOO LIGHTS *1959.*

These miniature candleholders were also used to carry remaining stocks of the early Whimsies. The various colored, oval-shaped bases with an extension to hold the candle, measure 1-3/4" wide by 1-3/4" deep and are mold-marked with Mark Type 25 in the recessed base.

No. 345.  CAMEL - from the 1958 Zoo Set (Set 8) of the early Whimsies.
No. 346.  HUSKY - from the 1956 Polar Set (Set 6) of the early Whimsies.
No. 347.  WEST HIGHLAND TERRIER - from the 1957 Pedigree Dogs (Set 7) of the early Whimsies.
No. 348.  BABY POLAR BEAR - from the 1956 Polar Set (Set 6) of the early Whimsies.
No. 349.  BABY POLAR BEAR - from the 1956 Polar Set (Set 6) of the early Whimsies.
No. 350.  CORGI - from the 1957 Pedigree Dogs (Set 7) of the early Whimsies.
No. 351.  HARE - from the 1954 (Set 7) of the early Whimsies.
No. 352.  LLAMA - from the 1958 Zoo Set (Set 8) of the early Whimsies.
No. 353.  BOXER - from the 1957 Pedigree Dogs (Set 7) of the early Whimsies.
No. 354.  SNOWY OWL - from the 1958 North American Animals (Set 9) of the early Whimsies.

FIG. 41

FIG. 41.  ALSATIAN - from the 1957 Pedigree Dogs (Set 7) of the early Whimsies.

## ANGEL TRAYS AND FIGURINES

*1959 - early 1960's.*

A set of three different Angel figures (standing, sitting and kneeling) sold either separately, mounted on trays similar to the Whimtrays or candleholders similar to the Disney Candleholder (see No.310). These figures have been found with green, pink, yellow and blue glazes.

FIG. 42.  ANGEL CANDLEHOLDER - measures 2" along each side of the black triangular base and is mold-marked WADE on the underside. Unlike the multi-

**FIG. 42.**

colored Zoo Lights, these triangular candleholders have so far only been found in black.

No. 355.  ANGEL DISH - measures 2" high and is mold-marked "ANGEL DISH" WADE PORCELAIN MADE IN ENGLAND.

No. 356.  ANGEL FIGURE (standing) - measures 1-1/2" high and is unmarked.

No. 357.  ANGEL FIGURE (kneeling) - measures 1-3/8" high and is unmarked.

No. 358.  ANGEL DISH - measures 2" high and is mold-marked "ANGEL DISH" WADE PORCELAIN MADE IN ENGLAND.

# WHIMTRAYS *1958 - 1965* and "BOULDRAY" and "PEERAGE" TRAYS

*late 1960's - early 1970's.*

The original Whimtrays were created to utilize excess stock of the early Whimsies. The trays, which were made in various color glazes, were made both in England and Ireland. For more information on these Whimtrays see *The W of W pg.114.*

No. 359.  ALSATIAN - from the 1957 Pedigree Dogs (Set 7) of the early Whimsies.

No. 360.  MONKEY - from the 1955 (Set 4) of the early Whimsies.

No. 361.  CANDLEHOLDER - measures 2-3/4" high. This candleholder base is similar to the Zoo Light candleholders but with a metal horse, resembling the "Bouldray" or "Peerage" lines, screwed to the base. Only the porcelain base was made by Wade which is mold-marked with Mark Type 25.

No. 362.  LADY "BOULDRAY" TRAY - the metal figurine is mounted on a tray similar to the Whimtrays and is mold-marked "BOULDRAY" WADE PORCELAIN 2 MADE IN ENGLAND. Only the tray was made by Wade.

*ANGELIC! A George Wade & Son Ltd. advertisement as it appeared in the September 1963 issue of Tableware. Note the horse and foal dish in the bottom right hand corner.*

**FIG. 43.**

FIG. 43.  "BOULDRAY" TRAY
  A. PELICAN - measures 2-1/4" high. The metal bird is mounted on a base similar to No.362.
  B. HORSE - measures 2-3/4" high. The metal horse is mounted on a base similar to No.362.

FIG. 44.  "PEERAGE" TRAY
  A. GIRL WITH BASKET measures 2-3/4" high. The metal figure is mounted on a porcelain base similar to the Whimtray but marked "Peerage" WADE PORCELAIN MADE IN ENGLAND.
  B. KNIGHT IN ARMOUR - measures 2-3/4" high. The metal figure is mounted on a porcelain base similar to the Whimtray but marked "Peerage" WADE PORCELAIN MADE IN ENGLAND. The knight is named "Guy of Warwick."

141

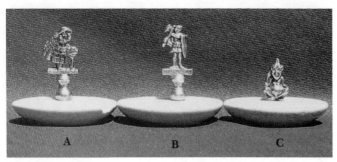

FIG. 44.

> C. ELF-measures 2" high. The metal figure is mounted on a porcelain base similar to the Whimtray but marked "Peerage" WADE PORCELAIN MADE IN ENGLAND.

No. 363.     BOXER - from the 1957 Pedigree Dogs (Set 7) of the early Whimsies.

No. 364.     CAMEL - from the 1958 Zoo Set (Set 8) of the early Whimsies.

No. 365.     COCKATOO - from the 1958 Zoo Set (Set 8) of the early Whimsies.

FIG. 45.

FIG. 45.     SWAN WHIMTRAY - from the 1959 Farm Animals (Set 10) of the early Whimsies. This is a rare combination.

# DOG DISH *circa 1957.*

A set of colored dishes mounted with either a Terrier or Spaniel dogs. The dishes are impressed with Mark Type 26 on the base. For the Terrier tray see *The W of W No.285 pg.44.*

No. 366.     SPANIEL DOG DISH - measures 1-5/8" high by 4" across.

# TEENAGE POTTERY *early 1960's.*

A 1961 Wade catalogue lists four different 1950's pop stars featured on guitar shaped brooches and heart-shaped trinket boxes or caskets. The four stars were Cliff Richards, Tommy Steele, Frankie Vaughan and Marty Wilde. Two of

these characters, Marty Wilde and Cliff Richards were also available as cameo plaques. The heart-shaped casket used in this line was later re-used for the Prince Charles and Lady Diana Spencer wedding commemorative. See No.1027.

No. 367.     FRANKIE VAUGHAN HEART-SHAPED CASKET - measures 1-5/8" high by 3-1/2" across. The covered dish is mold-marked with Mark Type 25 on the underside of the base.

No. 368.     MARTY WILDE HEART-SHAPED CASKET - measures 1-5/8" high by 3-1/2" across. The covered dish is mold-marked with Mark Type 25 on the underside of the base.

No. 369.     MARTY WILDE. This molded likeness of Marty Wilde measures 2-3/4" high by 1-7/8" across. This item is usually found applied to an oval-shaped plaque. See FIG.46.

FIG. 46.

FIG. 46.     TEENAGE POTTERY OF POP STARS. A Wade advertisement as it appeared in the October 1960 issue of *Pottery and Glass.*

> A. MARTY WILDE HEART-SHAPED CASKET - see No.368 for details.
> B. TOMMY STEELE HEART-SHAPED CASKET - measures 1-5/8" high by 3-1/2" across. The covered dish is mold-marked with Mark Type 25 on the underside of the base.
> C. CLIFF RICHARDS HEART-SHAPED CASKET - measures 1-5/8" high by 3-1/2" across. The covered dish is mold-marked with Mark Type 25 on the underside of the base.
> D. CLIFF RICHARDS GUITAR BROOCH - measures 2-3/8" long and is marked with a transfer type mark similar to Mark Type 25.
> E. TOMMY STEELE GUITAR BROOCH - measures 2-3/8" long and is marked with a transfer type mark similar to Mark Type 25.

F. **FRANKIE VAUGHAN GUITAR BROOCH** - measures 2-3/8" long and is marked with a transfer type mark similar to Mark Type 25.

G. **MARTY WILDE GUITAR BROOCH** - measures 2-3/8" long and is marked with a transfer type mark similar to Mark Type 25.

H. **MARTY WILDE CAMEO PLAQUE** - measures 3-3/4" by 2-3/4" and is marked with Mark Type 26.

I. **FRANKIE VAUGHAN HEART-SHAPED CASKET** - see No.367 for details.

J. **CLIFF RICHARDS CAMEO PLAQUE** - measures 3-3/4" by 2-3/4" and is marked with Mark Type 26.

# GARDNER MERCHANT TRINKET BOX *1986.*

This trinket box was a special issue for Gardner Merchant Catering to celebrate their hundredth anniversary.

No. 370.    **GARDNER MERCHANT TRINKET BOX** - measures 1-5/8" high by 3" wide. The trinket box is marked with Mark Type 20 along with the wording: "Gardner Merchant a century of catering service 1886-1986."

# EVERLASTING CANDLES *1953 - 1954* and CLOCKS and POWDER JARS *1990 - 1992.*

Promotional literature from George Wade & Co. Ltd. describes the Everlasting Candles as "These delightful candles are made in a special non-absorbent and heat-resisting translucent porcelain body, and will burn for several hours on a single filling of pink paraffin." The first candles introduced were available with small flower sprays of gold all-over pattern decoration. British and foreign patents were applied for. However, the candles were not a success on the market and were soon withdrawn from production.

In the 1990, Wade Ceramics Ltd. produced two attractive lines of co-ordinated giftware. The lines, KAWA and JACOBEAN, consisted of eleven different shapes, with similar shapes for each design. The two lines were withdrawn from production in 1992, after only a short run.

No. 371.    **EVERLASTING CANDLES** - measures 8-1/2" high with a 4" diameter base which has a transfer Mark Type 19 on the underside of the recessed base.

No. 372.    **KAWA CLOCK** - measures 6-1/4" high by 5" across the base by 2-1/2" deep and is marked with Mark Type 27B on the underside of the base.

No. 373.    **KAWA POWDER JAR** - measures 2-3/4" high by 3-3/4" diameter base and is marked with Mark Type 27B on the underside of the base.

FIG. 47.    **RANGE OF THE JACOBEAN LINE OF GIFTWARE.** The range consists of three planters (large, medium and small), clock, covered ginger jar, vases (small, medium and large), large covered jar, trinket box and

**FIG. 47.**

pedestal bowl. The Kawa range, not illustrated, has similar items in its range.

No. 374.    **JACOBEAN POWDER JAR** - measures 2-3/4" high by 3-3/4" diameter base and is marked with Mark Type 27B on the underside of the base.

No. 375.    **JACOBEAN CLOCK** - measures 6-1/4" high by 5" across the base by 2-1/2" deep and is marked with Mark Type 27B on the underside of the base.

No. 376.    **EVERLASTING CANDLES** - measures 8-1/2" high with a 4" diameter base which has a transfer Mark Type 19 on the underside of the recessed base.

*An illustration of the "Edwardian Giftware" line.*

143

## WADE EDWARDIAN GIFTWARE *1988 - 1990.*

A collection of giftware in the "Queensway Pattern." Items available were: Photo Frame 5-1/2" high, Large Vase 7-3/4" high, Medium Vase 5-1/2" high, Large Ewer 7-1/4" high with an 8-3/4" diameter basin, Medium Ewer 5-1/4" high with a 6-1/2" diameter basin and three planters, 5" high, 4-1/4" high and 3-1/2" high.

## BOOTS TEDDY BEARS *1988 - 1989.*

Most years, around Christmas, Wade supplies the Boots chain of drug stores with items ranging from teapots to bookends. Most often the items are marked with words stating the item is made exclusively for Boots by Wade but this is not always the case.

No. 377.   **TEDDY BEAR BOOKEND** - measures 6-3/8" high and is unmarked. There is a hole with a plastic plug in the base to fill the bookend with sand to give it stability.

No. 378.   **TEDDY BEAR UTILITY JAR** - measures 5-1/4" high and is unmarked. The utility jar was designed as a holder for kitchen utensils.

No. 379.   **TEDDY BEAR BOOKEND** - measures 6-3/8" high and is unmarked. There is a hole with a plastic plug in the base to fill the bookend with sand to give it stability. This bookend is the pair to No. 377.

## T.V. PEN & PENCIL HOLDER.

This utility holder, for use on the desktop, is believed to have been issued in the late 1970's or early 1980's as a private order.

No. 380.   **T.V. PEN & PENCIL HOLDER** - measures 3-1/2" high by 2-5/8" square at the base and is mold-marked on the recessed base WADE SM ENGLAND. The SM is quite stylized.

## CANDLEHOLDERS *circa 1957 - early 1960's.*

No. 381.   **OAK LEAF CANDLEHOLDER** - measures 1-7/8" high by 4-1/4" long. Only the porcelain leaf was supplied by Wade and this is mold-marked with Mark Type 25.

No. 382.   **OAK LEAF CANDLEHOLDER** - color variation of No.381. These oak leaf candleholders were issued circa the late 1950's early 1960's.

FIG. 48.

144

FIG. 48.   **CHRISTMAS CANDLE HOLDERS** (circa 1960 - 1961). A pair of boxed candleholders in the form of green holly leaves with red berries. The leaves, which are 4" long, are unmarked.

## PRICE'S PATENT CANDLE COMPANY LIMITED *1963 - 1982.*

For a number of years, George Wade & Son Ltd. produced candleholders for Price's Patent Candle Company Limited. None of these candleholders were marked "Wade." However, most of them bear the impressed contract number. For additional information see *The W of W* pg.117.

No. 383.   **FLOWER LIGHT LEAF HOLDER** - measures 6-1/4" long by 1-3/8" high and is unmarked. This item was produced between 1963-1973 (224,000 pieces were made).

No. 384.   **PLAIN ROUND HOLDER** - measures 4" in diameter and has an impressed MADE IN ENGLAND mark on the underside of the base.

No. 385.   **CUBE HOLDER** - measures 2" square by 2" high and is mold-marked WADE ENGLAND S58/1 on the recessed base.

No. 386.   **TULIP HOLDER** - measures 1-3/4" high by 2" in diameter at the top and is mold-marked S2/18 on the underside of the base.

No. 387.   **TULIP HOLDER** - measures 1-3/4" high by 2" diameter at the top and is mold-marked S2/18 on the underside of the base.

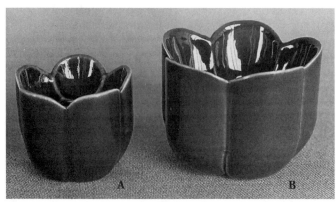

FIG. 49.

FIG. 49.   A. **TULIP HOLDER SMALL** - measures 1-3/4" high by 2" diameter at the top and is mold-marked S2/18 on the underside of the base.

B. **TULIP HOLDER LARGE** - measures 2-1/4" high by 2-7/8" diameter and is unmarked.

No. 388.   **VENETIAN SCATTER HOLDER** - measures 1-3/4" high by 3" diameter and is mold-marked S2/16 on the underside of the recessed base. The holder was produced in various colors between 1970 - 1982 (109,000 pieces were made).

No. 389.   **PLAIN ARCH HOLDER** - measures 1-1/2" high by 5-1/2" long and is mold-marked S2/6 on the underside of the recessed base.

**MONEY BANKS**

and

**PROTOTYPE MODELS.**

By

George Wade & Son Ltd.,

Wade, Heath & Co. Ltd.

and

Wade Ceramics Ltd.

mid 1950's - 1993.

# MONEY BANKS.

*By George Wade & Son Ltd. and Wade, Heath & Company Ltd. circa early 1960's - 1993.*

As well as giftware items, decorative money boxes have proven most popular as incentives and promotional items over the past few years. The Wade Potteries have produced a number of attractive money boxes since the early 1960's with the BAMBI money box and BENGO money box (based on the T.V. PETS figurine) being the earliest. The terms "money box" and "money bank" are interchangeable as companies often refer to these items using either term.

No. 390.  TOADSTOOL MONEY BANK - measures 5-1/2" high by 6" wide and is unmarked. The money bank was made by George Wade & Son Ltd. in 1987.

No. 391.  FAWN MONEY BANK - measures 5-1/4" high by 5" long and is marked with Mark Type 19. The money bank was made by George Wade & Son Ltd. in 1987.

No. 392.  KENNEL MONEY BANK - measures 4-1/2" high by 5-1/4" long and is unmarked. The money bank was made by George Wade & Son Ltd. in 1987.

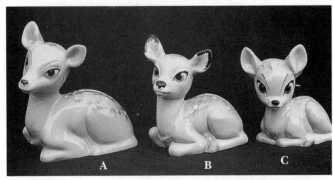

FIG. 50

FIG. 50  A. FAWN MONEY BANK (1987) - see No. 391 for details.
B. BAMBI MONEY BOX (1960's).
C. BLOW-UP DISNEY BAMBI (1961 - 1965).

No. 393.  "BREW GAFFER" MONEY BANK (1989 - 1990) - measures 5-1/4" high by 3-3/4" across the base and is marked: Made exclusively for LYONS TETLEY by WADE. The money bank was used as a promotional item by Lyons Tetley from September 1989 to the end of July 1990. The offer appeared on all Tetley Catering tea bags.

No. 394.  NATWEST PANDA MONEY BOX (1989) - measures 4-1/2" high and can be found with or without WADE ENGLAND molded on the underside of the base. This money box, in the form of a Panda which is the emblem of the World Wide Fund for Nature, replaced the popular Piggy Family money banks. The Panda money box was given as a gift to the under seven-year old customers of the bank who opened a NatWest World Savers account. For every account opened, the National Westminster Bank donated £1.00 to the World Wide Fund for Nature.
We would like to acknowledge National Westminster Bank's ownership and copyright of the Panda Money Box design.

No. 395.  PETER THE POLAR BEAR MONEY BOX (1988) - measures 6" high and is unmarked. This was a special promotion for Thorton's Toffee.

No. 396.  LYONS' VINTAGE VAN MONEY BANK (1990) - measures 5-1/4" high by 8" long and is marked with Mark Type 27B on the base. It is also marked Manufactured Exclusively for Lyons Tetley.

*Advertisement for the "Brew Gaffer" Money Box.*

*Advertisement for Tetley Vintage Money Box.*

**No. 397.** **MONSTER MUNCH MONEY BANK (1987-1988)-** measures 6-1/2" high and has an impressed mark: WADE ENGLAND, on the underside of the base.

**No. 398.** **LETTER BOX MONEY BANK** - measures 7" high by 4-3/4" diameter base and is unmarked. On the reverse side of the letter box money bank the molded logo reads: THORNTONS ESTD 1911.

**No. 399.** **TETLEY VINTAGE VAN MONEY BANK (1990)** - measures 5-1/4" high by 8" long and has an impressed mark on the base: MANUFACTURED EXCLUSIVELY FOR LYONS TETLEY. MADE IN ENGLAND. This promotion was exclusive to a specific Cash & Carry store between March and November of 1990.

## "PIGGY" MONEY BANKS

### late 1950's early 1960's.

In the late 1950's, Wade, Heath & Co. Ltd. introduced a series of money banks in the form of pigs, generally known as "piggy banks." These money banks measure 5" high by 6-1/2" long and had Mark Type 19 on the underside of the tummy. A variety of decorations were used, often employing similar decals to those used on the Harmony and Flair tableware. FIG.51 illustrates a piggy bank with a flower decoration, the decoration number of which is not known. Other examples are illustrated in FIG.52.

**FIG. 51.** **"PIGGY" BANK with unknown decoration.**

**FIG. 51.**

**FIG. 52.** Additional "Piggy" bank decorations.

    A - decoration No. 6261 "Roses" on a yellow glaze. A similar style, decoration No. 6263 had "Violets" on a white glaze.

    B - decoration No. 6269 "Parasols" on a yellow glaze.

    C - decoration No. 6264 solid black glaze with red eyes, nose and inside of ears.

    D - decoration No. 6262 "Stars" on a white glaze.

    E - decoration No. 6281 "Safeway" multicolored on white glaze. The reverse side of this piggy bank shows footprints with the words "Watch your step," a traffic light and a puppy sitting at the curb with the words "Paws at the kerb."

**FIG. 52A.**

**FIG. 52B.**

FIG. 52C.

FIG. 52D.

FIG. 52E.

## ADDITIONAL PROTOTYPE MODELS, COLOR VARIATIONS and LIMITED ADDITIONS *mid 1950's - late 1950's.*

This section illustrates a number of prototype items which did not go into production along with prototype items which did go into production, but with glazes differing from the final retail line item. Also shown are items with limited edition decorations differing from the standard decorations used in the retail line.

No. 400.   BOWL. This experimental piece, modelled by William Harper, measures approx. 3" in diameter and is unmarked.

No. 401.   BOWL. This prototype bowl measures 4" in diameter and is unmarked. The piece was modelled by William Harper and was the basis for the Primrose Bowl design.

No. 402.   TREASURE CHEST COVERED DISH. This experimental blue/green glazed finish piece was modelled by William Harper and eventually went into production as item No.308 in *The W of W pg.44.*

No. 403.   COVERED SHORE CRAB DISH. Prototype of the production model shown as item No.305 in *The W of W pg.44.*

No. 404.   COVERED SHORE CRAB DISH. Color variation of item No.403 above.

No. 405.   STACKING ASHTRAYS. Prototype version of the ashtrays including a ceramic base. The base did not go into production. See also items No.459-463 in this book.

No. 406.   TREASURE CHEST COVERED DISH. This experimental green glazed finish piece was modelled by William Harper and eventually went into production as item No.308 in *The W of W pg.44.*

No. 407.   PINEAPPLE BOWL - measures 4-1/2" by 3" and is unmarked. This experimental item designed by William Harper did not go into production.

No. 408.   LIZARD ASHTRAY - measures 3-1/2" high by 5" and is unmarked. This experimental item designed by William Harper did not go into production.

No. 409.   TREE STUMP LIDDED BOX - measures 2" high by 3" in diameter and is unmarked. This experimental item designed by William Harper did not go into production.

No. 410.   ROSE BOX - measures 3" high by 4" across and is unmarked. This experimental item designed by William Harper did not go into production.

No. 411.   VASE - measures 11-1/2" high. This decoration was applied to mold No. 342 in a limited number.

No. 412.   SEATED LADY - measures 7-1/4" high. This figurine was modelled by Frank Garbutt and decorated by Georgina Lawton circa 1950.

No. 413.   WALL PLAQUE - measures 13-1/4" in diameter and is one of two pieces decorated by Georgina Lawton, one of which, was presented to the late Sir George Wade.

No. 414.   VASE - measures 11" high and is a matching piece to the Wall Plaque No. 413 above. As with the plaque, this vase is one of two pieces decorated by Georgina Lawton.

## WADE LIGHTING RANGE *1990-1991.*

In mid 1991 Wade Ceramics Ltd. produced a wide range of decorative table lamps in various shapes, sizes and exclusive lithograph decorations. The lamps were complete with a hardwood plinth, brass lampholder and riser and gold color cable. The lamps were banded in 24 carat gold and matching shades were available. Wade continues to supply Astbury Lighting with lamp bases but no longer markets lamps as one of its own retail lines.

FIG. 53. "JACOBEAN" table lamps available in three sizes, TJ10 - 14" high, TJ12 - 16" high and TJ14 - 18" high. These table lamps were designed to compliment the "Jacobean" line of giftware.

FIG. 54. "KAWA" table lamps available in three sizes, GJ8 - 12" high, GJ10 - 14" high and GJ12 - 16" high. These table lamps were designed to compliment the "Kawa" line of giftware.

FIG. 53.

FIG. 55.

FIG. 54.

FIG. 55. "MARIKO" table lamps available in three sizes, RT10 -
     14" high, RT12 - 16" high and RT14 - 18" high. The base
     of this shape lamp was also available in mushroom and
     transparent blue craquelle glaze.
FIG. 56. "HANA" table lamps available in three sizes, GV10 - 14"
     high, GV12 - 16" high and GV14 - 18" high.

FIG. 56.

**TANKARDS and SOUVENIRS.**

**By**

**Wade, Heath & Co. Ltd.**

**and**

**Wade (Ireland) Ltd.**

**mid 1940's - 1991.**

# TANKARDS and SOUVENIRS.

### BY WADE, HEATH & CO. LTD. and WADE (IRELAND) LTD. mid 1940's - 1991.

Along with their lines of retail giftware and tableware, Wade, Heath & Co. Ltd. has had a long history of supplying various companies and organizations with souvenir items. Many of these items took the form of wall plates, miniature to full size tankards and various shaped pottery trays and vases. For more illustrations of Wade souvenir items see *The W of W pgs. 60, 61 and 62.*

## WALL PLATES.

No. 415.    **NOVA SCOTIA WALL PLATE** - measures 9-1/2" in diameter and has Mark Type 19 on the base.

No. 416.    **LONDON MAP WALL PLATE** - measures 8" in diameter and has Mark Type 19 on the base.

No. 417.    **WELLYPHANT PLATE** - measures 7-5/8" in diameter and is marked: WELLYPHANT WORLD, A Limited Edition of 5000 Designed by Stuart Hampson, WADE MADE IN ENGLAND. This plate was produced in 1991 for the late Vic Hampson. The design is based on a story about Wellyphants written by Vic Hampson. There are six characters in the story whose names all begin with "W." The fellow on the plate is named Wilfred Wellyphant. All the Wellyphants live on the Wellyphant islands which are somewhere between India and Africa where it rains hard every day at two o'clock in the afternoon and that is why all Wellyphants wear Wellington boots.

No. 418.    **MARITIME LOBSTER & TRAP WALL PLATE** - measures 9-1/2" in diameter and has Mark Type 19 on the base.

**FIG. 57.**

**FIG. 57.**    **ISLE OF WIGHT WALL PLATE** - measures 9-1/2" in diameter and has Mark Type 17 on the base.

## TANKARDS *mid 1950'S - mid 1980'S.*

The barrel tankards listed in an April 1960 Wade Price List included all sizes from jumbo to miniature; however, in a June 1966 Price List only the one pint and the half pint sizes were listed. It is most likely these latter two sizes con-

tinued in production for sometime after 1966. Wade literature advised customers that special orders would be accepted with a proofing charge for quantities under 250 pieces. Prices allowed for tankards in either ivory, cream or amber glazes with either gold or silver finish.

**FIG. 58.**

**FIG. 59.**

**FIG. 58.**    **DOGHOUSE TANKARD** - this one pint tankard was listed in a 1960 Wade Price List. The dark brown and honey glazed tankard measures 4-3/4" high and has Mark Type 19 on the base.

**FIG. 59.**    **"PUNK PIG" TANKARD** - measures 4-1/4" high and has Mark Type 19 on the base. The lettering on the reverse side of the tankard reads: TO COMMEMORATE THE DISAPPEARING WONDERS OF NATURE THIS TANKARD IS DEDICATED TO THAT NOBLE BEAST - THE CHAUVINIST PIG.

No. 419.    **BARREL TANKARD, JUMBO (4 PINT)** - measures 7-1/2" high and has Mark Type 19 on the base.

No. 420.    BARREL TANKARD, ONE PINT - measures 5" high and has Mark Type 19 on the base.

No. 421.    BARREL TANKARD, HALF PINT - measures 3-3/4" high and has Mark Type 19 on the base.

No. 422.    BARREL TANKARD, MINI - measures 2" high and has Mark Type 19 on the base.

No. 423.    DRUM HORSE TRADITIONAL TANKARD - this unusual grey glazed one pint tankard measures 4-3/4" high and has Mark Type 19 on the base.

No. 424.    LAKEHEAD UNIVERSITY TANKARD - measures 6" high and has Mark Type 37 on the base.

## TYRE DISHES.

No. 425.    TYRE DISH "ITALA" - the 5" diameter dish is No.13 from Series 5 and is marked: An "RK" Product By WADE OF ENGLAND.

No. 426.    TYRE DISH "SUNBEAM" - the 5" diameter dish is No.4 from Series 4 and is marked: A "MOKO" Product By WADE ENGLAND.

**FIG. 60.**

No. 427.    TYRE DISH "NASSAU, BAHAMAS" - the 5" diameter dish has Mark Type 19 on the base.

FIG. 60.    TYRE DISH "BRIGHTLINGSEA" - this 5" diameter dish is marked: A DEE CEE Souvenir by Wade on the underside of the base. This dish dates from 1957.

## POTTERY TRAYS.

The items in FIG.60 and FIG.61.(B) along with a number of other Wade products were customized with the names of popular holiday resorts, exclusively for Desmond Cooper & Co. The backstamp on these items included the wording "DEE CEE" along with a description of the souvenir. The comic pigs, elephants and cottages made by Wade (Ireland) Ltd. were also customized for this company.

**FIG. 61.**

FIG. 61.    POTTERY TRAYS -
A. "STOCKPORT" - measures 4-1/2" in diameter and has Mark Type 19 on the base. The base is also marked: Davenport Caravans Ltd. 312d Buxton Road Stockport Cheshire.
B. "REMEMBER ABERDOVEY" - measures 4-1/2" in diameter. The dish is marked: "DEE-CEE" A Souvenir of Wales by Wade England.

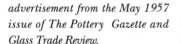

No. 428. POTTERY TRAY "REVERSING FALLS" - the 4-1/2" diameter tray has Mark Type 19 on the base. This souvenir item has the following wording: The Reversing Falls Saint John - Lancaster, New Brunswick, Canada.

No. 429. POTTERY TRAY "COVERED BRIDGE" - the 4-1/2" diameter tray has Mark Type 19 on the underside of the base.

No. 430. POTTERY TRAY "ANN OF GREEN GABLES" - the 4-1/2" diameter tray has Mark Type 19 on the underside of the base.

No. 431. POTTERY TRAY "ANN OF GREEN GABLES" - the 4-1/2" diameter tray has Mark Type 19 on the underside of the base.

No. 432. MINIATURE "PLYMOUTH" TANKARD - measures 2" high and has Mark Type 37 on the underside of the base.

No. 433. MINIATURE "TRADITIONAL" TANKARD - measures 2" high and has Mark Type 19 on the underside of the base.

## LESNEY TRAYS. *circa 1968 - 1975.*

A series of porcelain trays and dishes produced exclusively for LESNEY INDUSTRIES LTD. The Wade Pottery supplied only the porcelain base. The metal ornament was supplied and mounted on the tray or dish by Lesney Industries Ltd.

No. 434. LESNEY TRAY "HORSE DRAWN BUS" - measures 6" long by 3-1/2" wide by 2-1/2" high overall. The tray is mold-marked An R.K. Product by Wade of England on the underside of the recessed base.

No. 435. LESNEY TRAY "WINDSOR CASTLE" - measures 6" long by 3-1/2" wide. The tray is mold-marked An R.K. Product by Wade of England on the underside of the recessed base.

FIG. 62.

FIG. 63.

FIG. 62. LESNEY TRAYS.
A. "DOUBLE DECKER BUS" - measures 6" long by 3-1/2" wide by 2-1/4" high. The tray is mold-marked An R.K. Product by Wade of England on the underside of the recessed base.

B. "OPEN DOUBLE DECKER BUS" - measures 6" long by 3-1/2" wide by 2-1/2" high. The tray is mold-marked An R.K. Product by Wade of England on the underside of the recessed base.

FIG. 63. LESNEY TRAYS.
A. "DUKE OF CONNAUGHT" - measures 6" long by 3-1/2" wide by 2-1/2" high. The tray is mold-marked An R.K. Product by Wade of England on the underside of the recessed base.
B. "SANTA FE" - measures 6" long by 3-1/2" wide by 2-1/4" high. The tray is mold-marked An R.K. Product by Wade of England on the underside of the recessed base.

FIG. 64. LESNEY TRAY "PIKE" - measures 6" long by 3-1/2" wide and is mold-marked An R.K. Product by Wade of England on the underside of the recessed base. The metal fish was made in either green or white colors.

FIG. 64.

## SOUVENIR DISHES.

No. 436. SOUVENIR DISH "TOWER BRIDGE" - measures 4" long by 3" wide by 1-1/2" high and has Mark Type 26 on the underside of the base. This tray was produced circa 1957.

FIG. 65. SOUVENIR DISHES.
A. "SCOTTISH PIPER" - measures 4-1/2" long by 4" wide and is mold-marked S42/9 (reserved line) on the underside of the base. The porcelain base has a brown glaze and is the only part of the dish made by Wade.
B. "CITY OF LONDON" - measures 4-1/2" long by 4" wide and is mold-marked S42/9 (reserved line) on the underside of the base. The porcelain base has a brown glaze and is the only part of the dish made by Wade.

FIG. 66. SOUVENIR DISH "MERMAID" - measures 4-1/2" long by 4" wide and is mold-marked S42/9 (reserved line) on the underside of the base. The porcelain base has a brown glaze and is the only part of the dish made by Wade.

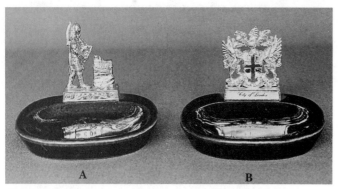

FIG. 65.

FIG. 66.

## "CADDIE" SET *1954*.

The "Caddie" set consists of teapot made in 4 and 5 cup sizes, golf ball sugar and golf bag creamer. In *The W of W pg.39 No.397*, we illustrated the golf bag creamer as a miscellaneous pitcher. Further research has shown this to be part of the "Caddie" set. It is interesting to note that the teapot in the set is the one referred to as "Scottie Teapot" in *The W of W pg.146*. "Scottie Teapot" was the name given to this style of tea pot in the Wade Heath Design Book. It is most probable that the name was changed when the teapot neared the end of its production life and the creamer and sugar were added to give the item more appeal and practicality.

No. 437.   GOLF BALL SUGAR - measures 2" high by 3" in diameter and has Mark Type 17 on the base.

No. 438.   GOLF BAG CREAMER - measures 3-1/2" high and has Mark Type 16 on the base.

## SOUVENIR DISHES and TRAYS.

FIG. 67.   SOUVENIR TRAYS.

A. "CITY OF STOKE-ON-TRENT"- measures 4-3/8" in diameter and has Mark Type 19 on the base. The tray is also marked: With the compliments of the Lord Mayor, Councillor, The Rev. Arthur Perry, on the underside of the base.

B. "THE YORKSHIRE INSURANCE COMPANY LTD." - measures 4-3/8" in diameter and has Mark Type 19 on the base.

No. 439.   PIN TRAYS - a boxed set of two 4-3/8" diameter trays each with Mark Type 19 on the base. The tray on the left shows a horse drawn Governess Car - 1900. The tray on the right shows an early motor driven Benz - 1898.

No. 440.   NUT DISH - measures 5" overall by 1-1/8" high and has Mark Type 17 on the base. The dish shows an illustration of the popular Toronto, Canada, landmark "Casa Loma."

No. 441.   NUT DISHES - a boxed set of two 4-1/8" diameter dishes each with Mark Type 19 on the base. Each dish is illustrated with the City of London Crest.
This shape dish was also produced, in 1957, as a boxed four-piece set under the name "BEACON BRIDGE" bowls. These bowls had no decoration except for a white rim and an individual glaze in either red, green, black or yellow.

FIG. 68.   NUT DISHES "18TH CENTURY COSTUME DESIGN" - both dishes measure approx. 4" in diameter and have Mark Type 19 on the base.

*Illustration from the November 1954 issue of The Pottery Gazette and Glass Trade Review.*

154

FIG. 67.

FIG. 68.

# MISCELLANEOUS TANKARDS.

No. 442.   TRADITIONAL TANKARD "BRITISH COLUM-BIA" - this one pint tankard measures 4-1/2" high and has Mark Type 19 on the base.

No. 443.   TAVERN TANKARD - measures 4-7/8" high and has Mark Type 19 on the base.

No. 444.   ROLL OUT THE BARREL TANKARD "WINSTON CHURCHILL " - first introduced in 1940, the tankard measures 5-3/4" high and has Mark Type 7 on the base.

FIG. 69.   ROLL OUT THE BARREL TANKARD "SOLDIER" - first introduced in 1940, the tankard measures 6" high and has Mark Type 7 on the base.

FIG. 69.

FIG. 70.

FIG. 70.   TANKARD "ROOSEVELT AND CHURCHILL" - first introduced circa 1942, the tankard measures 5-1/2" high by 7-1/2" across and has Mark Type 7 on the base. The words "Let's Drink to Victory, Let's Drink to Peace" are molded on the side of the tankard.

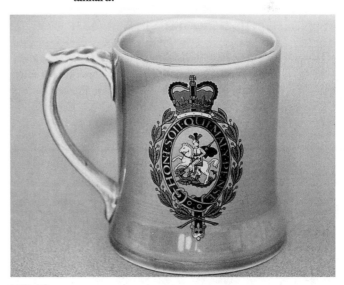

FIG. 71.

FIG. 71.   TRADITIONAL TANKARD "HONI SOIT QUI MAL Y PENSE" - this one pint tankard measures 4-1/2" high and has Mark Type 37 on the base.

No. 445.   TRADITIONAL TANKARD "ROTHMAN'S OF PALL MALL" - this one pint tankard measures 4-1/2" high and has Mark Type 19 on the base.

No. 446.   TRADITIONAL TANKARD "THE SAME AGAIN PLEASE" - this one pint tankard measures 4-1/2" high and has Mark Type 19 on the base.

No. 447.   McCALLUM JUG, LARGE - measures 6-3/4" high and has Mark Type 14 on the base. These character jugs were also produced with multicolored, hand-decorated finish and are usually found with a Wade Regicor mark.

**No. 448.** McCALLUM JUG, MEDIUM - measures 4-1/2" high and has Mark Type 14 on the base.

**No. 449.** McCALLUM JUG, SMALL - measures 2-3/4" high and has Mark Type 14 on the base.

**FIG. 72.** TOBY JUG - this green miniature jug measures 2-7/8" high and has Mark Type 10 on the base.

**FIG. 72.**

**FIG. 73.** CRANKY TANKARDS -
A. "THE HANGOVAH"- measures 4-3/4" high and has Mark Type 3 on the base.
B. "THE HYPERFLOOGIE" - measures 3-3/4" high and has Mark Type 7 on the base. These two Cranky tankards are the pre-WWII versions of the Cranky tankards illustrated in *The W of W pgs. 51, 129 and 130.*

**FIG. 73.**

**No. 450.** TANKARD "RYERSON POLYTECHNICAL INSTITUTE" - measures 6" high and has Mark Type 19 on the base

**No. 451.** TANKARD "LUDWIG VAN BEETHOVEN" - measures 6" high and has Mark Type 17 on the base. This commemorative tankard has a picture of the composer on one side and the wording Ludwig van BEETHOVEN 1770 - 1827 on the reverse side. It is most probable that similar tankards with different decorations were produced.

**No. 452.** TANKARD "W. A. MOZART" - measures 7-3/8" high and has Mark Type 17 on the base.

**No. 453.** McCALLUM ASHTRAY - measures 4-3/4" in diameter and is marked Wade Regicor England on the base.

## "TRUMPS" DISHES *1957.*

Four dishes depicting whimsical portrayal of the Joker and his royal colleagues. These dishes were sold in boxed sets of four.

**No. 454.** KING OF SPADES POTTERY TRAY - measures 4-1/4" in diameter and has Mark Type 19 on the base.

**No. 455.** QUEEN OF HEARTS POTTERY TRAY - measures 4-1/4" in diameter and has Mark Type 19 on the base.

**No. 456.** QUEEN OF CLUBS POTTERY TRAY - measures 4-1/4" in diameter and has Mark Type 19 on the base.

**No. 457.** KING OF DIAMONDS POTTERY TRAY - measures 4-1/4" in diameter and has Mark Type 19 on the base.

## POTTERY TRAYS.

**No. 458.** BAG PIPES POTTERY TRAY - measures 4-1/4" in diameter and has Mark Type 19 on the base.

**No. 459.** STACKING ASHTRAY - measures 3-7/8" across the cigarette rest and is mold-marked Wade Porcelain Made in England.

**No. 460.** STACKING ASHTRAY - measures 3-7/8" across the cigarette rest and is mold-marked Wade Porcelain Made in England.

**No. 461.** STACKING ASHTRAY - measures 3-7/8" across the cigarette rest and is mold-marked Wade Porcelain Made in England.

**No. 462.** STACKING ASHTRAY - measures 3-7/8" across the cigarette rest and is mold-marked Wade Porcelain Made in England.

**No. 463.** STACKING ASHTRAY - measures 3-7/8" across the cigarette rest and is mold-marked Wade Porcelain Made in England. The stacking ashtrays were designed by William Harper in the late 1950's.

## LONDON SOUVENIR TANKARDS *1957.*

**No. 464.** "TRAFALGAR SQUARE" MINIATURE TRADITIONAL TANKARD - measures 2" high and has Mark Type 19 on the base.

**No. 465.** "PICCADILLY CIRCUS" MINIATURE TRADITIONAL TANKARD - measures 2" high and has Mark Type 19 on the base.

**No. 466.** "TOWER BRIDGE" MINIATURE TRADITIONAL TANKARD - measures 2" high and has Mark Type 19 on the base.

## HARLEQUIN TRAYS *1957-1958.*

The Harlequin trays, a series of multicolored dishes, were sold in boxed sets of four. Each dish was mold-marked Wade Porcelain Made in England.

**No. 467.** "HARLEQUIN TRAY" - measures 3" square and has Mark Type 25 on the recessed base.

**No. 468.** "HARLEQUIN TRAY" - measures 3" square and has Mark Type 25 on the recessed base.

**No. 469.** "HARLEQUIN TRAY" - measures 3" square and has Mark Type 25 on the recessed base.

A George Wade & Son Ltd. advertisement as it appeared on the cover of the October 1960 issue of The Pottery Gazette and Glass Trade Review.

No. 470.   "HARLEQUIN TRAY" - measures 3" square and has Mark Type 25 on the recessed base.

FIG. 74.   "READY MIX CONCRETE" POTTERY TRAYS. Each triangular shaped tray measures 4-1/2" from base to apex. Tray 'A' illustrates a Ready Mix delivery truck and tray 'B' illustrates an elephant version of delivering Ready Mix concrete.

FIG. 75.   "READY MIX CONCRETE" CIGARETTE BOX. This design was applied to the Wade-Heath standard shape No. 242. Mark Type 19 is applied only to the underside of the lid.

FIG. 74.

FIG. 75.

157

FIG. 76.

FIG. 78.

FIG. 77.

FIG. 79.

FIG. 76.   "MRS. GAMP" POTTERY TRAY, (late 1950's). The tray measures 4-3/8" across and is marked Wade England Dickens. This tray is from a series that featured six different subjects based on Dickens' characters.

FIG. 77.   "PEARS" SOAP DISH (1987) - measures 5-3/4" long by 4-1/2" wide and has Mark Type 20 on the base. The dish was issued to celebrate the 30th Anniversary of Miss Pears.

# MISCELLANEOUS TANKARDS, JUGS and VASES.

No. 471.   "HUMBER COLLEGE" TRADITIONAL TANKARD - measures 4-3/4" high and has Mark Type 19 on the base.

No. 472.   "PROFESSIONAL MERCHANDISER" TRADITIONAL TANKARD - measures 4-3/4" high and has Mark Type 19 on the base.

No. 473.   NEW BRUNSWICK JUG - measures 4" high and has Mark Type 19 on the base.

No. 474.   NOVA SCOTIA JUG - measures 4" high and has Mark Type 19 on the base.

FIG. 78.   JUG - A. BALMORAL CASTLE - measures 3-1/4" high and has Mark Type 19 on the base.
B. TRURO - measures 5" high and is marked "A Desmond Cooper Souvenir" by Wade. See also FIGS. 60 and 61.

FIG. 79.   NATIONAL WESTMINSTER BANK MUG (1987 - 88). The mug measures 3-5/8" high by 3" in diameter and has Mark Type 20 on the base. This mug was made available to the Junior account holders as a special promotion through the Piggy Press Magazine. This special promotion was made available along with the NatWest Piggy Bank Family toward the end of its run. The Piggy Bank Family was replaced by the introduction of the Panda Money Box in January 1989; however, the Piggies were made available until January 1991. For more information on the Piggy Bank Family see *The W of W pg.116.*

No. 475.   "PICCADILLY CIRCUS" TRADITIONAL TANKARD - measures 4-3/4" high and has Mark Type 19 on the base.

No. 476. **"CHEERIO" TRADITIONAL TANKARD** - measures 4-3/4" high and has Mark Type 19 on the base.

No. 477. **"ROYAL CANADIAN AIR FORCE" TRADITIONAL TANKARD** - measures 4-1/2" high and has Mark Type 17 on the base.

No. 478. **"BUCKINGHAM PALACE" TRADITIONAL TANKARD** - measures 4-1/2" high and has Mark Type 19 on the base.

# VETERAN CAR SERIES *1956-1967.*

In the mid 1950's, Wade, Heath & Co. Ltd. began producing a very profitable line of giftware featuring reproductions of Veteran Cars. All the designs were proofed and authenticated by the Veteran Car Club of Great Britain. In the early days of production, the line consisted of half pint and one pint tankards, cigarette box and tyre dishes. Over the years, miniature tankards, oil jugs and funnels were also added to the line as were a series of full-size water jugs. The miniature funnels appear to have had a very short run as the only record of these was found in trade literature dated September 1959.

*JUGS FOR VETERAN CARS series V and VI from the Wade, Heath & Co. Ltd. Design Book.*

In 1956, tankards were presented to all entrants of the London to Brighton Veteran Car Rally. A number of these tankards featured a picture of "Genevieve" the car that featured in the film of the same name. The designs for these tankards had been vetted by Mr. Norman Reeves.

The following illustration shows twenty-four of the twenty-seven designs on the items produced in the Veteran Car series. For illustrations of No.25, a 1904 six h.p. Wolseley and No.26, a 1925 Austin Seven from the series are illus-

**FIG. 80.**

trated in the section on Wade (Ireland) Ltd. Records indicate that No.27, the last design in the series was a Model T Ford. To date, we have been unable to locate an illustration of this design. Series I, II, III, IV, V and VI were also produced as miniature tankards but with an abbreviated backstamp. Series I - IV were a two-color print in black outline with brown "earth." Series V onwards were a multi-colored print. For more information see *The W of W pg. 148.*

No. 479. **FUNNEL** - measures 3-1/2" high and is marked: A "MOKO" PRODUCT by Wade England. This hard-to-find item from the Veteran Car series features a 1909 Spyker which is No.8 from series 3.

No. 480. **"SUNBEAM 1904" HALF PINT TANKARD** - measures 3-3/4" high and is marked: A "MOKO" Product by Wade England.

No. 481. **"BENZ 1899" ONE PINT TANKARD** - measures 4-1/2" high and is marked: A "MOKO" PRODUCT by Wade England.

**FIG. 80.** VETERAN CAR ASHTRAY - measures 5-7/8" in diameter by 1-1/2" high.

**FIG. 81.**

## SERIES I (1956)

BENZ

FORD

DARRACQ

## SERIES II (1957)

SUNBEAM

ROLLS-ROYCE

BABY PEUGEOT

## SERIES III (1958)

DE DION BOUTON

SPYKER

## SERIES IV (1959)

LANCHESTER

OLDSMOBILE.

CADILLAC

## SERIES V (1961)

WHITE STEAM CAR.

ITALA

BUGATTI

SUNBEAM

## SERIES VI (1962 approx.)

ALFA ROMEO

BUGATTI

BENTLEY

## SERIES VII (1963 approx.)

1913 VAUXHALL

1925 M.G.

1907 FIAT F2

## SERIES VIII (1964 approx.)

DUESENBERG

MERCEDES

HISPANO-SUIZA

Note: For Series IX, See Text

# DECORATIVE SOUVENIR ITEMS.

No. 482.    BUD VASE - measures 4-3/4" high and has Mark Type 19 on the base (see also No.490).

FIG. 81.    AN ASSORTMENT OF DECORATIVE GIFTWARE. These black glazed items were decorated with at least four different white flower arrangements. All pieces illustrated have Mark Type 19 on the base and were produced in a number of shapes in the late 1950's - early 1960's.
A. BOWL - measures 4-1/2" high by 10" across.
B. BUD VASE - measures 5-3/4" high.
C. BUD VASE - measures 6-3/4" high.
D. BOWL - measures 4-1/2" high by 10" across.
E. JUG - measures 5-3/4" high.
F. BUD VASE - measures 4-3/4" high.
G. POTTERY TRAY - measures 4" in diameter.
H. POTTERY TRAY - measures 4" in diameter.
I. JUG - measures 5-3/4" high.
J. JUG - measures 5-3/4" high.

No. 483.    BARREL TANKARD - this one pint tankard measures 5" high and has Mark Type 19 on the base. This copper lustre tankard is sometimes found with applied advertising.

FIG. 82.    BARREL ASHTRAY (1959). This man-sized ashtray measures 2-1/2" high by 6" in diameter and has Mark Type 19 on the base.

FIG. 82.

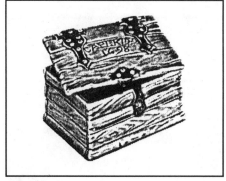

FIG. 83.

**FIG. 83.** **"CAPTAIN KIDD'S TREASURE CHEST" (1959) - a candy or cigarette box with lid as a matching piece to the Barrel Ashtray illustrated in FIG.82.**

# BUDDIES *circa 1960.*

The bud vases named Clarence and Clara were produced in the early 1960's and sold individually boxed.

No. 484.    BUDDIES "CLARA" - measures 4-1/2" high and has Mark Type 19 on the base.

No. 485.    BUDDIES "CLARENCE" - measures 4-1/2" high and has Mark Type 19 on the base.

# TOPLINE *1963.*

In March 1963, Wade, Heath & Co. Ltd. introduced a new range of vases, storage jars and pottery trays in a very contemporary style, designed by Michael Caddy. The range was available in seven basic patterns decorated in six different styles identified as shape Nos. 528 L/S, 528 S/S, 530, 531, 532 and 533.

Using Style No.101 as an example, the decorations were as follows:

Shape 528 L/S - 3 purple prints around bottom, banded black to top and with gold foot.

Shape 528 S/S - 4 purple prints and gold foot.

Shape 530 - 3 purple prints, black neck inside and out and gold round top.

Shape 531 - 2 purple prints, black neck, gold foot and black top.

Shape 532 - 5 purple prints, black neck and black top of lid.

Shape 533 - 3 purple prints, black neck and black top of lid.

# SOUVENIR ITEMS.

No. 486.    SHAVING MUG - measures 3-1/8" high by 4" diameter and has Mark Type 19 on the base. The Victorian barber scene, illustrated on one side only has a sign hanging on the wall informing customers "we close on Sundays."

No. 487.    "NOVA SCOTIA" SOUVENIR VASE - measures 4-1/2" high and has Mark Type 19 on the base. The reverse side of the vase shows the Provincial Flag of the province.

No. 488.    "NEW BRUNSWICK" SOUVENIR VASE - measures 4-1/2" high and has Mark Type 19 on the base. The reverse side of the base has a posy of violets.

No. 489.    "NEW BRUNSWICK" SOUVENIR JUG - this half pint jug measures 3-3/4" high and has Mark Type 19 on the base. This unusual jug is based on the Plymouth tankard with the addition of the spout.

*Display of TOPLINE ware by Wade, Heath & Co. Ltd.*

FIG. 84.

FIG. 84.     "LITTLE NELL" BUD VASE - measures 4-1/2" high and has Mark Type 19 on the base.

No. 490.     BUD VASE - measures 5-1/2" high and has Mark Type 19 on the base. (See also No.482 and FIG.81).

## SHAVING MUGS *circa mid 1960's - mid 1980's.*

For a number of years Wade, Heath & Co. Ltd. have supplied various soap and brush manufacturers with a variety of shaving mug designs. Two of the major companies were Addis Ltd. and Culmak Ltd. For information on Addis shaving mugs see *The W of W pgs. 46 and 115.*

The Culmak Ltd. shaving mugs were offered in a set named The Naval Set. A set of three shaving mug designs based on the theme of Admiral Horatio Nelson were issued in a boxed set along with a shaving brush and soap.

No. 491.     SHAVING MUG - measures 3-3/8" high and has Mark Type 20 on the base.

No. 492.     "ADMIRAL LORD HORATIO NELSON" SHAVING MUG - measures 3-1/4" high by 7-1/4" from

FIG. 85.

spout to back of handle and has Mark Type 19 on the base. Issued by Culmak Ltd.

No. 493.     "NELSON'S COLUMN" SHAVING MUG - measures 3-1/4" high by 7-1/4" from spout to back of handle and is marked Wade Made in England on the base. Issued by Culmak Ltd.

No. 494.     "H.M.S. VICTORY" SHAVING MUG - measures 3-1/4" high by 7-1/4" from spout to back of handle and is marked Wade Made in England on the base. Issued by Culmak Ltd.

No. 495.     "VETERAN CAR" SHAVING MUG - measures 3-1/2" high by 7-3/4" from spout to back of handle and has Mark Type 19 on the base. This shaving mug was made for ADDIS Ltd. as part of their shaving gift set range. See also *The W of W pg.115.*

FIG. 85.     NAVAL SET. The complete package of the Nelson's Column shaving mug, brush and soap as offered by Culmak Ltd.

## AIRLINER SERIES *1959-early 1970's.*

A series of candy boxes, round or square dishes and two sizes of tankards produced by Wade, Heath & Co. Ltd. in collaboration with B.O.A.C., all boxed either individually or in pairs. The designs featured four B.O.A.C. airliners, D.H.Comet 4, Bristol Britannia 312, Boeing 707 and the Douglas DC 7C with full information about each printed on the underside of the dishes and on the reverse side of the tankards.

FIG. 86.     A. POTTERY TRAY - measures 4-1/4" by 4-1/4" and illustrates a Boeing 707. The following appears on the reverse side of the tray: Boeing 707. Engines: Rolls Royce Conway Pure Jet. Length: 152 ft. 11 ins. Span: 142 ft. 5 ins. All-up Weight: 295,000 lbs. Average Cruising Speed: 530 mph. Max. Range. 6,650 miles.
B. ONE PINT TANKARD - measures 4-3/4" high and illustrates a Bristol Britannia 312 and has the following on the back of the tankard: Bristol Britannia 312. Engine: Bristol Proteus 755 Turbo-prop. Length: 124 ft. 3 ins. Span: 142 ft. 3 ins. All-up Weight: 180,000 lbs. Average Cruising Speed: 360 mph. Max.Range: 4,400 mls.
Both, the tray and tankard are marked: Reproduction by Wade of England in Collaboration with B.O.A.C.

FIG. 86.

# SOUVENIR POTTERY TRAYS and TANKARDS.

No. 496.   "NEW BRUNSWICK" TRADITIONAL TANKARD - measures 3-3/4" high and has Mark Type 19 on the base.

No. 497.   "NASSAU BAHAMAS" TRADITIONAL TANKARD - measures 3-3/4" high and has Mark Type 19 on the base.

No. 498.   "NEW BRUNSWICK" POTTERY TRAY - measures 5-1/4" square and has Mark Type 19 on the base.

No. 499.   TAUNTON TRADITIONAL CIDER MUG - measures 3-1/4" high by 6" across the handles. The following appears on the base: A limited number of these traditional Cider Mugs were reproduced by Wade Potteries for the TAUNTON CIDER COMPANY.

FIG. 87.   LOVING CUP (1985) - measures 5" high by 5" diameter. This cup was a special "one off" designed by Barbara Cooksey as a parting gift from Wade, Heath to William Walker on his retirement as Commercial Manager. Billy had worked with George Wade & Son Ltd. for one year in 1939 and with Wade, Heath from 1940 - 1985. Billy's wife, Joan, had also worked at Wade, Heath as a Free Hand Paintress between 1945 - 1953.

FIG. 87.

FIG. 88.   LOVING CUP "YEAR OF THE SCOUT 1907 - 1982" - measures 3-1/4" high. This loving cup was issued to celebrate the 75th Anniversary of the Scouts. The cup is marked on the base: Produced for Commemorative House by Wade Potteries England.

FIG. 88.

164

No. 500.   "PRINCE EDWARD ISLAND" TRADITIONAL TANKARD - this half pint tankard measures 3-3/4" high and has Mark Type 19 on the base. The illustration on one side of the tankard shows a Maritime Lobster and miniature trap with the Prince Edward Island coat of arms on the reverse.

## LONDON SOUVENIR DISHES.

These dishes, depicting well-known London scenes, were sold either individually boxed or in boxes of four. For illustrations of the round London Souvenir Dishes issued in 1957, see *The W of W pg. 62, Nos. 635, 636, 638 and 639.*

No. 501.   "TOWER BRIDGE" POTTERY TRAY - measures 4-1/4" square and has Mark Type 19 on the base.

No. 502.   "HOUSES OF PARLIAMENT" POTTERY TRAY - measures 4-1/4" square and has Mark Type 19 on the base.

## SHELL DISHES *early 1950's.*

The Shell dishes were produced as both a reserved line as well as gift items. A number of glazes were used for these dishes some of which were highlighted in gold. It is most probable that some, if not all of these dishes, were produced at the Wade (Ireland) Pottery. An illustration in the Spring 1956 *Jolly Potter* shows this shell dish alongside the 1953 coronation dish.

No. 503.   SHELL DISH - measures 3-1/2" across and has Mark Type 15 on the base.

No. 504.   SHELL DISH - measures 3-1/2" across and has the following mold-marked on the base: "A  Made in England."

No. 505.   SHELL DISH - measures 3-1/2" across and has Mark Type 15 on the base along with the following molded mark: "A  BCM/OWL."

## POTTERY TRAYS.

No. 506.   "GUERNSEY" POTTERY TRAY - measures 4-1/4" square and is marked "A Wade Product" on the base.

No. 507.   "PICCADILLY CIRCUS" POTTERY TRAY - measures 4-1/4" square and has Mark Type 19 on the base.

FIG. 89.   "ORCHARD" Pottery Trays and Marmalade Jars.

## EMETT DISHES *1958.*

Rowland Emett has been a prolific artist of eccentric cartoon characters, often in an Edwardian style. Many of Emmett's illustrations have appeared in the magazine, *Punch* and also in *Life Magazine* and eventually on Wade Pottery trays. Emett, whose daughter was a Wade collector in the 1950's, was approached by the Wade Pottery to draw designs for reproduction on pottery trays and later, small vases. Unfortunately these vases were never produced.

The original designs were drawn to the actual size as they would appear on the final product. This would give both the artist and client a true idea of how the illustration would eventually appear. The next stage was to re-draw the illustration to one and one half times larger. This enabled the lines to be drawn in a clear and distinct style ready for photographing for the transfer reproduction.

No. 508.   EMETT DISH - measures 4-1/4" square and is marked "EMETTS" by Wade of England "Town Carriage for a Ninth Earl."

No. 509.   EMETT DISH - measures 4-1/4" square and is marked "EMETTS" by Wade of England "Dog & Dogstar."

No. 510.   EMETT DISH - measures 4-1/4" square and is marked "EMETTS" by Wade of England "Pastoral Interlude."

## POTTERY ACCESSORIES - ANIMAL THEME.

No. 511.   POTTERY TRAY "POODLE"- measures 4-1/4" in diameter and has Mark Type 19 on the base.

FIG. 90.   A. ASHTRAY "HORSES"- measures 2-5/8" high by 2-3/4" square and has Mark Type 19 on the base.
B. WALL PLATE "HORSES" - measures 8" in diameter and has Mark Type 19 on the base.
C. HALF PINT TANKARD "HORSES" - measures 3-3/4" high and has Mark Type 19 on the base.

## BALLET DISHES *circa late 1950's.*

No. 512.   BALLET DISH - measures 4-1/4" square and is marked: Ballet Wade of England.

No. 513.   BALLET DISH - measures 4-1/4" square and is marked: Ballet Wade of England.
For additional shapes and information see *The W of W pg.110.*

FIG. 90.

FIG. 89.

## MY FAIR LADY SOUVENIR TRAYS and TANKARDS *1958*.

A range of standard Wade pottery shapes were decorated with characters from the highly popular musical, My Fair Lady, which played in the West End of London and Broadway in New York for a number of years in the late 1950's. The My Fair Lady items were distributed, in England, by Kenleys Limited (see also advertisement below). Musical tankards were also made by Wade (Ireland) Ltd. featuring the tune "On the Street Where You Live" from the musical. Non-musical tankards were also produced and both the musical and non-musical tankards were also distributed by Kenleys Limited.

FIG. 91.    A. "MY FAIR LADY" SWEET DISH - measures 4-1/4" square and has Mark Type 19 on the base. The tray shows Eliza as a Flower Seller.

B. "MY FAIR LADY" SWEET DISH - measures 4-1/4" square and has Mark Type 19 on the base. The tray shows Eliza and Henry Higgins.

FIG. 91.

## MAMBO *1957*.

In *The W of W pgs. 110 and 111* mention is made of the "Zamba" line of giftware issued in 1957. In the January 1957 issue of *The Pottery Gazette and Glass Trade Review* a full page advertisement appeared illustrating nine shapes in the "Mambo" pattern which was similar in shape and pattern design to "Zamba."

A similar advertisement, featuring the nine items shown in the January issue, was featured in the June 1957 issue of *The Pottery Gazette and Glass Trade Review* but this time under the name "Zamba." So far we have been unable to find any reason for the name change.

*Miscellaneous Flower Bowls by Wade, Heath & Co. Ltd. Circa 1960.*

# FLOWERS, JUGS and VASES.

By

Wade & Co.

and

Wade, Heath & Co. Ltd.

late 1920's - 1960.

# FLOWER JUGS and VASES.

## By Wade & Co. and Wade Heath & Co. Ltd.
### Late 1920's - 1960.

The major product of Wade, Heath & Co. Ltd. was, from its inception as Wade & Co. through to the late 1930's, most definitely their range of teapots. However, the late 1920's, the company greatly extended its products to include what was to become a very popular line of decorative flower jugs and related tableware items.

An article in the July 1933 issue of *The Pottery Gazette and Glass Trade Review*, notes that there was a growing interest, by both the trade and the buying public, in the increased range of wares being produced by the pottery. The article went on to describe these additional lines as "...gaily painted decorations on cream glazed ware - articles for table use, such as fruit sets, sandwich sets, preserve jars, bowls, vases and flower jugs." It is towards these latter two items, vases and flower jugs, that this section of the book is primarily directed.

In 1933, an interesting new vase shape was introduced to the range of "occasional ware" the "Don" shape which was made available in two sizes. The advertisements, Wades' Modern Ware, shows a version of the "Don" vase on the left with decoration No. 3377 and the "Orb" shape with decoration No. 3379 second from left. The hand decorated flower jug on the right is in the "Eros" shape with decoration No. 3217.

New flower jug shapes were added to the line in 1935, the most popular being the "Flaxman," "Richmond," and the "Orpheum," to which were applied a variety of attractive decorations. The fact that these jugs featured the impressed name of the shape along with the decoration number appeared to have a great psychological effect on the purchaser who liked to see the marks. This unique marking helped the sale of the items.

An article in a March 1935 trade magazine noted that the Wade, Heath Pottery was producing a "giant flower jug, some 16" in height...being particularly useful for a window recess..." It was also mentioned that this particular item was referred to, by the pottery workers, as the "Soudan Major."

For the Christmas trade of 1935, Wade, Heath & Co. Ltd. produced "the Big Bad Wolf" musical jug which was described as "...a piece of relief modelling which conveys a definite story...Produced in bas relief, there is the story of the house as built by the builder pig, whilst the handle of the jug represents the big, bad wolf."

For an illustration of this musical jug see No.626 in the color section.

The extremely popular "Snow White" musical jug was introduced in 1938 along with a new series of "Flaxman" matt-glazed ornamental wares in new shapes and colorings. It was also at this time that the flower jug modeled along the lines of a garden bird bath was introduced.

In 1939, the beautiful "Lambeth Walk" jug was introduced. This design was made both in a regular version and as a musical jug version playing the tune "Doing the Lambeth Walk" from the popular London West End production of "Me and My Gal."

# WADES' MODERN WARE
### SERVICEABLE — ARTISTIC — DISTINCTIVE
## HAVE YOU SEEN OUR NEW LINE "ORCADIA WARE"?
### WADE · HEATH · & CO. LTD., HIGH STREET POTTERY, BURSLEM, STOKE-ON-TRENT
MR. H. J. BERRY, 12, THAVIES INN, LONDON, E.C.1.

| Mr. J. G. Macintyre, 61, Williams Street..................DUBLIN. | Messrs. Myott, Son & Co., 40, Wellington Street East  TORONTO. |
|---|---|
| Mr. J. Macnab, 19, Waterloo Street..............GLASGOW, C.2. | Mr. L. A. Solomon, 8, Progress Lane..............CAPE TOWN. |
| Messrs. A. T. Fondeville & Co., 116, East 27th Street  NEW YORK. | "Vedeka" Heerengracht, 252...................AMSTERDAM, C. |

*WADES' MODERN WARE. The Pottery and Glass Trade Review, September 1933.*

SNOW WHITE MUSICAL JUG. *The Pottery Gazette and Glass Trade Review, September 1938.*

During the WWII years, Wade, Heath & Co. Ltd. continued to produce decorated flower jugs, though somewhat in limited quantities, for the export market. Production for the home market was restricted to plain white, undecorated ware. It wasn't until the late 1940's that the pottery again started producing decorative ware for the home market. By the mid 1950's, Wade, Heath & Co. Ltd. had, to all intents and purposes, ceased production of flower jugs, and was concentrating on the production of tableware and advertising items. For further information on Wade, Heath & Co. Ltd. flower jugs see *The W of W pgs. 47-49, and pgs. 120-124.*

No. 514.    FLOWER JUG - decoration No.4486, shape No. 164 and and has Mark Type 7 on the base. The flower jug measures 11-3/4" high. This Flower Jug is also marked "Sample" and was in limited production in 1936.

No. 515.    ORCADIA VASE - measures 6-1/4" high with decoration No. 3399 and Mark Type 2A on the base.

No. 516.    ORCADIA VASE - measures 6" high and is marked ROSKYL POTTERY on the base.

No. 517.    FLOWER JUG - measures 11" high with shape No."Elite 93" and Mark Type 2 on the base.

No. 518.    ORCADIA FLOWER JUG - measures 6-1/2" high with decoration No.7404 and Mark Type 2A on the base.

No. 519.    ORCADIA VASE - measures 6-1/4" high with decoration No. 3408 and Mark Type 2A on the base.

No. 520.    ORCADIA VASE & FLOWER HOLDER - measures 5-1/2" high and has Mark Type 2A on the base. An illustration of this vase in the July 1933 issue of *The Pottery Gazette and Glass Trade Review,* refers to this shape as the "Don" vase with decoration No. 3377.

An advertisement from the February 1937 issue of *The Pottery Gazette and Glass Trade Review.*

No. 521.    ORCADIA VASE - measures 7-1/2" high and has Mark Type 1A on the base.

No. 522.    ORCADIA VASE - measures 7" high with decoration No. 3405 and Mark Type 1A on the base.

No. 523.    ORCADIA VASE - measures 5-3/4" high with decoration No. 3407 and Mark Type 2A on the base.

No. 524.    VASE, "PHOENIX" shape - measures 5" high with decoration No. 2766 and Mark Type 2 on the base. The decoration on this vase, although similar to the Orcadia decoration is not marked as such.

No. 525.    FLOWER JUG - measures 6-1/8" high with shape No.89 and Mark Type 2 on the base.

No. 526.    FLOWER JUG - measures 9" tall with shape No. 90 and Mark Type 4 on the base.

No. 527.    FLOWER JUG - measures 8" high with shape No. 169 and Mark Type 7 on the base.

No. 528.    FLOWER JUG - measures 9" high with shape No. 154 and Mark Type 6 on the base.

No. 529.     FLOWER JUG - measures 8-3/4" high and has shape No. 401 on the base. This flower jug is from the elegant Empress line which was in production circa early to late 1950's. For more information on the Empress line see *The W of W pg. 131.*

No. 530.     FLOWER JUG - measures 8" high with shape No. 122, decoration No. 4806 and Mark Type 7 on the base.

No. 531.     FLOWER JUG - measures 7-1/2" high with shape No. 113, decoration No. 186 and Mark Type 4 on the base.

No. 532.     FLOWER JUG - measures 7" high and has Mark Type 10 on the base.

No. 533.     FLOWER JUG - measures 5-1/4" high and has Mark Type 10 on the base.

FIG. 92.     FLOWER JUG "BLACK FROST" - decoration No. 6282.

FIG. 92.

FIG. 93.     "BLACK FROST". Additional Flower Jug shapes for decoration No. 6282 from the Wade, Heath Design Book. It is safe to assume that the fourth jug is shape No. S 538.

S 535     S 536     S 537.

FIG. 93.

No. 534.     FLOWER JUG - measures 5-5/8" high with Mark Type 19 on the base.

No. 535.     JUG - measures 3-7/8" high and has Mark Type 19 on the base.

No. 536.     FLOWER JUG - measures 9" high with shape No. 146 and Mark Type 7 on the base.

No. 537.     FLOWER JUG - measures 6-3/4" high with shape No. 114 and Mark Type 2 on the base.

No. 538.     FLOWER JUG - measures 6-1/2" high with decoration No. 1913 and Mark Type 2 on the base.

No. 539.     FLOWER JUG - measures 9" high with shape No. 146 and Mark Type 4 on the base.

No. 540.     VASE - measures 7" high with shape No. 214, decoration No. 3843 and Mark Type 2 on the base.

No. 541.     FLOWER JUG - measures 7-1/4" high and has Mark Type 1 on the base.

No. 542.     FLOWER JUG - measures 7" high with shape No. 13 and Mark Type 2 on the base.

No. 543.     FLOWER JUG - measures 7-1/2" high with shape No. 13 and Mark Type 7 on the base.

No. 544.     FLOWER JUG - measures 5-5/8" high with shape No. 106M and Mark Type 5 on the base.

No. 545.     FLOWER JUG - measures 5-5/8" high with shape No. 106M and Mark Type 5 on the base.

No. 546.     FLOWER JUG - measures 5-5/8" high with shape No. 106M and Mark Type 5 on the base.

No. 547.     FLOWER JUG - measures 5-1/4" high with shape No. 113M and Mark Type 2 on the base.

No. 548.     FLOWER JUG - measures 9" high with shape No. 123 and Mark Type 4 on the base.

No. 549.     FLOWER JUG - measures 9" high with shape No. 123 and Mark Type 4 on the base.

No. 550.     FLOWER JUG - measures 9" high with shape No. 119, decoration No. 4377 and is marked Wade Heath England Registration No. 812659. The jug is marked sample on the base.

No. 551.     FLOWER JUG - measures 9" high with shape No. 119, decoration No. 186 and Mark Type 4 on the base.

No. 552.     FLOWER JUG - measures 9" high with shape No. 173 and Mark Type 6 on the base.

No. 553.     FLOWER JUG - measures 7-3/4" high with shape No. 173 and Mark Type 7 on the base.

No. 554.     FLOWER JUG - measures 7-1/2" high with shape No. 149M/S and Mark Type 4 on the base.

No. 555.     FLOWER JUG - measures 7-1/4" high with shape No. 106 and Mark Type 2 on the base.

No. 556.     FLOWER JUG - measures 5-1/2" high with shape No. 406 and Mark Type 14 on the base.

No. 557.     FLOWER JUG - measures 5-1/2" high with shape No. 405 and Mark Type 10 on the base.

No. 558.     JUG - measures 4" high and has Mark Type 6 on the base.

No. 559.     JUG - measures 4" high and has Mark Type 6 on the base.

No. 560.     FLOWER JUG - measures 5-5/8" high with shape No. 149Min. and Mark Type 6 on the base.

No. 561.     FLOWER JUG - measures 8-3/4" high with shape No. 106 and Mark Type 4 on the base.

No. 562.     FLOWER JUG - measures 8" high and has Mark Type 2 on the base. This flower jug was first produced in 1927 and the production of it ran into the early 1930's.

# MODERN ARTISTIC & DISTINCTIVE WARE

Teapots, Jugs, Vases, Butter and Cheese Dishes, Morning, Fruit and Supper Sets in attractive designs, Cafetieres, Vegetable Dishes.

## WADE, HEATH & CO., LTD.,
### High Street Pottery,
### Burslem, Stoke-on-Trent.

London Showrooms: H. J. BERRY, 12, Thavies Inn, E.C.1
'Phone: Central 9943.
Scotland: Mr. John Macnab, 19, Waterloo Street, Glasgow, C.2.
Ireland: Mr. J. G. Macintyre, 61, William Street, Dublin.
U.S.A.: Messrs. A. J. Fondeville & Co., 116, East 27th Street, NEW YORK.
Canada: Messrs. Myott, Son & Co., 40, Wellington Street East, TORONTO.
South Africa: Mr. L. A. Solomon, 8, Progress Lane, CAPETOWN

*MODERN ARTISTIC & DISTINCTIVE WARE. The Pottery and Glass Trade Review, March 1934.*

No. 563. FLOWER JUG - measures 9" high with shape No. 106 and Mark Type 4 on the base.

No. 564. FLOWER JUG - measures 8-3/4" high with shape No. 120 and is marked Roskyl Pottery on the base.

No. 565. FLOWER JUG - measures 7-1/2" high with shape No. 147 and Mark Type 6 on the base.

No. 566. FLOWER JUG - measures 7-1/2" high with shape No. 148 and Mark Type 4 on the base.

No. 567. FLOWER JUG - measures 8-3/4" high with shape No. 120 and Mark Type 2 on the base.

No. 568. HANDLED FLOWER VASE - measures 6-1/2" high with decoration No. 3627, shape No. 94 and Mark Type 2 on the base.

No. 569. JUG - measures 5-1/2" high and has Mark Type 17 on the base.

No. 570. JUG - measures 5-1/2" high with shape No. 407 and Mark Type 10 on the base.

No. 571. JUG - measures 5-1/2" high with shape No. 407 and Mark Type 19 on the base.

No. 572. "BIRDBATH" FLOWER JUG - measures 10-1/4" high with shape No. 143 and Mark Type 6 on the base.

No. 573. "BIRDBATH" FLOWER JUG - measures 10-1/4" high with shape No. 143 and Mark Type 10 on the base.

No. 574. "BIRDBATH" FLOWER JUG - measures 10-1/4" high with shape No. 143 and Mark Type 10 on the base.

No. 575. "BIRDBATH" FLOWER JUG - measures 10-1/4" high with shape No. 143 and Mark Type 7 on the base.

No. 576. FLOWER JUG - measures 9" high with shape No. 334 and Mark Type 6 on the base.

No. 577. FLOWER JUG - measures 8-1/4" high with shape No. 92 and Made in England (ink stamp) marked on the base.

No. 578. FLOWER JUG - measures 9" high with shape No. 121, decoration No. 5785 and Wade Heath England Registration No. 812930 marked on the base. See also No.373 in *The W of W pgs. 48 and 122.*

No. 579. FLOWER JUG - measures 8-7/8" high with shape No. S302 and Mark Type 6 on the base.

No. 580. VASE - measures 6-1/2" high with shape No. 359 and Mark Type 7 on the base.

No. 581. "BIRDBATH" FLOWER JUG - measures 8" high with shape No. 143M and Mark Type 7 on the base.

No. 582. JUG "ROSS" shape - measures 4-1/2" high with decoration No. 3411 and Mark Type 1 on the base.

No. 583. FLOWER JUG - measures 6-1/4" high and has Mark Type 7 on the base.

No. 584. FLOWER JUG - measures 8-3/4" high with decoration No. 3757 and Mark Type 2 on the base.
This item also has the name "Castile 15" impressed into the base.

FIG. 94.

FIG. 94.    "FLOWER JUG" - measures 8-3/4" high with decoration No. 3765 and Mark Type 2 on the base. This item also has the name "Castile 15" impressed into the base.

No. 585.    COFFEE POT - measures 7-1/2" high and has Mark Type 1 on the base. The name England is also impressed into the base.

No. 586.    FLOWER JUG - measures 7-3/4" high with shape No. 150, decoration No. 4007 and Mark Type 2 on the base.

No. 587.    FLOWER JUG - measures 8-1/2" high with decoration No. 3585 and Mark Type 2 on the base.

No. 588.    FLOWER JUG - measures 11-1/4" high with shape No. 112 and Mark Type 2 on the base.

No. 589.    FLOWER JUG - measures 8-3/4" high with shape No. 106, decoration No. 3801 and Mark Type 2 on the base.

No. 590.    HANDLED FLOWER VASE - measures 6-1/2" high with shape No. 94 and Mark Type 2 on the base. This item has the name Richmond impressed into the base.

No. 591.    COVERED JAR - measures 5" high and has Mark Type 1 on the base.

No. 592.    FLOWER JUG - measures 6-1/4" high and has Mark Type 7 on the base. This flower jug is similar to No.583.

No. 593.    VASE - measures 7-1/8" high with shape No. 213 and Mark Type 2 on the base.

No. 594.    FLOWER JUG - measures 8-3/4" high with shape No. 123, decoration No. 3926 and Mark Type 4 on the base.

No. 595.    FLOWER JUG - measures 8-1/2" high with shape No. 135 and Mark Type 4 on the base.

No. 596.    FLOWER JUG - measures 8-3/4" high with shape No. 147 and Mark Type 7 on the base.

No. 597.    FLOWER JUG - measures 8-1/2" high with shape No. 144 and Mark Type 10 on the base.

No. 598.    FLOWER JUG - measures 6-1/4" high with shape No. 89 and Mark Type 4 on the base.

No. 599.    FLOWER JUG - measures 5-5/8" high with decoration No. 3493 and WADEHEATH WARE Reg. Shape No. 707794 Made in England stamped on the base.

No. 600.    VASE - measures 5" high with shape No. 216 and Mark Type 4 on the base.

No. 601.    FLOWER JUG - measures 7-1/2" high with shape No. 172 and Mark Type 6 on the base.

No. 602.    FLOWER JUG - measures 11-3/4" high with shape No. ELITE 93, decoration No. 128 and Mark Type 4 on the base.

No. 603.    FLOWER JUG - measures 9" high with shape No. 106, decoration No. 205 and Mark Type 4 on the base.

No. 604.    PLATE - measures 5" in diameter and has Mark Type 7 on the base.

No. 605.    FLOWER HOLDER - measures 5-3/4" high with shape No. 243 and Mark Type 7 on the base.

No. 606.    JUG - measures 5" high and has Mark Type 2 on the base.

No. 607.    VASE - measures 9" high with shape No. 17, decoration No. 3516 and Mark Type 2A on the base.

No. 608.    BUTTER DISH - measures 3-1/2" high by 7" in diameter with decoration No. 3302 and Mark Type 1 on the base. See No.359 in *The W of W pg.47*.

No. 609.    FLOWER JUG - measures 5-1/2" high with shape No. 131Min. and Mark Type 4 on the base.

No. 610.    VASE - measures 3-1/2" high and has Mark Type 10 on the base.

No. 611.    VASE - measures 3-3/4" high and has Mark Type 6 on the base.

No. 612.    VASE - measures 5" high with shape No. 19, decoration No. 3405 and Mark Type 2 on the base.

No. 613.    FLOWER JUG - measures 7-1/2" high and has Mark Type 7 on the base.

No. 614.    VASE - measures 6-1/4" high and has Mark Type 2 on the base.

No. 615.    VASE - measures 5" high and has Mark Type 1 on the base. This vase is shape No.216.

No. 616.    FLOWER JUG - measures 5-1/8" high with decoration No.4044, shape No.132 Min. and Mark Type 2 on the base.

No. 617.    FLOWER JUG - measures 9" high with shape No.155 and Mark Type 7 on the base.

No. 618.    VASE - measures 6-1/2" high with shape No.359 and Mark Type 7 on the base.

No. 619.    VASE - measures 6-1/2" high with shape No.359 and Mark Type 7 on the base.

No. 620.    VASE - measures 11-1/2" high with decoration No.4968 and Mark Type 10 on the base.

No. 621.   VASE & FLOWER FROG - measures 6-3/4" high with decoration No.3452 and Mark Type 2 on the base.

No. 622.   VASE - measures 8-3/4" high with shape No.332, decoration No.4976 and Mark Type 10 on the base.

WADEHEATH WARE. *The Pottery Gazette and Glass Trade Review,* September 1937.

## "LAMBETH WALK" SET - 1939.

A set consisting of four beer mugs and pitcher. The pitcher was produced in both musical and non-musical versions. The design was based on the popular West End musical comedy "Me and My Gal." The musical jug plays the tune "Doing the Lambeth Walk," one of the more popular songs from the show.

No. 623.   "LAMBETH WALK" MUG - the mug is 4-3/4" high and is marked WADEHEATH on the base.

No. 624.   "LAMBETH WALK" PITCHER - the pitcher is 10-3/8" high to the top of the figure on the handle and is marked WADEHEATH on the base.

No. 625.   "LAMBETH WALK" MUG - the mug is 4-3/4" high and is showing the reverse of No.623. The mug is marked WADEHEATH on the base.

## "BIG BAD WOLF" MUSICAL JUG - 1935.

This musical jug was produced by Wade, Heath & Co. Ltd. under their agreement with Walt Disney to manufacture Mickey Mouse Nursery Ware. The relief molded jug features scenes from the children's story "The Three Little Pigs." The jug plays the tune "Who's Afraid of the Big Bad Wolf."

No. 626.   "BIG BAD WOLF" MUSICAL JUG - measures 9-3/4" high to the top of the wolf's hat and is ink stamped Wadeheath England on the inside rim of the base.

## MISCELLANEOUS WARE.

No. 627.   BASKET - measures 7-1/2" high by 10" overall and has Mark Type 6 on the base.

No. 628.   BOWL - measures 3-1/4" high by 7-3/4" in diameter and has Mark Type 7 on the base.

No. 629.   VASE - measures 8-3/4" high with decoration No.4004, shape No.107 and Mark Type 2 on the base.

No. 630.   FOOTED CAKE PLATE - measures 3-1/2" high by 7-3/4" in diameter and has Mark Type 7 on the base. Wadeheath produced the plate only.

No. 631.   FLOWER JUG - measures 3" high with decoration No.3857, shape No.124 and Mark Type 2 on the base.

No. 632.   FLOWER JUG - measures 3" high with shape No.214 and Mark Type 4 on the base.

No. 633.   VASE - measures 8-1/2" high with shape No.90, decoration No.3491 and Mark Type 2 on the base.

No. 634.   VASE - measures 8-3/4" high with shape No. 217 and Mark Type 2 on the base.

No. 635.   FLOWER JUG - measures 8-1/2" high with shape No. 135 and Mark Type 2 on the base.

No. 636.   FLOWER JUG - measures 8-7/8" high with shape No. 110, decoration No. 3491 and Mark Type 2 on the base.

No. 637.   VASE - measures 5-1/2" high with shape No. 243 and with Mark Type 6 on the base.

No. 638.   BUTTER DISH - measures 7" long by 5-1/2" wide and 4" high to top of finial. The butter dish has Mark Type 7 on the base.

No. 639.   JAM DISH - with Mark Type 6 on the base along with the impressed name "FAIRY COTTAGE."
The jam dish measures 3" square by 4" high to the top of finial. This jam dish was produced as late as 1939 and would therefore also have a Mark Type without the word "FLAXMAN."

No. 640.   TEAPOT "QUEEN" shape - measures 5-1/4" high with decoration No. 6239 and Mark Type 1 on the base.

## "FLAXMAN" BUD VASES
### CIRCA EARLY 1960's.

In the early 1960's, Wade, Heath & Co. Ltd. introduced a line of sculptured bud vases in all over single glaze colors. The range was given the name "Flaxman," reintroducing a famous Wade, Heath name from the past. The following illustration shows eight shapes from the "Flaxman" bud vase range.

*"FLAXMAN" Bud Vase Range.*

## "CHELSEA" ORNAMENTAL WARE *1962.*

A limited line of ornamental ware produced by Wade, Heath & Co. Ltd. consisting of flat bowls, footed bowls and vases in matte finish. Examples are shown in the following illustration.

POTTERY GAZETTE

*and Glass Trade Review · November 1962*

*Ornamental ware of quality by*

WADE

*"CHELSEA" Ornamental Ware.*

**TEAPOTS, TEA CADDIES and CREAM & SUGARS.**

**By Wade & Co., Wade Heath & Co. Ltd.**

**and**

**Wade Ceramics Ltd.**

**late 1920's - 1992.**

## TEAPOTS, TEA CADDIES and CREAM & SUGARS.

From its very early days as Wade & Co. to the present time as Wade Ceramics Ltd., over a century later, the Wade potteries have been renowned for their variety of teapots. In the late 19th century, the emphasis was on practical, but decorative, teapots for every day use. Today, many of the teapots, though by no means all, are of the decorative, collectable type. Many examples of both early and recent teapots are illustrated in the color pages and described in this section.

Between the 1890's and the 1930's, Wade often manufactured teapot sets which comprised of a teapot, teapot stand, creamer, sugar and milk jug. Some of the shapes that lent themselves ideally to the teapot sets were the "Eton" shape, the "Queen" shape and the "Pekin" shape, many of which are illustrated in reproductions of Wade advertisements in this section.

In the 1920's and 1930's, Wade, Heath & Co. Ltd. produced a particularly useful shape teapot, the "Compacto." This spoutless teapot, with sunken lid, was directed mainly to the hotel, restaurant, and cafe trade where it proved to be most popular. The "Compacto" teapot was manufactured in a number of sizes and with numerous decorations. Also popular during these years were the three-piece sets comprising teapot, hot water pot and tray. See Nos. 657, 658 and 659. The popular "Compacto" shape teapot was also available as a three-piece set.

*A WADEHEATH advertisement for "Queen" shape No. 3211 teapot as it appeared in the October 1933 issue of The Pottery Gazette and Glass Trade Review.*

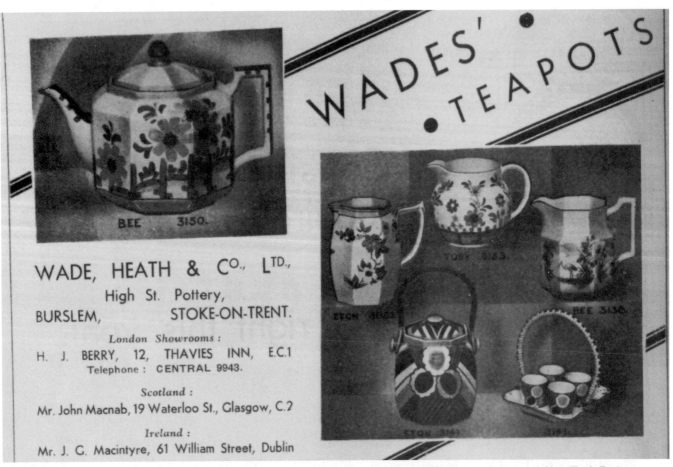

*An advertisement for WADES' TEAPOTS as it appeared in the February 1932 issue of The Pottery Gazette and Glass Trade Review.*

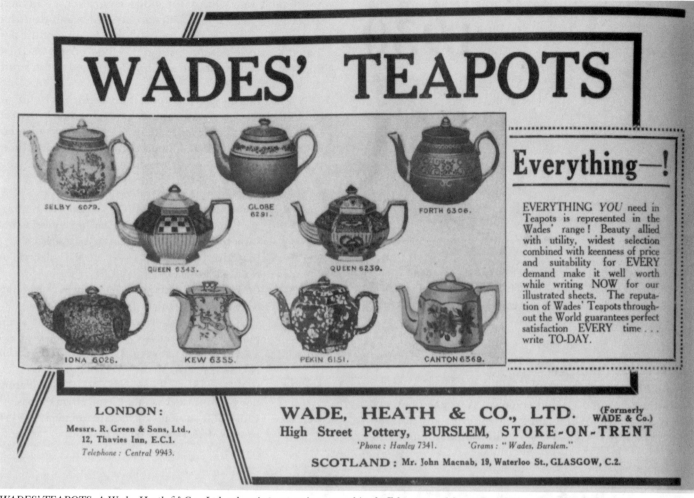

WADES' TEAPOTS. A Wade, Heath & Co., Ltd. advertisement as it appeared in the February and September 1931 issues of The Pottery Gazette and Glass Trade Review.

No. 641.    TEAPOT "Pekin" shape - with decoration No. 6148 and Mark Type 1 on the base. The teapot is 7-1/4" high to top of finial.

No. 642.    COOKIE JAR - measures 7-1/4" high to top of finial and has Mark Type 7 on the base.

No. 643.    HOT WATER POT - measures 7-1/4" high to top of finial and has Mark Type 7 on the base.

No. 644.    COOKIE JAR - with decoration No. 6274 and Mark Type 1 on the base. The cookie jar is 7-1/4" high to top of finial. This decoration was also referred to as "the old Davenport style."

No. 645.    "BIRD'S NEST" TEAPOT - measures 6" high and has Mark Type 7 on the base.

No. 646.    COOKIE JAR - measures 6" high and has Mark Type 7 on the base.

No. 647.    TEAPOT - with decoration No. 3945 and Mark Type 2 on the base. The teapot is 6-1/2" high.

No. 648.    TEAPOT "Windsor" shape - measures 6" high and is mold-marked Made in England along with Mark Type 7 on the base.

FIG. 95.    COOKIE JAR - measures 8-1/2" high and is marked Wade England on the base.

FIG. 95.

177

FIG. 96.

FIG. 96.    COOKIE JAR & COFFEE POT (late 1930's). For the cookie jar see No.646 in the color section. The matching coffee pot measures 7-1/2" high and has Mark Type 7 on the base.

## WALT DISNEY TABLEWARE
*circa mid 1930's - late 1930's.*

In the mid 1930's, an agreement was reached between Wade, Heath & Co. Ltd. and Walt Disney Productions for Wade, Heath to produce a series of both adult and children's tableware. One of the most sought after sets in these series is the Snow White tableware set. This was introduced in the Fall of 1938 to coincide with the opening of the animated movie. The set consisted of "good quality earthenware pictorially embossed and suitably picked out in brush work colorings."

The range included teapots, cheese dish, biscuit jar, butter dish, cream cheese, hot water jug, toast rack, egg set, breakfast cruet, individual salt and pepper, honey jar, circular tray, sugar and cream and coffee pot. In addition to this line a musical jug was produced which was available with any one of four different tunes.

No. 649.    "DONALD DUCK" TEAPOT - measures 6-1/2"high and is marked Wadeheath England by Permission Walt Disney. This teapot was also made in a smaller size.

No. 650.    COOKIE JAR - measures 7-1/4" high (decoration No.6148) and has Mark Type 2D on the base.

No. 651.    COFFEE POT - measures 7-3/4" high (decoration No.6148) and has Mark Type 2D on the base.

No. 652.    CIRCULAR TRAY - measures 9" in diameter (decoration No.6148) and has Mark Type 2D on the base.

No. 653.    TEAPOT - measures 6-1/2" high (decoration No.6148) and has Mark Type 2D on the base.

No. 654.    COVERED SUGAR - measures 3-3/4" high (decoration No.6148) and has Mark Type 2D on the base.

No. 655.    CREAMER - measures 4" high (decoration No.6148) and has Mark Type 2D on the base.

WADES' TEAPOTS. A Wade, Heath & Co. Ltd. advertisement as it appeared in the April 1933 issue of The Pottery Gazette and Glass Trade Review.

# MISCELLANEOUS TEAPOTS, COFFEE POTS, MUGS, CREAMERS and SUGARS.

**Fig. 97.**

**Fig. 97.**    OLD ENGLISH CASTLE TEAPOT - measures 5" high by 8-1/2" from spout to handle by 5-1/4" wide. The teapot is mold-marked Old English Castle Made in England along with Mark Type 7 on the base.

**No. 656.**    COFFEE POT - measures 7-3/4" high and has Mark Type 7 on the base.

**No. 657.**    TEAPOT - measures 5-1/2" high (decoration No. 6026) and has Mark Type 1 on the base.

**No. 658.**    HOT WATER POT - measures 5-1/2" high (decoration No. 6026) and has Mark Type 1 on the base.

**No. 659.**    TRAY - measures 8-1/4" long by 7-1/4" wide (decoration No. 6026) and has Mark Type 1 on the base.

**No. 660.**    HOT WATER POT - measures 7-1/4" high and has Mark Type 5 on the base.

**No. 661.**    TEAPOT - measures 5-3/4" high and has Mark Type 4 on the base.

**No. 662.**    TEAPOT - measures 5" high and has Mark Type 7 on the base.

**FIG. 98.**    TEAPOT - decoration No. F.H. 4813 (maroon and green decoration).

**FIG. 98.**

**No. 663.**    TEAPOT - measures 6-1/4" high and has Mark Type 8A on the base.

**No. 664.**    TEAPOT "Bramble" - measures 6" high and has Mark Type 12 on the base.

**No. 665.**    CREAMER "Bramble" - measures 2-3/4" high and has Mark Type 12 on the base.

**No. 666.**    SUGAR "Bramble" - measures 1-3/4" high and has Mark Type 12 on the base.

**No. 667.**    TEAPOT "Bramble" - single color glaze with Mark Type 10 on the base. The teapot is 5-3/4" high.

**No. 668.**    TEAPOT "Bramble"- golden turquoise with Mark Type 12A on the base. The teapot is 6" high.

**FIG. 99.**    TEAPOT "Bramble" - decoration No. 6027 (decorated leaves and berries on white background).Note the new shaped teapot and lid finial used for this decoration along with decoration No. 5038 "Golden Turquoise" (*The W of W No. 487 pg.55*) and No.667 above. The "Golden Turquoise" decoration was also applied to the regular "Bramble" teapot with the "branch" finial.

SHAPE

SIZES MADE

DATE PRODUCED

LITHO NUMBER

OPEN/RESERVED

COLOURS USED

PATTERN No. 6027

BRAMBLE        WHITE BODY
(RD.    TIPPED
PRINTED IN    EN COLOURS:-
HAR.          RED    371
HEATHS    BLACK    2CY

**FIG. 99.**

**No. 669.**    TEAPOT "Kew" shape - measures 5-1/2" high and has Mark Type 1 on the base.

**No. 670.**    TEAPOT "Nelson" shape - measures 5" high (decoration No. 4883) and has Mark Type 13 on the base.

**No. 671.**    HOT WATER POT - measures 5-1/2" high and has Mark Type 1 on the base.

**No. 672.**    TRAY - measures 8-1/4" long by 7-1/4" wide and has Mark Type 1 on the base.

**No. 673.**    "EAGLE" TEAPOT - measures 6" high (decoration No. 5078) and has Mark Type 13 on the base.

**No. 674.**    SUGAR - measures 2" high (decoration No. 5078) and has Mark Type 13 on the base.

No. 675.   CREAMER - measures 3-1/2" high (decoration No. 5078) and has Mark Type 13 on the base.

No. 676.   MILK JUG - measures 4-1/2" high (decoration No. 5078) with Mark Type 13 on the base.

No. 677.   CREAMER - measures 3-1/2" high and has Mark Type 16 on the base.

No. 678.   SUGAR - measures 2" high and has Mark Type 16 on the base.

No. 679.   TEAPOT "Nelson" shape - measures 5-1/2" high and has Mark Type 16 on the base.

No. 680.   PLATE "Chintz Floral & Butterfly" (Pattern No. L. 4810) - measures 8-3/4" in diameter and has Mark Type 7 on the base.

No. 681.   TEAPOT "Chintz Floral & Butterfly" (Pattern No. L. 4810) - measures 5-1/2" high and has Mark Type 7A on the base.

No. 682.   CUP "Chintz Floral & Butterfly" (Pattern No. L. 4810) - measures 2-3/4" high and is ink stamped on the base: Made in England A.

No. 683.   SAUCER "Chintz Floral & Butterfly" (Pattern No. L. 4810) - measures 5-3/4" in diameter and has Mark Type 7A on the base.

No. 684.   TEAPOT "Nelson" shape - measures 5-1/4" high (decoration No. 6017) and has Mark Type 10 on the base.

No. 685.   TEAPOT "Floral Trellis" - measures 6-1/2" high to top of finial. This was a special order for Ringtons Limited and has a special backstamp incorporating the pattern name along with the names of Wade and Rington.

No. 686.   SUGAR "Floral Trellis" - measures 2-3/4" high and has a similar backstamp to No.685.

No. 687.   CREAMER "Floral Trellis" - measures 3-3/4" high and has a similar backstamp to No.685.

No. 688.   TEAPOT "Old Coach House, York" - measures 6-1/2" high and has Mark Type 37 on the base.

No. 689.   TEAPOT "Finn MacCoul" - measures 6-1/2" high and has Mark Type 27A on the base. A crest decoration "Together we Progress" appears on the other side of the teapot.

# CO-ORDINATED TEAPOTS and MUGS

*early 1990's - to date.*

Four sets of mugs and teapots produced as a general retail line utilizing the standard Wade shapes Albert and Samantha. The "Hedgerow" teapot (Albert shape) was accompanied by three matching mugs and the "Village Scenes" teapots (Albert shape) with two matching mugs. The "Chatsworth" teapot (Samantha shape) was available with two decorations accompanied by three co-ordinated mugs. The "Chatsworth" sets were discontinued in 1993. In 1990 co-ordinated "Floral" teapots (Albert shape) and mugs were available for a short time in "Pansy", "Lily" and "Poppy" patterns.

FIG. 100.   An illustration showing the "Hedgerow," "Village Scenes" and "Chatsworth" teapot sets.

ailable: 'Hedgerow' Teapot & three Mugs;

FIG. 100.

## ANNIVERSARY TEAPOTS *1991 - to date.*

A set of four all-over color teapots in either silver, gold, ruby or pearl highlighted in either gold or silver.

FIG. 101.   An illustration showing the "Anniversary" teapots.

## TEA CADDIES.

No. 690.   TEA CADDY "Chinese Rose" decoration (late 1980's) - measures 3-1/2" high and has Mark Type 20 on the base.

No. 691.   TEA CADDY "Poinsettia" decoration (late 1980's) - measures 3-1/2" high and has Mark Type 20 on the base.

No. 692.   TEA CADDY "Snow Man" decoration (late 1980's) - measures 3-1/2" high and has Mark Type 20 on the base.

No. 693.   RINGTONS LTD. TEA CADDY (1989). This 5" high tea caddy was a special order for Ringtons Ltd. The design is based upon an original "Maling" cathedral jar produced for Ringtons in the late 1920's.

No. 694.   RINGTONS LTD. TEA CADDY (1987). This 3-1/2" high tea caddy was issued to commemorate the 80th Anniversary of Ringtons Ltd. which was established in 1907. The design is based upon an original "Maling" cathedral jar produced for Ringtons in the late 1920's.

FIG. 102.   RINGTONS LTD. TEA CADDY (1991). This tea caddy measures 3" square at the top, 2-1/2" square at the base by 5-1/2" high to the top of the lid.

FIG. 101.

FIG. 103.

FIG. 102.

FIG. 103. **RINGTONS LTD. TEA CADDY (1993).** This tea caddy measures 2-1/2" square at the top, 3" square at the base by 5-1/2" high to the top of the lid. It is the intention of Ringtons Ltd. to launch a new jar every two years.

## SPECIAL TEAPOTS.

No. 695. "CAT BURGLAR" TEAPOT - measures 6-1/2" high and was a special design originated, by Wade, for Boots Drug Store chain in the late 1980's. A "CAT BURGLAR" cookie jar was also availabale.

No. 696. "MACY'S" TEAPOT (1989) - measures 5-3/4" high and is marked: Made in England expressly for R.H. Macy & Co. Inc., New York N.Y. 10001 ©MACY.

No. 697. "VALOR GAS" TEAPOT (1990) - measures 6" high and is marked: Valor a Limited Edition of 1000 by Wade. The teapot as illustrated shows a decal of the Venetian fire place and the reverse side shows the Victorian Jubilee fire place. The wording on the lid reads: Valor Masters of the living flame.

No. 698. "CROSS STITCH" TEAPOT (late 1980's) - measures 6-1/2" high and has Mark Type 20 on the base.

FIG. 104. "RSPB" TEAPOT (1989) - measures 4-3/8" high to top of finial and has a blue decoration on a white background. The teapot is marked : Wade Potteries RSPB to celebrate 100 years. Made in England.

FIG. 105. MINIATURE TEAPOT & CREAMER (circa late 1930's) - the creamer measures 2" high and the teapot 3-1/4" high. These items are from similar molds to the Walt Disney children's dishes and are marked "England."

FIG. 106. "RIDGEWAYS" TEAPOT KEY RING - measures 1" high by 1-1/2" overall and is unmarked.

FIG. 104.

FIG. 105.

FIG. 106.

# FELINE SERIES, VILLAGE EVENTS, TUTTI-FRUITTI and MISCELLANEOUS TEAPOTS.

No. 699.     "CAT-FISH" TEAPOT (1989-1990) - measures 5" high and is from the Feline Collection of Whimsical Teapots designed by Judith Wootton.

No. 700.     "CAT-FISH" TEAPOT, Mini (1989-1992) - measures 4-1/2" high and is from the Feline Collection of Whimsical Teapots.

No. 701.     "TUTTI-FRUITTI" CREAMER (1990-1992) - measures 3-1/4" high and is mold-marked Wade England. The Tutti-Fruitti series was designed by Barbara Cooksey.

No. 702.     "TUTTI-FRUITTI" COVERED SUGAR (1990-1992) - measures 4" high and is mold-marked Wade England.

No. 703.     "TUTTI-FRUITTI" TEAPOT (1990-1992) - measures 5-1/2" high and is mold-marked Wade England.

No. 704.     "CAT-LITTER" TEAPOT (1989-1990) - measures 6-1/4" high and is from the Feline Collection of Whimsical Teapots.

No. 705.     "CAT-LITTER" TEAPOT, Mini (1989-1992) - measures 5-1/4" high and is from the Feline Collection of Whimsical Teapots.

No. 706.     "CAT-NAP" TEAPOT, Mini (1989-1992) - measures 5-1/2" high and is from the Feline Collection of Whimsical Teapots.

No. 707.     "CAT-NAP" TEAPOT (1989-1990) - measures 6-3/8" high and is from the Feline Collection of Whimsical Teapots.

No. 708.     SINGLE CUP TEAPOT "Grapevine" pattern (mid 1980's to date) - measures 3-3/4" high and is from the Regency Collection of fine bone china.

No. 709.     TETLEY "SIDNEY" TEAPOT (1990) - measures 5-3/4" high and is marked: Made exclusively for LYONS TETLEY by Wade. The "Sidney" teapot was designed by Judith Wootton.

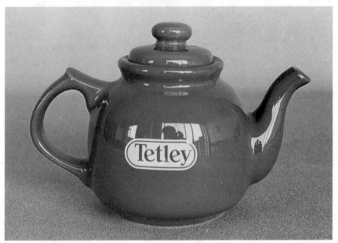

FIG. 107.

FIG. 107.     TETLEY TEAPOT (late 1980's) - measures 4-1/2" high by 7" overall and has an all-over blue glaze with white lettering. The teapot is marked on the base: Two cup teapot specially made by Wade Potteries for Lyons Tetley Ltd.

No. 710.     SINGLE CUP TEAPOT "Pot Pourri" (mid 1980's to date) - measures 4-1/8" high and is from the Regency Collection of fine bone china.

No. 711.     SINGLE CUP TEAPOT "Blue Dresden" (mid 1980's to date) - measures 4" high and is from the Regency Collection of fine bone china.

No. 712.     "CRICKET MATCH" TEAPOT (1991-1992) - measures 6" high and has Mark Type 27B on the base. The teapot is from the Village Events series of Teapots.

No. 713.     "GENIE" TEAPOT (1990-1991) - measures 8-1/4" high and has Mark Type 27B on the base. The copper lustre version illustrated was in production for one year only and was replaced with an all-over, less expensive yellow version still in production.

No. 714.	"WEDDING" TEAPOT (1991 to date) - measures 7" high and has Mark Type 27B on the base. The teapot is from the Village Events series of teapots.

## COCKLESHELL COVE COLLECTION.

No. 715.	"HELTER SKELTER" TEAPOT (1990 - 1993) - measures 7-1/4" high and has Mark Type 27B on the base. The teapot is from the Cockleshell Cove series of Collector Teapots.

No. 716.	"HELTER SKELTER" MUG (1990 - 1993) - measures 3-3/4" high and has Mark Type 27B on the base. The mug is from the Cockleshell Cove Collection.

No. 717.	"PUNCH & JUDY" TEAPOT (1990 - 1993) - measures 6-3/4" high and has Mark Type 27B on the base. The teapot is from the Cockleshell Cove series of Collector Teapots.

No. 718.	"PUNCH & JUDY" MUG (1990 - 1993) - measures 3-3/4" high and has Mark Type 27B on the base. The mug is from the Cockleshell Cove Collection.

No. 719.	"LA BELLA VISTA" MUG (1990 to date) - measures 3-3/4" high and has Mark Type 27B on the base. The mug is from the Cockleshell Cove Collection.

No. 720.	"LA BELLA VISTA" TEAPOT (1990 to date) - measures 7-3/4" high and has Mark Type 27B on the base. The teapot is from the Cockleshell Cove series of Collector Teapots.

## BOOTS TEAPOTS and MUGS.

No. 721.	"RINGMASTER" TEAPOT (1990) - measures 5" high and is marked: Designed exclusively for Boots by Wade Ceramics.

No. 722.	"RINGMASTER" MUG (1990) - measures 3-3/4" high and is marked: Designed exclusively for Boots by Wade Ceramics.

No. 723.	"NOAH'S ARK" MUG (1990) - measures 3-3/4" high and is marked: Designed exclusively for Boots by Wade Ceramics.

No. 724.	"NOAH'S ARK" TEAPOT (1990) - measures 5-1/4" high and is marked: Designed exclusively for Boots by Wade Ceramics.

No. 725.	"JUNGLE FUN" TEAPOT (1990) - measures 5" high and is marked: Designed exclusively for Boots by Wade Ceramics.

No. 726.	"JUNGLE FUN" TEAPOT (1990) - measures 5" high and is a variation of No.725 with a low, shorter spout. This version was not sold in the Boots Drug Stores.

No. 727.	"JUNGLE FUN" MUG (1990) - measures 3-3/4" high and is marked: Designed exclusively for Boots by Wade Ceramics.

## ENGLISH LIFE TEAPOTS, MUGS and CADDIES *1988 to date unless noted otherwise.*

No. 728.	"POST OFFICE" TEAPOT - measures 5-1/4"high and is marked Wade England.

No. 729.	"POST OFFICE" MUG - measures 3-3/4" high and is marked Wade England.

No. 730.	"POST OFFICE" TEA CADDY (1988-1990) - this metal caddy measures 4-1/4" high and is marked Wade England.

No. 731.	"PRIMROSE JUNCTION" TEAPOT - measures 5-5/8" high and is marked Wade England.

No. 732.	"PRIMROSE JUNCTION" MUG - measures 3-5/8" high and is marked Wade England.

No. 733.	"PRIMROSE JUNCTION" TEA CADDY (1989-1990) - this metal caddy measures 4-1/4" high and is marked Wade England.

No. 734.	"POLLY'S CAFE" TEAPOT - measures 5" high and is marked Wade England.

No. 735.	"POLLY'S CAFE" TEA CADDY (1991 to date) - measures 4-1/2" high and has Mark Type 27B on the base.

No. 736.	"POLLY'S CAFE" MUG - measures 3-5/8" high and is marked Wade England.

No. 737.	"T. POTTS CHINA SHOP" MUG - measures 3-5/8" high and has Mark Type 27B on the base.

No. 738.	"T. POTTS CHINA SHOP" TEAPOT - measures 6" high and has Mark Type 27B on the base.

No. 739.	"FLORIE'S FLOWERS" TEAPOT - measures 5-7/8" high and is marked Wade England.

No. 740.	"FLORIE'S FLOWERS" MUG - measures 3-5/8" high and is marked Wade England.

No. 741.	"POLICE STATION" TEAPOT - measures 6-1/4" high and has Mark Type 27B on the base.

No. 742.	"POLICE STATION" MUG - measures 3-5/8" high and is marked Wade England.

No. 743.	"ANTIQUE STORE" TEA CADDY (1991 to date) - measures 5-1/4" high and has Mark Type 27B on the base.

No. 744.	"ANTIQUE STORE" TEAPOT - measures 5-7/8" high and is marked Wade England.

No. 745.	"ANTIQUE STORE" MUG - measures 3-5/8" high and is marked Wade England.

No. 746.	"ANTIQUE STORE" TEA CADDY (1989-1990) - this metal caddy measures 4-1/4" high and is marked Wade England.

No. 747.	"FISH AND CHIP SHOP" MUG - measures 3-5/8" high and is marked Wade England.

No. 748.	"FISH AND CHIP SHOP" TEAPOT - measures 5-3/4" high and is marked Wade England.

No. 749.	"QUEEN VICTORIA PUB" TEAPOT - measures 5-5/8" high and is marked Wade England.

No. 750.	"QUEEN VICTORIA PUB" MUG - measures 3-1/2" high and is marked Wade England.

No. 751.	"QUEEN VICTORIA PUB" TEA CADDY (1991 to date) - measures 5-1/4" high and has Mark Type 27B on the base.

No. 752.	"QUEEN VICTORIA PUB" TEA CADDY (1989-1990) - this metal tea caddy measures 4-1/4" high and is marked Wade England.

No. 753.	"MERRY CHRISTMAS" MUG (1991to date) - measures 3-5/8" high and has Mark Type 27B on the base.

No. 754.	"CHRISTMAS CAROL" TEAPOT (1990 to date) - measures 6" high and has Mark Type 27B on the base.

No. 755.	"CHRISTMAS TREE" TEAPOT (1989-1991) - measures 5-3/4" high and is marked Wade England.

No.756.	"CHRISTMAS TREE" TEAPOT (1989 to date) - measures 5-3/4" high and is marked Wade England.

No. 757. CHRISTMAS TREE TEAPOT (1989 to date) - measures 5-3/4" high and is marked Wade England.

No. 758. "SANTA'S GROTTO" TEAPOT (1989 to date) - measures 6" high and is marked: Made by Wade Potteries PLC.

No. 759. "CONSERVATORY" MUG - measures 3-5/8" high and is marked Wade England.

No. 760. "CONSERVATORY" TEAPOT - measures 5-1/4" high and is marked Wade England.

No. 761. "CONSERVATORY" TEA CADDY (1991 to date) - measures 4-1/2" high and has Mark Type 27B on the base.

## ENGLISH LIFE PLATES *1992 - 1993.*

A series of six designs taken from the English Life teapots and applied to 9-5/8" diameter and 7-3/4" diameter "deep" plates. Each plate is marked "English Life Collector Plates, Designs by Barry Smith and Barbara Wootton for Wade U.K." The designs were: Florie's Flowers, General Store Post Office, Antiques, Fish and Chip Shop, Primrose Junction and the Queen Victoria Pub. See FIG.108.

ENGLISH LIFE PLATES Six designs 19 & 24cm approx. ENGLISH LIFE TEAPOTS AND MUGS Fishmonger & Pet Shop. COCKLESHELL ...VE TEAPOTS Pier Theatre & Lighthouse.

WADE

**FIG. 108.** An illustration of Wade Teapots, Mugs and Plates.

## BOOTS TEAPOTS, MUGS and COOKIE JARS *1991 - 1992.*

No. 762. "DRUMMER BOY" TEAPOT (1991) - measures 6-3/4" high and has Mark Type 27B on the base.

No. 763. "GYMKHANA" TEAPOT (1991) - measures 6-1/4" high and has Mark Type 27B on the base.

No. 764. "WHITE RABBIT" TEAPOT (1992) - measures 8-1/4" high and has Mark Type 27B on the base.

No. 765. "DRESSAGE" TEAPOT (1992) - measures 6-3/4" high and has Mark Type 27B on the base.

No. 766. "FISH" MUG (1992) - measures 4" high and has Mark Type 27B on the base.

No. 767. "CATS" MUG (1992) - measures 4" high and has Mark Type 27B on the base.

No. 768. "CATS" TEAPOT (1992) - measures 5-1/2" high and has Mark Type 27B on the base.

No. 769. "GOOSE FAIR" TEAPOT (1991) - measures 6-1/2" high and has Mark Type 27B on the base.

No. 770. "GOOSE FAIR" COOKIE JAR (1991) - measures 10-1/2" high and has Mark Type 27B on the base.

No. 771. "PEASANT" COOKIE JAR (1991) - measures 10-1/2" high and has Mark Type 27B on the base.

No. 772. "PEASANT" TEAPOT (1991) - measures 6-1/2" high and has Mark Type 27B on the base.

No. 773. "FRUITS" TEACUP & SAUCER (1992). The teacup measures 3-1/2" high by 4-3/8" in diameter The saucer measures 7-3/4" in diameter Both items have Mark Type 27B on their bases.

No. 774. "FRUITS" TEAPOT (1992) - measures 5-1/2" high and has Mark Type 27B on the base.

## THE NATIONAL TRUST TEAPOTS *1989.*

A series of two teapots produced for The National Trust. Not shown is the "ALFRISTON LODGE" which was based on the English Life "Flories Flowers" teapot with an amended roof. Both National Trust teapots were designed by Dorn Williams.

No. 775. "BLAISE HAMLET COTTAGE" TEAPOT - measures 5" high. This design, based on a cottage at Blaise Hamlet near Bristol, was applied to the English Life Conservatory shape teapot.

## CLOWN TEAPOTS *1992 - to date.*

A set of two teapots designed by Judith Wootton as a general retail line. The clowns take their name from the style of their tie. Both teapots have Mark Type 27B on their bases. In 1993, Wade Ceramics produced a range of four items, utilizing the "clown" decoration, to be sold in Boot's Drugstores. See FIGS. 206 and 207.

No. 776. "BOW" TEAPOT - measures 7-3/8" high.

No. 777. "KIPPER" TEAPOT - measures 7-5/8" high.

## OWL AND PUSSY CAT TEAPOTS *1992 - 1993.*

A teapot design featuring the Owl and the Pussy Cat with a Five Pound Note finial. The teapots measure 6-1/4" high and are mold-marked Wade England on the under-

FIG. 109.

NEW FROM WADE
# MEMORIES

MEMORIES ARE MADE OF THESE
NEW NOVELTY TEAPOTS FROM WADE

THE OWL & THE PUSSY CAT in Green, Blue & Honey.
CLOWNS - Bow & Kipper.

**WADE**
Wade Ceramics Limited

Royal Victoria Pottery, Westport Road, Burslem, Stoke-on-Trent, Staffordshire, ST6 4AG, England, U.K.
Telephone: (0782) 577323   Fax: (0782) 834284

A BEAUFORD GROUP COMPANY

**FIG. 109.** An illustration showing both the "Clown" and "Owl and Pussy Cat" teapots.

side of the base. They were available in three colors: all-over yellow, all-over blue and all-over dark green. See FIG.109.

## MISCELLANEOUS TEAPOTS.

No. 778.   "LIGHTHOUSE" TEAPOT (1991 to date)- measures 7-1/2" high and has Mark Type 27B on the base. This teapot is from the Cockleshell Cove series. See also Nos.715, 716, 717, 718, 719 and 720.

No. 779.   "PET SHOP" TEAPOT ( 1992 to date)- measures 5-3/8" high and is marked Wade England. This teapot is part of the English Life series. A matching 3-3/4" high mug is also available.

No. 780.   "FISHMONGERS" TEAPOT ( 1992 to date)- measures 6" high and is marked Wade England on the

base. This teapot is part of the English Life series.

No. 781.   "COCKLESHELL PIER THEATRE" TEAPOT(1991 to date) - measures 6-3/8" high and is marked Wade England. This teapot is part of the English Life series.

No. 782.   "SANTA'S CHRISTMAS" TEAPOT (1991-1993)- measures 5-1/2" high and has Mark Type 27B on the base.

No. 783.   "WADELAND FIRE ENGINE COMPANY" TEAPOT (1993 to date) - measures 5" high and has Mark Type 27B on the base.

No. 784.   "APRES SKI" TEAPOT (1991 - 1993) - measures 5-1/2" high and has Mark Type 27B on the base.

## TETLEY TEA TABLEWARE *1992.*

A series of tableware items designed by Wade especially for Lyons Tetley. Each piece was made available to those who sent in a number of tokens along with a fee as detailed in Tetley Collectables Teafolk Catalogue 1992. A number of other items were also available through this catalogue but they were not made by Wade. Those items made by Wade are marked: An Original Design for Lyons Tetley by Wade England.

No. 785.    "GAFFER" COOKIE JAR - measures 8-3/8" high.
No. 786.    "GAFFER" TOAST RACK - measures 2-3/4" high by 6" long.
No. 787.    "GAFFER & SIDNEY" TEAPOT - measures 5" high.

## WILLIAMSON & MAGOR TEA CADDIES *1990 and 1993.*

A set of two elephant tea caddies designed by Wade, exclusively for Williamson & Magor well known distributors of tea since 1869. Each piece is marked Handcrafted and Produced Exclusively for Williamson & Magor by Wade Royal Victoria Pottery.

No. 788.    "EARL GREY" TEA CADDY - measures 7-1/4" high.
No. 789.    "ENGLISH BREAKFAST" TEA CADDY - measures 7-1/4" high. In 1993 a dark blue, high glaze, version of the "English Breakfast" tea caddy was also produced by Wade for Williamson & Magor.

## HARRODS STORAGE JARS *1993.*

A set of storage jars designed as a special order for Harrods by Judith Wootton. The jars were made in four colors, cream, green, burgundy and blue. See FIG.110.

HARRODS STORAGE JAR. - ACTUAL ORDER - J.Wootton

**FIG. 110.    An Original Design for the Harrods Storage Jar.**

Farmhouse Teapot.

**FIG. 111.**

# FARMHOUSE RANGE *1993*.

A proposed range of kitchen ware comprising teapot, storage jar, milk jug, creamer and sugar. This design by Judith Wootton was launched at the NEC, Birmingham, in February 1993 but at the time of writing has yet to go into production. See FIG.111.

**FIG. 111.    FARMHOUSE RANGE. Preliminary designs for teapot and storage jar.**

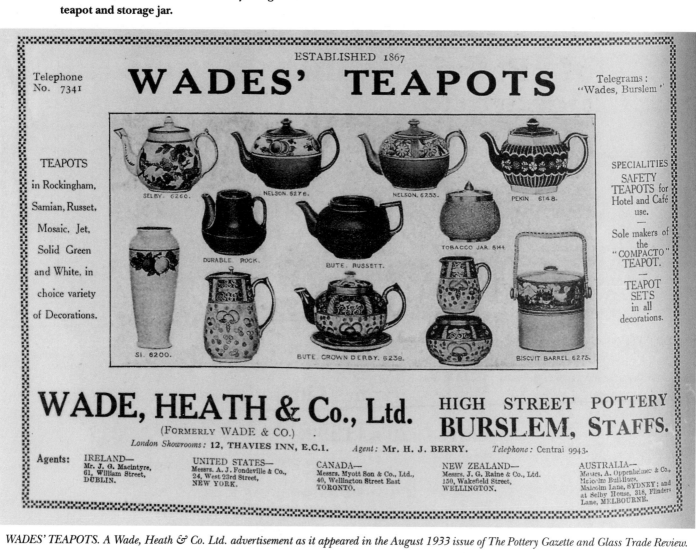

*WADES' TEAPOTS. A Wade, Heath & Co. Ltd. advertisement as it appeared in the August 1933 issue of The Pottery Gazette and Glass Trade Review.*

**TABLEWARE.**

**By Wade, Heath & Co. Ltd.**

**and**

**Wade Ceramics Limited.**

**early 1920's - 1992.**

# TABLEWARE *early 1920's - 1993.*

In the late 1980's, the Wade (Ireland) Ltd. pottery was completely re-tooled for the production of full lines of tableware. The new lines were launched at the Birmingham and Frankfurt Spring Fairs of 1989. Unfortunately, due to strong competition from their well-established competitors in the tableware field, the Wade lines did not sell as well as expected and all production of tableware ceased in the Spring of 1993.

## MISCELLANEOUS TABLEWARE.

No. 790.   "THE McCALLUM" WATER JUG - measures 6-3/4" high and has Mark Type 16 on the base. For additional information see *The W of W No.396 pgs.49 and 123.*

No. 791.   FLOWER JUG - shape No.131 Min., measures 5-1/2" high and has Mark Type 4 on the base.

No. 792.   "GOTHIC" COVERED DISH - shape No.361, measures 2-1/4" high by 6" long by 4-1/4" wide. The dish has Mark Type 9 on the base.

No. 793.   "FRIED GREEN TOMATOES" MONEY BOX (1992) - measures 5-1/4" high by 6" in diameter. The money box has Mark Type 27B on the base. This money box was issued in a limited number to coincide with the opening of the movie of the same name distributed by Rank Film Distribution in the UK.

No. 794.   WALL PLAQUE (1936) - pattern No.180, measures 12-1/2" in diameter and has Mark Type 4 on the base. This plaque was also issued with similar background design but featuring either a bird or a butterfly.

No. 795.   BREAD & BUTTER PLATE - measures 7-3/4" in diameter and has Mark Type 7 on the base.

No. 796.   DINNER PLATE - measures 10-3/4" in diameter and is marked Wade "Hedgerow" England.

No. 797.   BOWL - measures 2-1/2" high by 9" in diameter at the rim and has Mark Type 17 on the base.

No. 798.   OVAL PIN DISH - measures 4-1/4" long by 3-3/4" across and has Mark Type 19 on the base.

No. 799.   HONEY POT - measures 4-1/8" high and has Mark Type 7 on the base.

No. 800.   CUP & SAUCER "MODE SHAPE." The cup measures 2-1/2" high and the saucer measures 5-5/8" in diameter. Both items are marked Wade England "Diamonds" on the underside of the base.

No. 801.   CEREAL BOWL - measures 1-1/2" high by 6-1/4" in diameter and has Mark Type 15 on the base.

No. 802.   "ROOSTER" CUP & SAUCER. The cup measures 2-1/4" high and is marked Made in England A. The saucer measures 5-5/8" in diameter and has Mark Type 7A on the base.

No. 803.   "ROOSTER" CHEESE DISH COVER - measures 6-3/4" in diameter and is unmarked. For more information on the "Rooster" pattern see *The W of W FIG.99 pg.138.* At the time of writing *The World of Wade,* we were under the impression that the Robert Barlow design was a preliminary design for the Flair "Cockerel" pattern. Further research shows that the "Rooster" pattern was produced somewhat earlier

(circa mid 1940's) than the Flair tableware "Cockerel." The backstamp indicates that this pattern was produced for export only.

FIG. 112.   COVERED BOX - measures 1-1/2" high (lid off) by 4" in diameter. This mottled green box with yellow and red flower finial is marked on the underside of the lid, Wade England No. 126.

FIG. 112.

No. 804.   COVERED BOX - pattern No.4274, measures 2-1/8" high by 3-1/2" long by 2-1/2" wide. The box has Mark Type 7 on the base.

No. 805.   COVERED CAMEO DISH - measures 1-1/2" high by 3" in diameter. This piece is believed to be a Wade product and is unmarked.

No. 806.   COVERED CAMEO DISH - measures 1-1/2" high by 3" long by 2-1/2" wide. This piece is believed to be a Wade product and is unmarked.

## FALSTAFF WARE *circa 1960 - 1970.*

The Falstaff ware was produced by Wade, Heath & Co. Ltd. as a special order for Falstaff of Birmingham. It was this company that applied the metal fittings to the ware and then distributed the finished items to their wholesalers. The dates of production are not recorded but it is most probable that the ware was produced sometime between 1960 and 1970. Items reported in this line, other than those illustrated, are the teapot, milk jug, butter dish, honey jar and salad bowl.

No. 807.   "FALSTAFF" CLARET JUG - measures 10" high and is mold-marked Wade Falstaff. This is an unfinished item before the application of the metal fittings as found in a Wade storage room. It has not been determined if this design actually went into production. See also FIG. 213.

FIG. 113.   CLARET JUG - This cobalt blue jug measures approx. 10" high and is mold-marked Wade Falstaff England. During one of our visits to the Wade Pottery, we found an example of the claret jug, without the metal fittings, in an all-over white glaze with applied flower decoration. It was thought, by Wade personnel, that this was probably an experimental piece. See No.807 in the color section.

FIG. 113.

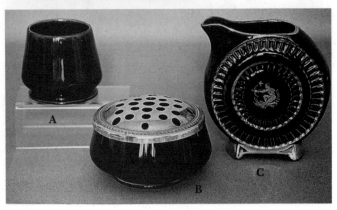

FIG. 114.

No. 808. DUCOR STORAGE JAR - measures 9-3/4" high. This is the large size version of the storage jar. It was also produced in medium and small sizes.

FIG. 115.    DUCOR decoration and backstamp.

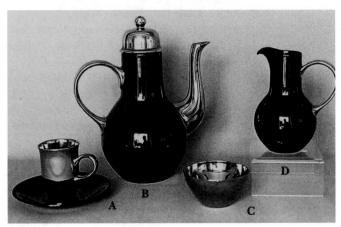

FIG. 116.

FIG. 114.    "FALSTAFF" OCCASIONAL WARE.
A. SUGAR BOWL - this cobalt blue bowl measures 3" high and is mold-marked Wade Falstaff England.
B. POSY BOWL - this cobalt blue bowl measures 3-1/4" high by 5-1/4" in diameter and is mold-marked Wade Falstaff England.
C. FOOTED JUG - this cobalt blue jug, although similar in color to the Falstaff ware, was not made for Falstaff but for Wade (PDM) Ltd. at a later date. The jug measures 5-3/4" high and has Mark Type 45 on the base.

## DUCOR WARE *circa mid 1950's.*

A line of coffee sets, storage jars and occasional pieces were manufactured by Wade, Heath & Co. Ltd. on an exclusive basis for Ducor. This company was formed by Duncan Fox who bought out Corfields in approx. mid 1960's. The name Ducor was arrived at by taking the first two letters of Duncan and combining them with the first three letters of Corfield. All of the Ducor items made by Wade were designed by the freelance designer Michael Caddy.

FIG. 117.

FIG. 116.    DUCOR COFFEE SET.
A. CUP& SAUCER - the cup measures 3" high and the saucer measures 5-1/2" in diameter.
B. COFFEE POT - measures 9-3/4" high to the top of finial.
C. SUGAR BOWL - measures 2" high by 3-5/8" in diameter.
D. CREAMER - measures 5-3/4" high.

**FIG. 117.** **DUCOR DOME STORAGE JAR.** This jar was made in three sizes: large, medium and small. The item shown in the line drawing was produced with a variety of decorations; blue background and black decoration on back and front and with silver bands and silver finial; black background with print decoration, gold bands and finial; opaque white background with pink and green print decoration and gold bands and finial (as illustrated) . These three color variations were also made without the print decoration. For additional decorations see also No.808 in the color section.

**FIG. 118.** **FIG. 119.**

**FIG. 118.** **DUCOR STORAGE JAR.** This jar, given the decoration name "Siamese," was made in two sizes, medium and small and in two color variations: opaque white background with pink and green print and gold finial; blue background with black decoration and gold finial.

**FIG. 119.** **"RIVIERA" STORAGE JAR.** - Pattern No. 6286 was produced in three sizes: large, medium and small and in three glaze variations: white, blue and yellow. Six different prints were applied to this shape all having gold finials. This shape was originally made for Ducor, but, as with many special orders, permission was given to change the decoration and enter the item in the Wade retail line.

## "IMPERIAL" DECORATIVE WARE

*circa mid 1950's.*

The "Imperial" pattern, decoration 6165, was introduced in early 1955 by Wade, Heath & Co. Ltd. and applied to a variety of their standard shapes. The background color was in either maroon or black with white flowers highlighted in gold. The handles of the jugs were all-over glazed with a gold finish.

No. 809.  "IMPERIAL" JUG - measures 5-1/2" high and has Mark Type 16 on the underside of the base.

*IMPERIAL. A Wade, Heath & Co. Ltd. advertisement as it appeared in the March 1955 issue of The Pottery Gazette and Glass Trade Review.*

## MISCELLANEOUS TABLEWARE *continued.*

No. 810.  STORAGE JAR - measures 9-1/2" long by 4-1/4" wide by 3-1/8" high with shape No.104 and Mark Type 7 on the base. Not shown is the lid originally marketed with this item.

No. 811.  TRAY - measures 8-1/2" long by 4-1/2" wide and is marked Wadeheath by permission Walt Disney. This item is from the same range of occasional ware as the butter dish, No.838.

## DECORATION NO.1629 *circa early 1920's - mid 1930's.*

This decoration described as "...styles in richly gilt blue-and-gold "Derby" decorations,..." in the July 1931 issue of *The Pottery Gazette and Glass Trade Review*, was a hand painted decoration applied to a wide range of tableware items. The line was manufactured by Wade & Co. in the early 1920's through to the mid 1930's when the company became Wade, Heath & Co. Ltd.

No. 812.  PITCHER - measures 7-1/4" high (decoration No. 1629) and has Mark Type 4 on the base.

No. 813.  PLATE - measures 5-3/4" square (decoration No. 1629) and has Mark Type 1B on the base.

191

No. 814.  CREAMER - measures 2-1/2" high (decoration No. 1629) and has Mark Type 1B on the base.

FIG. 120.  FRUIT BOWL AND NAPPY (circa early 1920's).
A. This 9-3/4" wide free-hand decorated bowl has a blue, orange, brown and green flower and leaf decoration with Mark Type "zero" on the base.
B. This 6-1/2" wide nappy has a similar mark and decoration to item "A" above.

FIG. 120.

## DECORATION NO.230 *circa 1938.*

This "Bon-Bon" dish or "Sweet" tray was designed by Robert Barlow for Wade, Heath & Co. Ltd. The original intention was that this design would be used for a complete line of tableware, but with the outbreak of WWII in 1939, this projected line did not fully develop. As well as the dish illustrated, a larger, 10" diameter by 3" high version (decoration No. 228) with Mark Type 4 on the base has been found. This decoration has green leaves and purple edged flowers.

No. 815.  FOOTED SWEET DISH - measures 6" in diameter by 2" high (decoration No. 230) and has Mark Type 6 on the base.

## DECORATION NO.4024 *circa 1937.*

A series of "COTTAGE" shaped biscuit barrels, teapots etc. was produced by Wade, Heath & Co. Ltd. in the late 1930's. According to the April 1938 issue of *The Pottery Gazette and Glass Trade Review,* during a visit to the 1938 British Industries Fair, Queen Mary purchased a "COTTAGE" teapot whilst visiting the Wade stand.

No. 816.  COOKIE JAR - measures 6" high by 5-1/2" long by 4-3/8" wide (decoration No. 4024) and has Mark Type 2 on the base.

## WADEHEATH "PANDA" NURSERY WARE *1939.*

The production of nursery tableware appears to have been a chief item of trade for Wade, Heath & Co. Ltd. On the occasion of the release of a new Walt Disney cartoon or a newspaper headline of a special event, Wade, Heath &

Co. Ltd. was quick to issue a children's set of dishes based on the event.

Such an occasion was the arrival of Ming, the baby giant panda, at the London Zoo in 1939.

To compliment the children's dishes, Wade, Heath also introduced a "Giant Panda" figure measuring 7-1/2" high. For illustrations of this figurine and the toy dishes see the following advertisement.

*WADEHEATH "PANDA" NURSERY WARE AND "GIANT PANDA" FIGURE. A Wade, Heath & Co. Ltd. advertisement as it appeared in the August 1939 issue of The Pottery Gazette and Glass Trade Review.*

## BASKET WARE "1" *circa 1946* and BASKET WARE "2" *circa 1955.*

Basket Ware "1" was the first complete line of tableware to be introduced by Wade, Heath & Co. Ltd. after WWII. Basket Ware "2" decoration was applied to the same shapes as the earlier decoration. This "modernization" of the line involved the addition of stainless steel holders and acrylic finials. For more information on these patterns, see *The W of W pgs. 131 and 137.*

No. 817.  BASKET WARE "2" BISCUIT BARREL - measures 8-1/2" high and has Mark Type 16 on the base.
No. 818.  BASKET WARE "1" BISCUIT BARREL - measures 6-3/4" high and has Mark Type 7 on the base.
No. 819.  BASKET - mold No. 250, measures 5-1/4" high and has Mark Type 7 on the base.

No. 820.    BASKET WARE "1" CRUET SET. The tray measures 5-1/2" in diameter and has Mark Type 7 on the base. The salt and pepper are both 2-1/2" high and are unmarked. The covered mustard is 2-3/4" high and is unmarked.

No. 821.    BASKET WARE "1" CREAMER - measures 3-1/8" high and has Mark Type 7 on the base.

No.822.    BASKET WARE "1" SUGAR - measures 2" high and is marked "NOVELTIO" Trade Mark Made in England. Items produced by Wade, Heath & Co. Ltd. but marked "NOVELTIO," was a special order for a London based export company and was backstamped with the company's own mark.

No. 823.    BASKET WARE "1" CREAMER - measures 3-1/8" high and is marked "NOVELTIO" Trade Mark Made in England.

No. 824.    BASKET WARE "1" TEAPOT - measures 6" high and has Mark Type 7 on the base.

# "QUACK QUACK" CHILDREN'S DISHES *1947 - circa mid 1950's.*

It was originally thought that this line of children's dishes was first produced in the 1930's. This, however, was not the case although it is most probable that the design, by Robert Barlow, was created prior to WWII.

The dishes were produced immediately after the end of the war by Wade, Heath & Co. Ltd. as an export only line. When the restrictions for decorated ware for home consumption were lifted in 1952, the line then went on sale in the U.K.

No. 825.    "QUACK QUACK" CEREAL DISH - measures 7-1/4" in diameter and has Mark Type 11A on the base.

No. 826.    "QUACK QUACK" PLATE - measures 6-1/4" in diameter and has Mark Type 11A on the base.

No. 827.    "QUACK QUACK" BOWL - measures 6-1/4" in diameter and has Mark Type 11A on the base.

No. 828.    "QUACK QUACK" SAUCER - measures 5-3/4" in diameter and has Mark Type 11A on the base.

No. 829.    "QUACK QUACK" CUP - measures 2-1/4" high by 3" in diameter at the top and has Mark Type 11A on the base.

FIG. 121.

FIG. 121.    "QUACK QUACK" PLATE - measures 6-1/2" in diameter and has Mark Type 11A on the base.

# "NODDY" and "BIG EARS" CHILDREN'S DISHES *circa 1955.*

Due to the great success of the "Quack Quack" children dishes and the earlier Walt Disney toy tea sets and the "Panda" Nursery Ware, Wade, Heath & Co. Ltd. issued a series of nursery wares based on the very popular TV series, Noddy, which in turn, was based on the Enid Blyton characters. The popularity of this nursery set gave rise to the figurines produced by George Wade & Son Ltd. a few years later.

Items in the set consisted of the following: tea cup and saucer, bread and butter plates, oatmeal bowls, baby plates, handled mugs small and large, unhandled beakers. Most items were marked: Wade England, ©1953 by Noddy Subsidiary Rights Co. Ltd. It would appear that the copyright year, 1953, refers to the date the Enid Blyton characters were registered since the 1955 advertisement indicates that this was a new nursery ware by Wade.

*ENID BLYTON'S "NODDY" AND "BIG EARS." A Wade, Heath & Co. Ltd. advertisement as it appeared in the May 1955 issue of The Pottery Gazette and Glass Trade Review.*

# WALT DISNEY CHILDREN'S DISHES

### 1934 - late 1950's.

In 1934, Wade, Heath & Co. Ltd. acquired the sole selling rights for the British Empire (excluding Canada) for reproducing the Walt Disney characters on tableware. The first set produced was a four piece children's dish set comprising: baby plate, cup and saucer, mug and plate. These were marketed in an attractive "Mickey Mouse" presentation box.

Due to the popularity of the children's set, Wade, Heath & Co. Ltd., in 1935, began producing a line of Mickey Mouse children's toy dishes. The sets were produced in three sizes: eight pieces, ten pieces and sixteen pieces, all in decorative presentation boxes.

The eight piece set consisted of two cups and saucer, two plates, teapot, sugar and creamer (presumably the teapot and lid were classed as two pieces). The ten piece set had two extra plates and the sixteen piece set had extra cups, saucers and plates.

Queen Mary, who appears to have been a regular customer of the Wade Potteries in the 1930's, is reported to have bought one of the Mickey Mouse toy tea sets at the BIF in 1938.

The Walt Disney "Lullaby Land" toy tea sets were produced by Wade, Heath & Co. Ltd. in 1935, and the "Snow White" toy tea set in 1938.

*MICKEY MOUSE NURSERY WARE. A Wade, Heath & Co. Ltd. advertisement as it appeared in the September 1934 issue of The Pottery Gazette and Glass Trade Review.*

No. 830. PLATE "MICKEY MOUSE" - measures 5-3/4" square and has Mark Type 2B on the base.

No. 831. SUGAR BOWL - measures 1-1/2" high and is unmarked.

No. 832. CREAMER - measures 2" high and is unmarked.

No. 833. SAUCER - measures 3-3/4" in diameter and has Mark Type 2C on the base.

No. 834. CUP "SLEEPY" - measures 1-7/8" high and is unmarked.

No. 835. SAUCER - measures 3-3/4" in diameter and has Mark Type 2C on the base.

No. 836. CUP "HAPPY" - measures 1-7/8" high and is unmarked.

No. 837. TEAPOT "SNOW WHITE" - measures 3-3/8" high and has Mark Type 2C on the base.

No. 838. BUTTER DISH "DOPEY" - measures 4-1/2" high by 7" in diameter and has Mark Type 2B on the base.

No. 839. SUGAR "HIAWATHA" - measures 1-1/2" high and is unmarked.

No. 840. CREAMER "FUNNY LITTLE BUNNIES" - measures 2" high and is unmarked.

No. 841. SAUCER "RING O' ROSES" - measures 4" in diameter and has Mark Type 7 on the base.

No. 842. CUP "SIMPLE SIMON MET A PIE MAN" - measures 1-7/8" high and is unmarked.

No. 843. SAUCER "LITTLE JUMPING JOAN" - measures 4" in diameter and has Mark Type 7 on the base.

No. 844. CUP "ABC TUMBLE DOWN D" - measures 1-7/8" high and is unmarked.

No. 845. TEAPOT "WHAT ARE LITTLE GIRLS MADE OF" - measures 3-3/8" high and has Mark Type 2C on the base.

FIG. 122. "MICKEY MOUSE" CHILDREN'S TOY DISHES (1935). The following items are either unmarked or marked with Mark Type 2C on the base.
A. Creamer - measures 2" high. Teapot - measures 3-3/8" high. Sugar - measures 1-1/2" high.
B. The four cups and saucers. The saucers are interchangeable as they have similar decorations but each cup has a different character decoration. The cups measure 1-7/8" high and the saucers measure 2-3/4" in diameter.
C. Plates. Each plate measures 5-1/8" in diameter.

FIG. 122A.

FIG. 122B.

FIG. 122C.

## "PINOCCHIO" NURSERY WARE *1940.*

For a very short time, in the early days of WWII, Wade, Heath & Co. Ltd. produced a line of children's toy tea and dinner sets with decorations based on the popular Walt Disney cartoon feature, *Pinocchio*. The decoration was applied to shapes similar to those used for the earlier Walt Disney issues of Snow White and the Seven Dwarfs, Mickey Mouse etc. Due to the war-time restrictions imposed on decorative tableware, this line appears to have had a very short run.

## HONEY POTS and TRAYS *circa mid 1930's - mid 1950's.*

A number of individual honey pots were produced by Wade, Heath & Co. Ltd. in the 1930's. However, individual pots lost appeal by the 1950's and were generally replaced by covered pots belonging to certain lines of tableware.

Ashtrays, sometimes referred to as "pin trays" were from the standard range of Wade, Heath tableware of the 1950's, with various hand-applied decorations.

No. 846. "BIRD FINIAL" HONEY POT - measures 3-3/4" high and has Mark Type 7 on the base.

No. 847. "FLOWER FINIAL" HONEY POT - measures 4-1/4" high and has Mark Type 4 on the base.

No. 848. ASHTRAY - decoration No. 4900, measures 4" long by 3" wide by 3/4" high and has Mark Type 13 on the base.

No. 849. ASHTRAY - decoration No. 6017, measures 4" long by 3" wide by 3/4" high and has Mark Type 10 on the base.

No. 850. "BEEHIVE" HONEY POT - measures 3-3/4" high and has Mark Type 6 on the base.

No. 851. "PEAR" HONEY POT - measures 4-1/8" high and has Mark Type 7 on the base.

PINOCCHIO" NURSERY WARE. *A Wade, Heath & Co. Ltd. advertisement as it appeared in the April 1940 issue of The Pottery Gazette and Glass Trade Review.*

195

WADEHEATH WARE. An advertisement as it appeared in the March 1938 issue of The Pottery Gazette and Glass Trade Review.

## "RUBYTONE" TABLEWARE 1953 - circa early 1960's.

This design, referred to as a "fancy" tea set, was made in four color variations of a design based on embossed bands and raised vine leaves and fruit.

The first design was "Rubytone" decoration No.6113, a rich red with gold vine leaves on a white background. Next came sets in two shades of green: "Regal Green" decoration No.6143 and "Greenstones" in a lighter shade of green. The last variation was a design of gold leaves and bands on a white background. For further information on these designs, see The W of W pgs. 52, 132 and 133.

No. 852.   DINNER PLATE - measures 8-3/4" in diameter and has Mark Type 17A on the base.

No. 853.   DESSERT PLATE - measures 6-3/4" in diameter and has Mark Type 17A on the base.

No. 854.   LARGE TEAPOT - measures 6-1/2" high by 11" overall and has Mark Type 17A on the base.

No. 855.   CUP & SAUCER - the saucer measures 5-1/2" in diameter and has Mark Type 16 on the base. The cup measures 2-1/2" high and has Mark Type 16 on the base.

No. 856.   COVERED SUGAR WITH HANDLES - measures 3-1/2" high and has Mark Type 16 on the base.

No. 857.   GRAVY BOAT & TRAY "REGAL GREEN" - the tray measures 6-1/2" long and has Mark Type 16 on the base. The gravy boat is 6"long by 3"high and has Mark Type 16 on the base.

No. 858.   GRAVY BOAT & TRAY - the tray measures 6-1/2" long and has Mark Type 16 on the base. The gravy boat is 6"long by 3"high and has Mark Type 16 on the base.

No. 859.   CREAMER - measures 6"long by 3-1/2"high and has Mark Type 16 on the base.

No. 860.   COVERED SUGAR WITHOUT HANDLES - measures 3-1/2" high and has Mark Type 16 on the base.

No. 861.   PLATTER - measures 11" long and has Mark Type 17A on the base.

## REGENCY SHAPE COFFEE and TEA SETS early 1950's - 1961.

The popular and much-used Regency shape was marketed with a variety of decorations. A tea set and a coffee set were introduced in 1952 with decoration No. 5002. See FIG.123. It is interesting to note that this decoration is very similar to decoration No. 4959 which is illustrated as item Nos.1007-1012 . The Regency shape was also used for the coffee set issued in the latter part of the 1950's and illustrated as item Nos. 862-867.

The bowl shown in FIG.123 indicates that decoration No. 5002 was applied to tableware shapes other than Regency.

REGENCY SHAPE. A Wade, Heath & Co. Ltd. advertisement as it appeared in the March 1952 issue of Pottery Gazette and Glass Trade Review.

**FIG. 123.**

**FIG. 124.**

**FIG. 123.** BOWL - decoration No. 5002, measures 6-1/4" in diameter and has Mark Type 10 on the base.

No. 862. COFFEE POT - measures 6-3/4" high and has Mark Type 19 on the base.

No. 863. CUP & SAUCER - the cup measures 2-3/8" high and has Mark Type 19 on the base. The saucer measures 5" in diameter and has Mark Type 19 on the base.

No. 864. CUP - measures 2-3/8" high and has Mark Type 19 on the base.

No. 865. SAUCER - measures 5" in diameter and has Mark Type 19 on the base.

No. 866. SUGAR - measures 1-3/4" high and has Mark Type 19 on the base.

No. 867. CREAMER - measures 1-7/8" high and has Mark Type 19 on the base.

## MISCELLANEOUS TABLEWARE *continued.*

No. 868. MILK JUG - measures 5-1/4" high and has Mark Type 10 on the base.

No. 869. VASE "SHAPE 3" - copper lustre decoration, measures 2-3/4" high and has Mark Type 13 on the base.

No. 870. VASE "SHAPE 1" - decoration 4900, measures 2-1/2" high by 3-3/4" in diameter and has Mark Type 13 on the base.

No. 871. DEMITASSE CREAMER - measures 2" high and has Mark Type 15 on the base.

No. 872. DEMITASSE CREAMER - measures 2" high and has Mark Type 16 on the base.

No. 873. DEMITASSE COVERED SUGAR - measures 2-1/4" high and has Mark Type 16 on the base.

No. 874. CUP & SAUCER - the cup measures 2-3/8" high and has Mark Type 17 on the base. The saucer measures 5-5/8" in diameter and has Mark Type 17 on the base. This cup and saucer is from the Regency shape line of tableware circa 1951-1960.

**FIG. 124.** DEMITASSE CUP & SAUCER - the cup measures 2-1/2" high and the saucer measures 4-1/2" in diameter. Both cup and saucer have Mark Type 10 on the base.

## COPPER LUSTRE WARE.

Between approx. 1935 and the early 1980's, Wade, Heath & Co. Ltd. produced a large variety of solid copper lustre items along with a variety of combination hand-painted designs and copper lustre. For illustrations of many solid copper lustre items produced by the pottery during the 1950's see. FIG.125 and also *The W of W pgs. 56 and 57.*

**FIG. 125.** A Wade, Heath & Co. Ltd. Catalogue Page circa early 1950's.

| | | |
|---|---|---|
| 1. | Candy Box | 6-3/4" L by 5" W |
| 2. | Cigarette Box | 5" L by 3-3/4" W |
| 3. | Ashtray | 4" L by 3" W |
| 4. | Finger Bowl | 4" diameter |
| 5. | Dandy Jug (cream) small size | 3" H |
| 6. | Dandy Jug (cream) large size | 3-1/2" H |
| 7. | Dandy Jug 42s | 4-1/2" H |
| 8. | Dandy Jug 36s | 5-1/4" H |
| 9. | Dandy Jug 24s | 6-1/4" H |
| 10. | Dandy Jug 30s | 5-3/4" H |
| 11. | Beer Mug | 5" H |
| 12. | Eagle Tea Pot and Stand | 6" H |
| 13. | Dandy Sugar small size | 1-3/4" H |
| 14. | Dandy Sugar large size | 2" H |
| 15. | Toby Jug (Pirate) | 5" H |
| 16. | Toby Jug (Highwayman) | 5" H |
| 17. | Lattice Jug 30s | 6" H |
| 18. | Lattice Jug 36s | 5" H |
| | Lattice Jug 42s (not shown) | 4-1/2" H |
| 19. | Nelson Tea Pot 30s | 5-1/2" H |
| 20. | Nelson Tea Pot 24s | 5-3/4" H |
| | Nelson Tea Pot 42s (not shown) | 4-1/2" H |
| | Nelson Tea Pot 36s (not shown) | 5" H |
| 21. | Dutch Jug 36s | 4-1/2" H |
| 22. | Dutch Jug 30s | 5-1/2" H |
| 23. | Dutch Jug 24s | 5-3/4" H |
| | Dutch Jug 42s (not shown) | 4" H |
| 24. | Diamond Jug 30s | 6" H |
| 25. | Diamond Jug 36s | 5-1/2" H |
| | Diamond Jug 42s (not shown) | 5" H |
| 26. | Stag Bowl | |
| 27. | Console Bowl | 11-1/4" L by 6" W |
| 28. | Stag Jug 42s | 5" H |
| | Stag Jug 36s (not shown) | 5-1/2" H |
| 29. | Polka Jug 30s | 6" H |
| | Polka Jug 36s (not shown) | 5-1/2" H |
| 30. | Stag Jug 30s | 6" H |

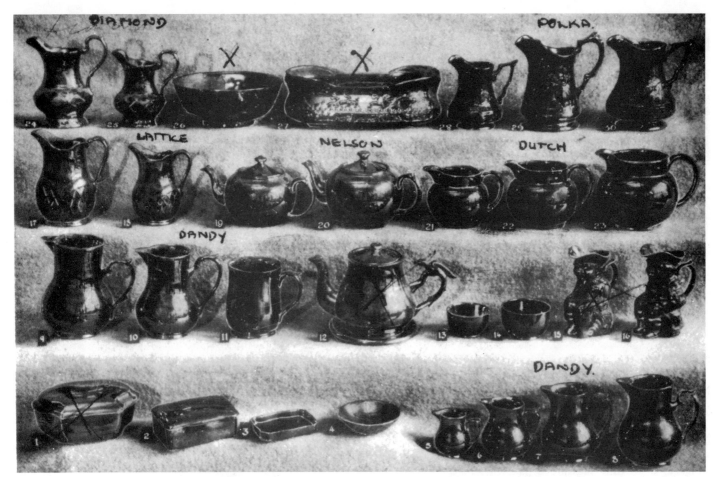

FIG. 125.

# "HEDGEROW" and "MEADOW" TABLEWARE *1950 - early 1960's.*

A series of print-and-enamel decorations were applied to Wade, Heath & Co. Ltd. standard range of dinner, tea and coffee ware including the very popular Regency shape.

No. 875.  PLATE "HEDGEROW" - decoration No. 4905, measures 11" in diameter and is marked Wade "Hedgerow" England.

No. 876.  PLATE "MEADOW" - decoration No. 4933, measures 8" in diameter and is marked Wade "Meadow" England.

No. 877.  SAUCER "HEDGEROW" - decoration No. 4905, measures 5-1/2" in diameter and is marked Wade "Hedgerow" England.

FIG. 126.

No. 878.  CUP "HEDGEROW" - decoration No. 4905, measures 2-1/4" high and is marked Wade "Hedgerow" England.

FIG. 126.  COVERED VEGETABLE DISH - decoration No. 4933, measures 9-3/4" across and is marked Wade "Meadow" England.

# MISCELLANEOUS TABLEWARE.

FIG. 127.  CUP & SAUCER "Orb" shape. The cups measure 2-3/4" high and have Mark Type 10B on the base. The saucers measure 5-5/8" in diameter and have Mark Type 7A on the base.

FIG. 128.  MISCELLANEOUS WARE.
A. PLATE - pattern No. 6108, measures 9-1/2" in diameter and has Mark Type 17 on the base.
This free-hand decorated plate was decorated in olive green, yellow, golden brown and sepia brown.
B. VETERAN CAR CIGARETTE BOX - mold No. 242, Rolls-Royce decoration. The cigarette box measures 5"long by 3-1/2" wide by 1-3/4"high and has Mark Type 19 on the base.
C. TANKARD - measures 5" high with a black silhouette decoration on a Harvest body. The tankard is unmarked.
D. TANKARD - measures 5" high with a black silhouette decoration of Sir George Wade on a Harvest body. The tankard is marked: With compliments of the season 1950.
E. DISH - decoration No. 5069 on shape No. "F,"

FIG. 127.

FIG. 128.

measures 10" overall by 6-3/4" wide. The dish has Mark Type 10 on the base. This dish has a lithograph spray centre on a white body with either green, blue or maroon outer band highlighted with gold edging.

F. PLATE - measures 9-1/2" in diameter and has Mark Type 17 on the base.

G. JUG - "Parasol" decoration, measures 5" high and is marked: A DEE CEE Souvenir by Wade.

H. PLATE - measures 9-1/2" in diameter and has Mark Type 19 on the base.

No. 879.   COVERED CANDY DISH - measures 4-1/2" high to top of finial and has Mark Type 19 on the base.

No. 880.   DANDY MILK JUG - measures 5-1/8" high and has Mark Type 19 on the base.

No. 881.   PLATE - measures 6-3/4" in diameter and has Mark Type 7A on the base.

No. 882.   CUP & SAUCER - the cup is 2-3/4" high and is marked Made in England A. The saucer measures 5-5/8" in diameter and has Mark Type 7A on the base.

No. 883.   PLATE - measures 6-1/2" square and has Mark Type

7A on the base.

No. 884.   CUP & SAUCER - the cup is 2-3/4" high and is marked Made in England A. The saucer measures 5-5/8" in diameter and has Mark Type 7A on the base.

No. 885.   PLATE - measures 6-3/4" in diameter and has Mark Type 7A on the base.

No. 886.   CUP & SAUCER - the cup is 2-3/4" high and is marked Made in England A. The saucer measures 5-5/8" in diameter and has Mark Type 7A on the base.

No. 887.   PLATE - measures 6-3/4" in diameter and has Mark Type 7A on the base.

No. 888.   SUGAR - measures 3" high and is marked Made in England A.

No. 889.   CREAMER - measures 3-1/2" high and has Mark Type 7 on the base.

No. 890.   PLATE - measures 6-3/4" in diameter and has Mark Type 7A on the base.

No. 891.   CREAMER - measures 3-1/2" high and has Mark Type 7A on the base.

No. 892.   CIGARETTE BOX - mold No. 242, decoration No.

199

6468. The cigarette box measures 5"long by 3- 1/2" wide by 1-3/4"high and has Mark Type 10 on the base.

No. 893.   ASHTRAY - decoration No. 6468, measures 4"long by 3"wide by 3/4"high and has Mark Type 10 on the base.

No. 894.   CUP - measures 2-3/4" high and is marked WADE "Ascot" England 6020 on the base.

No. 895.   CUP - measures 2-3/4" high and is marked WADE "Ascot" England 6020 on the base. Both item Nos. 894 and 895 have similar markings but different patterns.

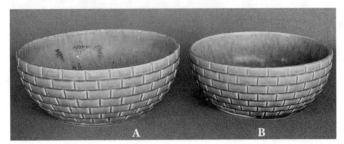

FIG. 129.

FIG. 129.   FRUIT BOWLS (circa late 1930's).
A. This green mottled bowl measures 3-1/4" high by 8-3/4" in diameter and has Mark Type 6 on the base.
B. This blue mottled bowl measures 3" high by 7-3/4" in diameter and has Mark Type 6 on the base.

## LATTICE WARE *1955.*

Having a hand-painted design in yellow, green and red on a "Mother-of-Pearl" lustre glaze and a lattice-embossed design, the complete Lattice Ware set was comprised of the following: teapot, sugar, creamer, milk jug, 5" round dish, 6" round dish, cheese dish, covered butter, honey pot, biscuit jar, mint sauce boat and stand, triple tray, salad bowl, salad servers, oval dish and cruet set.

For illustration of some of these shapes, see *The W of W pg. 138, FIG. 97* which illustrates Lattice Ware Decoration No. 6191.

No. 896.   DISH - measures 6-1/4" overall and has Mark Type 16 on the base.

No. 897.   CREAMER - measures 2-3/4" high and has Mark Type 16 on the base. This Lattice Ware creamer has an all-over silver glaze.

## "CAMBRIDGE" TABLEWARE *circa mid 1950's.*

Decoration No. 6016. All pieces are marked: Wade "Cambridge" England 6016.

No. 898.   PLATTER - measures 14-1/4" overall.
No. 899.   SAUCER - measures 5-1/2" in diameter.
No. 900.   CUP - measures 2-5/8" high.
No. 901.   PLATTER - measures 11-3/4" overall.
No. 902.   DINNER PLATE - measures 10-1/2" in diameter.
No. 903.   BREAD & BUTTER PLATE - measures 6-1/2" in diameter.

No. 904.   GRAVY BOAT & TRAY - the gravy boat is 8" long by 3-1/4" high and the tray is 7-3/4" long  by 5-1/4" wide.

No. 905.   CREAMER - measures 3" high. The two handled covered sugar (not shown) measures 4-1/8" high to the top of finial.

No. 906.   FRUIT BOWL - measures 5-1/4" in diameter.
No. 907.   SOUP BOWL - measures 7-1/2" in diameter.
No. 908.   SALAD PLATE - measures 8" in diameter.
No. 909.   VEGETABLE BOWL - measures 9" in diameter.

FIG. 130.

FIG. 130.   "ROSETTA" (mid 1950's). This 7-3/4" diameter plate, decoration No. 5097,  is from a dinner ware set using the same centre motif as the "Cambridge" pattern. All pieces in this set are marked: Wade "Rosetta" England 5097 along with Mark Type 10B.

FIG. 131.   DINNER WARE SET - with pink flowers and green leaves along with an overall applied gold decoration.
A. TAB HANDLED PLATE - measures 9-1/2" in diameter and has Mark Type 10 on the base.
B. CUP & SAUCER - the cup measures 2-3/4" high and the saucer is 5-1/2" in diameter.
Both items have Mark Type 10 on their bases.
C. PLATE - measures 6-1/2" in diameter and has Mark Type 10 on the base.
D. CREAMER - measures 2-3/4" high and has Mark Type 15 on the base.
E. SUGAR - measures 2-3/4" high by 4-1/2" in diameter at the top and has Mark Type 15 on the base.
F. OVAL TAB HANDLED PLATTER - measures 11" across and has Mark Type 17 on the base.

FIG. 131.

# TABLEWARE with SPRAYED BAND, LINE and FLOWER DECORATION.

No. 910.　GRAVY BOAT - measures 3"high by 8"long and has Mark Type 7 on the base.

No. 911.　DINNER PLATE - measures 10" in diameter and has Mark Type 7 on the base.

No. 912.　DESSERT PLATE - measures 9" in diameter and has Mark Type 7 on the base.

## "MODE" TABLEWARE - RED CRISS CROSS DECORATION early 1953.

This decoration was available as a full dinner set including a number of occasional pieces such as Sugar Shaker, similar in shape to the Salt and Pepper Shakers but double the size and the popular "snack" or "TV Tray" combination of plate and cup. All pieces have Mark Type 17 on the base.

No. 913.　TEAPOT - measures 6" high.

No. 914.　CREAMER - measures 2-1/2" high.

No. 915.　SUGAR - measures 2-5/8" high.

No. 916.　PLATTER - measures 13-1/2" in diameter.

No. 917.　BREAD & BUTTER PLATE - measures 6" in diameter.

No. 918.　DINNER PLATE - measures 10-1/4" in diameter.

No. 919.　BOWL - measures 6-1/2" overall.

No. 920.　CUP & SAUCER - the cup measures 2-1/2" high and the saucer measures 5-5/8" in diameter.

## "MODE" TABLEWARE - GREEN CRISS CROSS DECORATION mid 1953.

No. 921.　DINNER PLATE - measures 10-1/4" in diameter.

No. 922.　CUP & SAUCER - the cup measures 2-1/2" high and the saucer measures 5-5/8" in diameter.

No. 923.　BOWL - measures 6-1/2" overall.

## "MODE" TABLEWARE - DECORATION NO.6069. late 1954.

A similar decoration to the "Mode" Criss Cross decoration was introduced in 1954 as decoration No.6069. Unlike the diagonal stripes in the Criss Cross decoration, decoration No.6069 had one thick olive green vertical and one thick olive green horizontal band with three thin, red, yellow and black wavy lines to one side of each thick band.

## "ORB" TABLEWARE early 1950's.

All pieces have Mark Type 17 on the base unless noted otherwise.

No. 924.　DINNER PLATE - measures 8-3/4" in diameter.

No. 925.　BREAD & BUTTER PLATE - measures 6-3/8" in diameter.

No. 926.　CUP & SAUCER - the cup measures 2-7/8" high and the saucer measures 5-3/4" in diameter.

No. 927.　PLATTER - measures 11" overall.

No. 928.　BOWL - measures 6" in diameter.

No. 929.　DINNER PLATE - measures 8-3/4" in diameter and has Mark Type 10 on the base.

No. 930.　CUP & SAUCER - the cup measures 2-7/8" high and the saucer measures 5-3/4" in diameter.

No. 931.　BREAD & BUTTER PLATE - measures 6-3/8" in diameter.

No. 932.　CUP & SAUCER - the cup measures 2-7/8" high and the saucer measures 5-3/4" in diameter.

No. 933.　BOWL - measures 6" in diameter.

## "MODE" WARE SNACK SET 1953.

No. 934.　SNACK SET - decoration No. 6069. The plate measures 9-1/2" overall and has Mark Type 17 on the base. The cup is 2-1/2" high and is similar to the "Mode" shape cup.

FIG. 132.

**FIG. 132.** **SNACK SET "CARNIVAL"** - the plate measures 9-1/2" overall and has Mark Type 19 on the base. The cup is 2-1/2" high and is similar to the "Mode" shape cup.

**FIG. 133.**

*TRADITIONAL "ORB" SHAPE. A line of dinner and tea ware with a wide underglaze maroon border, stamped with gold decoration. A Wade, Heath & Co. Ltd. advertisement as it appeared in the December 1954 issue of The Pottery Gazette and Glass Trade Review.*

## "REGENCY" TABLEWARE
*circa late 1940's - 1960.*

No. 935. **WALL PLATE "SOMERSET COTTAGE"** - decoration No. 6101, measures 10-1/2" in diameter and has Mark Type 17 on the base.

No. 936. **BREAD & BUTTER PLATE "SOMERSET COTTAGE"** - decoration No. 6049, measures 6-3/4" in diameter and has Mark Type 10 on the base.

No. 937. **CUP "SOMERSET COTTAGE"** - decoration No. 6049, measures 2-5/8" high and has Mark Type 10 on the base.

No. 938. **SAUCER "SOMERSET COTTAGE"** - decoration No. 6049, measures 5-1/2" in diameter and has Mark Type 17 on the base.

No. 939. **PLATE "SPRINGTIME"** - measures 9" in diameter and is marked Wade England A.

FIG. 133. **WALL PLATE "SOMERSET COTTAGE"** - decoration No. 6048 from the Wade, Heath Design Book.

FIG. 134. **CENTRE HANDLED SANDWICH PLATE** - measures 10-1/2" in diameter and has Mark Type 17 on the base.

**FIG. 134.**

## ROMANCE WALL PLATES *1951 - 1960.*

The Romance wall plates comprised mainly of lithograph decorations of eighteen century romantic couples or various flower arrangements. These designs, which were usually applied to the "Regency" shape plates are also found on items produced by potteries other than Wade. These lithograph designs were from open stock made available to all potteries.

The Romance wall plates are most often found with the maroon, dark green or dark blue borders. The plates with light blue or especially yellow borders are the hardest to find.

No. 940. **WALL PLATE** - measures 10-1/2" in diameter and has Mark Type 10 on the base.

# PORCELAIN Cooking Ware

Attractive and modern in colour and design "WADE" Porcelain Oven-proof Cooking Ware has an extensive range including :—

Baking dishes, Casseroles, Tea and Coffee Pots, Hot Water Jugs, Hors d'oeuvres—large and small, Soups, etc.

It economises food and preserves the flavour by bringing it straight from the oven to the table and has the extra hygiene and easier cleaning of high class pottery.

*Send for full particulars and prices to*

GEORGE WADE & SON, LTD., *Manchester Pottery, Burslem*, STOKE-ON-TRENT.

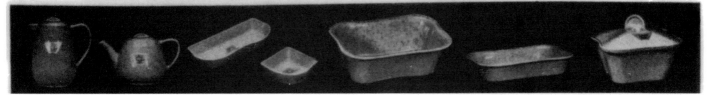

*PORCELAIN COOKING WARE as it appeared in the January 1940 issue of The Pottery Gazette and Glass Trade Review.*

No. 941.  WALL PLATE - measures 10-1/2" in diameter and has Mark Type 10 on the base.

No. 942.  WALL PLATE - measures 10-1/2" in diameter and has Mark Type 10 on the base.

No. 943.  WALL PLATE - measures 10-1/2" in diameter and has Mark Type 10 on the base.

## MISCELLANEOUS TABLEWARE.

FIG. 135.  MILK JUG "BRAMBLE" (circa early 1950's). This 5" high milk jug has an all-over turquoise glaze with Mark Type 10 on the base. This elongated shape is different from the usual Dandy Jugs used in the Bramble Ware.

No. 944.  NUT DISH "EMERALD GOLD" - measures 8"long by 5-1/4"wide and has Mark Types 10 and 12B on the base.

No. 945.  DISH "EMERALD GOLD"- measures 12"long by 8-3/4"wide and has Mark Types 10 and 12B on the base.

No. 946.  NUT DISH "GOLD BLUSH" - measures 8"long by 5-1/4"wide and has Mark Type12 on the base.

No. 947.  NUT DISH "GOLDEN TURQUOISE" - measures 5" in diameter and has Mark Types 10 and 12A on the base.

No. 948.  COVERED SUGAR "BRAMBLE" - measures 3-3/4"

FIG. 135.

high and has Mark Type 12 on the base. For further information see *The W of W pgs.54, 55, 140 and 141*.

No. 949.  NUT DISH - decoration No. 5068, measures 8"long by 5-1/4"wide and has Mark Type 14 on the base.

203

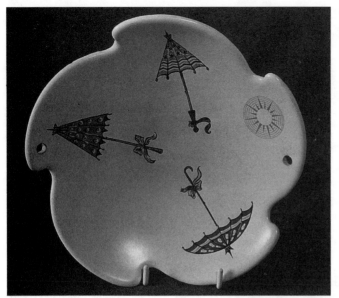

FIG. 136.

FIG. 136.   NUT DISH "PARASOL" (late 1950's) - measures 7"
in diameter and is marked: Wade England "Parasol."
For more information on the "Harmony" tableware
line which included the "Parasol" decoration see *The
W of W pgs. 136 and 137.*

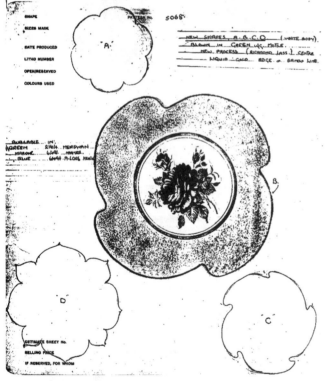

FIG. 137.

FIG. 137.   DECORATION NO. 5068 on dish shape "B" along
with additional new shapes "A," "C" and "D."

FIG. 138.   DECORATION NO. 5069 on dish shape "E" along
with additional new shapes "F" and "G."

## FLOWER POTS *circa early 1960's.*

For a short time in the early 1960's, Wade, Heath & Co.
Ltd. produced a quite extensive range of flower pots with

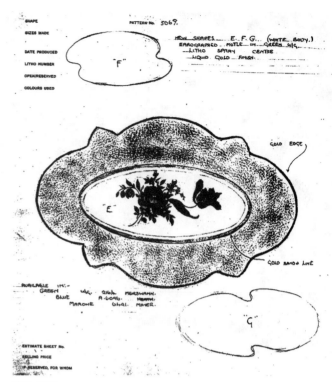

FIG. 138.

or without drip trays. The "Venetian" line was a fluted
design in single all-over glazes whilst their standard line
consisted of a variety of transfer decorations on plain or
multicolored backgrounds.

No. 950.   FLOWER POT - measures 2-1/2" high and has
Mark Type 19 on the base. See FIG.139 for the
matching round drip tray.

FIG. 139.   Examples from the "Standard Line" of Wade,
Heath & Co. Ltd. Flower Pots.

FIG. 140.   "VENETIAN" Line of Wade, Heath & Co. Ltd.
Flower Pots.

FIG. 141.   "SUMMER FESTIVAL" flower containers (1988).
Three sizes of planters, 5" high, 4-1/4" high and 3-
1/2" high were made available in white or either one
of two flower patterns: Dauphine or Clementine.
Two size "Log Planters" were also introduced. The
large log measures 3-1/2" wide by 10" long and the
small log measures 2-1/4" wide by 7" long.

## "FESTIVAL" WARE DECORATION
## NO.5070. *mid 1952 - late 1950's.*

This pattern, featuring embossed Polka dancing figures
under a honey glaze, was traced with copper lustre and
given the decoration number 5070. Originally thought to
have been issued in 1954, an advertisement in the July 1952
issue of *The Pottery Gazette and Glass Trade Review* shows it to
have been in production somewhat earlier. The original
line consisted of teapot, creamer, large milk jug, small milk
jug, sugar and dish. The handled tankard was added to the
line in 1955.

FIG. 139.

FIG. 140.

205

FIG. 141.

The items listed for decoration No.5070 were also issued with a light blue background as decoration No.6192. For more information on "Festival" Ware see *The W of W pgs. 56 and 143.*

No. 951.    NUT DISH "FESTIVAL" - measures 6" in diameter and has Mark Type 18 on the base.

No. 952.    SUGAR "FESTIVAL" - measures 2-1/4" high and has Mark Type 18 on the base.

No. 953.    CREAMER "FESTIVAL" - measures 4-1/4" high and has Mark Type 18 on the base.

# REGENCY WALL PLATES

*circa 1952 - late 1950's.*

These decorative wall plates, with single color borders and a variety of lithograph center designs, were based on the dinner plates from the standard line of Regency tableware.

No. 954.    REGENCY WALL PLATE - measures 10-1/2" in diameter and has Mark Type 10 on the base.

No. 955.    REGENCY WALL PLATE - measures 10-1/2" in diameter and has Mark Type 10 on the base.

No. 956.    REGENCY WALL PLATE - measures 10-1/2" in diameter and has Mark Type 10 on the base.

FIG. 142.    "DOG AND PHEASANT"REGENCY WALL PLATE. A print-and-enamel design taken from the Wade, Heath Design Book.

# DECORATION NO.5091 *circa early 1950's.*

No additional records have been found relating to this shape and decoration but with a gravy boat and two sizes of platters, it is safe to say that it was produced in a wide range of tableware items.

No. 957.    PLATTER - decoration No. 5091, measures 14-1/2" overall and has Mark Type 10 on the base.

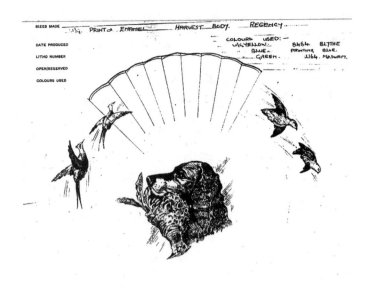

FIG. 142.

No. 958.    GRAVY BOAT - decoration No. 5091, measures 3-7/8" high and has Mark type 10 on the base.

No. 959.    PLATTER - decoration No. 5091, measures 12-1/2" overall and has Mark Type 10 on the base.

# "FLAIR" TABLEWARE *circa 1956 - early 1960's.*

The "Flair" line of tableware replaced the popular "Mode" shape of the early 1950's. The decorations illustrated were also used on the "Mode" shape shortly before the line was discontinued circa mid 1950's. For additional "Flair" decorations see *The W of W pgs. 138 and 139.*

The "Flair" tableware along with "Harmony" and "Harlequin" sets were also available in undecorated, two-tone versions. The color combinations are as follows. In each case the first color is used on the outside of the cup and the second color on the inside.

    a.)    Canada Green/Primrose
        Pattern No. 6227 G.P.

    b.)    Primrose/Canada Green
        Pattern No. 6228 P.G.

    c.)    Turquoise Blue/Rose Pink
        Pattern No. 6229 T.P.

    d.)    Rose Pink/Turquoise Blue
        Pattern No. 6230 P.T.

    e.)    Pearl Grey/Caramel
        Pattern No. 6231 G.C.

    f.)    Caramel/Pearl Grey
        Pattern No. 6232 C.G.

On each of the above color combination, the additional pieces in the sets were colored as follows:

    a.)    Saucers - same color as inside of cup (underside always white)

    b.)    Plates - same color as outside of cup (underside always white)

    c.)    Oatmeals (bowls) - same color as inside of cup (underside always white)

    d.)    Coupe Soups - same color as inside of cup (underside always white)

    e.)    Sugars - same color as outside of cup (solid color)

f.) Creamers - same color as inside of cup
(solid color)

g.) Teapot Base - same color as inside of cup
(solid color)
Teapot Lid - same color as outside of cup
(solid color)

Note: In the carton packed 21 piece "Harlequin" set (for some of these items see *The W of W pg. 139*) the bread & butter (or cake plate), sugar bowl and cream jug were always Canada Green.

No. 960.    BREAD & BUTTER PLATE "CARNIVAL" - measures 6-1/2" in diameter and has Mark Type 19 on the base.

No. 961.    CUP & SAUCER - the cup measures 2-1/2" high and has Mark Type 19 on the base. The saucer measures 5-3/4" in diameter and has Mark Type 19 on the base.

No. 962.    BREAD & BUTTER PLATE "SUNFLOWER" - measures 6-1/2" in diameter and has Mark Type 19 on the base.

No. 963.    CUP & SAUCER "SUNFLOWER" - the cup measures 2-1/2" high and has Mark Type 19 on the base. The saucer measures 5-3/4" in diameter and has Mark Type 19 on the base.

No. 964.    BREAD & BUTTER PLATE - decoration No. 6190, measures 6-1/2" in diameter and has Mark Type 19 on the base.

No. 965.    BREAD & BUTTER PLATE - measures 6-1/2" in diameter and has Mark Type 19 on the base.

No. 966.    CUP & SAUCER - the cup measures 2-1/2" high and has Mark Type 19 on the base. The saucer measures 5-3/4" in diameter and has Mark Type 19 on the base.

No. 967.    BREAD & BUTTER PLATE "FERN" - measures 6-1/2" in diameter and has Mark Type 19 on the base.

No. 968.    CUP & SAUCER "FERN" - the cup measures 2-1/2" high and has Mark Type 19 on the base. The saucer measures 5-3/4" in diameter and has Mark Type 19 on the base.

# MISCELLANEOUS TABLEWARE.

FIG. 143.    DECORATION NO. 6136. Free-hand underglaze decoration on a white body with an all-over pearl lustre finish and gold edging.

FIG.143.

A. NUT DISH - measures 4-1/8" in diameter and has Mark Type 19 on the base.
B. DANDY JUG - measures 5-3/4" high and has Mark Type 19 on the base.

No. 969.    ASHTRAY "NIAGARA FALLS" - measures 5" square and has Mark Type 17 on the base.

No. 970.    CREAMER - measures 2-3/4" high and has Mark Type 14 on the base.

No. 971.    SUGAR BOWL - "Darwin" decoration, measures 2-1/2" high and is marked "Wade England Darwin."

FIG. 144.    PLATE - "Darwin" decoration, measures 9-1/2" in diameter and is marked "Wade England Darwin." The "Darwin" decoration can be found in blue/white, green/white and brown/white color ways.

FIG. 144.

FIG. 145.

FIG. 145.    PLATE - measures 6-1/2" in diameter and has Mark Type 19 on the base.

No. 972.    CUP & SAUCER - the cup measures 2-1/2" high and has Mark Type 14 on the base. The saucer measures 5-5/8" in diameter and has Mark Type 14 on the base.

FIG. 146.

FIG. 147B.

No. 973.    CIGARETTE BOX - shape No. 242, measures 5"long
by 3-1/2"wide by 1-3/4"high and has Mark Type 10
on the base.

FIG. 146.    "RIBBON AND BOW" SAUCER - measures 5-5/8"
in diameter and has Mark Type 10B on the base. As
of this writing, it is not known if this pattern was produced in a full tableware set or just a coffee and/or
tea set. The ribbon is pale purple on a white background.

FIG. 147D.

FIG. 147.    ADDITIONAL TABLEWARE DECORATIONS.
A. Decoration No. 6155, free-hand underglaze decoration in red, yellow, olive green and black.

FIG. 147C.

FIG. 147A.

B. Decoration No. 6154, free-hand underglaze decoration in black, grey and green with an all-over pearl
lustre finish.
C. Decoration No. 6156, free-hand underglaze decoration in black, yellow, red, olive green and grey.
D. Decoration No. 6186, free-hand underglaze decoration similar to item "C" but with a dipped primrose
glaze.
E. Decoration No. 6103, hand-painted underglaze
decoration in yellow, green, grey and coral with
brown line edgings. This pattern was applied to the
"Mode-ware" line.

FIG. 147E.

F. Decoration No. 6212 "Plantain," transfer type decoration in yellow and black. This decoration was
applied to the "Flair" tableware line.
G. Decoration No. 6157, combination transfer and
hand decoration in black and green or black and
orange.
H. Decoration No. 6158, combination transfer and
hand decoration in black and green or black and
orange.
I. Decoration No. 6161, combination transfer and
hand decoration in yellow, green and orange.
J. Decoration No. 6160, free-hand underglaze decoration.

208

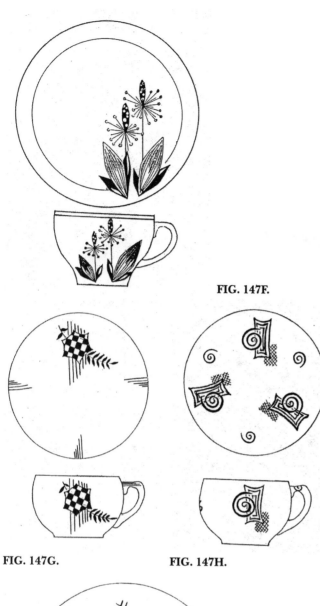

FIG. 147F.

FIG. 147G.　　　　FIG. 147H.

FIG. 147I.

FIG. 147J.

FIG. 147K.

FIG. 147L.

K. Decoration No. 6204, free-hand underglaze decoration in black and yellow.
L. Decoration No. 6162, transfer decoration of green stars and orange stripes.

## "TUTTI-FRUITTI" TABLEWARE
### 1990 - 1992.

This hand-painted tableware line was designed by Barbara Cooksey. The set was also available in single, all-over glazes of white, pink, red, blue, yellow or green. Most pieces are mold-marked Wade England on the underside of the base.

No. 974.　　COVERED CANISTER - measures 8" high.
No. 975.　　COVERED CANISTER - measures 7-1/4" high.

No. 976.    DINNER PLATE - measures 8-1/2" in diameter and
            has Mark Type 27B on the base.
No. 977.    TEAPOT - measures 6" high.
No. 978.    MILK JUG - measures 5-1/2" high.
No. 979.    COVERED SUGAR - measures 4-1/4" high.
No. 980.    CREAMER - measures 3-1/4" high.
No. 981.    TEAPOT - measures 5" high.
No. 982.    COVERED BUTTER DISH - measures 6-1/4" long
            by 4-5/8"wide by 4-1/2" high.
No. 983.    SALT - measures 3" high and is unmarked.
No. 984.    PEPPER - measures 3-1/4" high and is unmarked.
No. 985.    MUG - measures 4" high.
No. 986.    CUP & SAUCER - the cup measures 3-1/4" high by
            4" in diameter. The saucer measures 6-3/4" in diam-
            eter and has Mark Type 27B on the base.
No. 987.    FRUIT BOWL - measures 4-1/4" high by 9" in
            diameter.
No. 988.    COVERED CHEESE - the plate measures 8-1/4" in
            diameter and has Mark Type 27B on the base. The
            cover measures 4-1/2" high by 6" in diameter and is
            unmarked.

## "CLASSIC LINEN" TABLEWARE

*1989 - 1993.*

One of the most popular of the Wade lines of tableware
but unfortunately in production for a short time only. Each
piece is marked Made in Ireland Wade Classic Linen.

No. 989.    COFFEE POT - measures 9" high.
No. 990.    DINNER PLATE - measures 7-3/4" in diameter.
No. 991.    COFFEE CUP - measures 2-3/8" high by 2-7/8"
            indiameter.
No. 992.    SAUCER - measures 5-1/2" in diameter.
No. 993.    TEA CUP - measures 2-7/16" high by 3" in diameter.
No. 994.    SAUCER - measures 6-7/8" in diameter.
No. 995.    CREAMER - measures 3-3/4" high.
No. 996.    COVERED SUGAR - measures 3-7/8" high.
No. 997.    TEAPOT - measures 6" high.

## "MUSIC" TABLEWARE *1989 - 1991.*

This very contemporary design was available in full dinner, tea and coffee sets. Each piece is marked on the base:
"Music" a Peter Ting Design Exclusive to Wade UK Fine
Tableware. For additional items produced in the "Music"
pattern see FIG.148.

No. 998.    COVERED SUGAR - measures 3-7/8" high.
No. 999.    SALT - measures 3-5/8" high.
No. 1000.   PEPPER - measures 3" high.
No. 1001.   CREAMER - measures 4" high.

FIG. 148.    An illustration of the "MUSIC" pattern.

## BhS UTENSIL JAR *late 1980's.*

A kitchen utensil jar produced by Wade, Heath & Co.
Ltd for The British Home Stores.

No. 1002.   "BON APPETIT" UTENSIL JAR - measures 6-1/8"
            high by 4" in diameter and is marked  BhS Bon
            Appetit Tableware Made in Britain.

FIG. 148.

FIG. 149.

## "MEADOWLAND" TABLEWARE

*1989 - 1993.*

A full line of tableware designed by Barbara Cooksey,
each item is marked on the base: Meadowland Dishwasher
Safe Fine Tableware. For additional items produced in the
"Meadowland" pattern see FIG.149.

No. 1003.   SALT - measures 3-5/8" high.
No. 1004.   PEPPER - measures 3" high.

FIG. 149.   An illustration of the "MEADOWLAND" pattern.

## "SUMMER FRUITS" TABLEWARE
*1989 - 1993.*

A full line of tableware designed by Barbara Cooksey, each item is marked on the base: Summer Fruit Wade UK Fine Quality Tableware. For additional items produced in the "Summer Fruits" pattern see FIG.150.

No. 1005.   OPEN SUGAR - measures 2-1/2" high.
No. 1006.   GRAVY BOAT - measures 3-1/4" high.

FIG. 150.

FIG. 150.   An illustration of the "SUMMER FRUITS" pattern.

## "INDIAN TREE" LITHOGRAPH DECORATION No.4959.

This popular lithograph decoration was from "open stock" and therefore available to any pottery. This decoration is referred to as Lytho filled in with enamel.

No. 1007.   BOWL - measures 2-3/4" high by 9" in diameter and has Mark Type 10B on the base.
No. 1008.   PLATE - measures 6-3/4" in diameter and has Mark Type 10B on the base.
No. 1009.   CUP & SAUCER - the cup measures 2-3/4" high and has Mark Type 10B on the base. The saucer measures 5-3/4" in diameter and has Mark Type 7A on the base.
No. 1010.   SUGAR BOWL - measures 2-3/4" high by 4" in diameter and has Mark Type 7A on the base.
No. 1011.   CEREAL BOWL - measures 1-1/2" high by 6-1/4" in diameter and has Mark Type 10B on the base.
No. 1012.   PLATE - measures 10" in diameter and has Mark Type 10B on the base.

## MISCELLANEOUS TABLEWARE
*1986 - 1993.*

Illustrated below are a number of items and decorations produced by the Wade Potteries in the late 1980's and early 1990's.

FIG. 151.

FIG. 152.

211

FIG. 153.

FIG. 155.

FIG. 154.

FIG. 156.

FIG. 151.   A range of Wade "OVEN-TO-TABLE" tableware (1987 - 1989). Available in the following patterns: Country Blue, Herb Collection, Multi Splash and White.

FIG. 152.   "SPLASH" Breakfast Sets (late 1987- 1989). The sets were available in Blue, Peach or Multi-Colored and comprised Teapot, Milk Jug, Sugar Bowl, Creamer, Toast Rack and Salt and Pepper shakers.

FIG. 153.   "BLUE CHINTZ." This complete line of tableware was also produced in the "Rose Chintz" pattern.

FIG. 154.   "KINGS KITCHENWARE" (early 1990's - 1993). This all-over white or cream pattern was produced in the following items: Cheese Dish, Butter Dish, Milk Jug, Toast Rack, Salt and Pepper, Preserve Jar, Utensil Jar and Large or Medium Storage Jars. This

line was also available in solid green with gold trim or solid white with gold trim.

FIG. 155.   "FARMSTEAD" oven-to-table cookware. This range of cookware, created by Queensberry Hunt, was available either in "Chestnut" or "Kingfisher" blue.

FIG. 156.   "EXECUTIVE DESK SET" was designed and produced in 1993 for bulk orders only i.e. business gifts etc. Items available in this range were Desk Tidy, Pencil Holder, Letter Rack, Ink Well, Trinket Box, Ashtray, Bosuns Decanter and a Half Pint Tankard.

**ROYAL COMMEMORATIVES**

By George Wade & Son Ltd.

and

Wade, Heath & Co. Ltd.

1935 - 1990.

# ROYAL COMMEMORATIVES.

At the time of writing *The World of Wade*, it was believed that the Wade Potteries first introduced Royal Commemorative items to their lines with the proposed coronation of Edward VIII in 1937. Further research, however, has shown that the pottery produced commemorative ware for the Silver Jubilee of King George V and Queen Mary in 1935.

It appears that Wade, Heath & Co. Ltd. was one of the first British potteries to produce ware for the Silver Jubilee (see advertisement below). Samples of the ware were available to the trade as early as November 1934. The set consisted of a footed, handled mug; coffee mug, cup and saucer, square tea plate and a baby's cereal bowl.

*JUBILEE WARE "GEORGE V AND QUEEN MARY." A Wade, Heath & Co. Ltd. advertisement as it appeared in the November 1934 issue of The Pottery Gazette and Glass Trade Review.*

The Wade Potteries have continued to produce Royal Commemorative ware right up to and including the present time. With the increasing size of the royal family, commemorative items have started to appear at frequent intervals, a trend that might soon burn itself out.

The popular Bell's whisky decanters commemorating numerous royal occasions, have increased considerably in value. Be aware, however, that the high prices are for full containers, unopened and complete with the original presentation box or carton. For further information on Royal Commemoratives see *The W of W pgs. 63, 153, 154 and 155.*

FIG. 157.

FIG. 157.  MISCELLANEOUS COMMEMORATIVE ITEMS.
A. MUSICAL LOVING CUP "EDWARD VIII" - measures 5" high by 4-1/2" in diameter and has a Wadeheath Ware ink stamp on the base. The inscription on the back of the cup reads:
Coronation, King Edward VIII May 12th 1937. As Edward VIII abdicated prior to the coronation, this cup was not produced in great quantities. A similar loving cup was produced to commemorate the coronation of George VI and Queen Elizabeth. See *The W of W pgs 63 and 153.*
B. MUG "QUEEN ELIZABETH II" - measures 2-1/4" high and has Mark Type 14 on the base.
This mug was issued to commemorate the coronation of Queen Elizabeth II on June 2, 1953.
C. FRUIT BOWL - issued in 1953 to commemorate the coronation of Queen Elizabeth II. The bowl measures 9" across and has Mark Type 10 on the base.
D. LOVING CUP "CHARLES AND DIANA" (1981) - measures 3-1/4" high by 3-1/2" in diameter and has Mark Type 19 on the base.

No. 1013.  "BELL'S WHISKY DECANTER" - issued in 1981 to commemorate the marriage between H.R.H. Prince Charles and Lady Diana Spencer which took place on July 29, 1981.
This 75 cl size decanter is marked WADE on the underside of the recessed base.

No. 1014.  "BELL'S WHISKY DECANTER" - issued in 1988 to commemorate the birth of Princess Beatrice on August 8, 1988. This 75 cl decanter has Mark Type 27A on the underside of the recessed base.

No. 1015.  "BELL'S WHISKY DECANTER" - issued in 1990 to commemorate the birth of Princess Eugenie on March 23, 1990. This 75 cl decanter has Mark Type 27A on the underside of the recessed base.

No. 1016.  "BELL'S WHISKY DECANTER" - issued in 1990 to commemorate the 90th birthday of Queen Elizabeth the Queen Mother on August 4, 1990. This 75 cl decanter has Mark Type 27A on the underside of the recessed base. Also shown is the presentation box for the decanter.

No. 1017.  VASE - issued in 1981 to commemorate the marriage between H.R.H. Prince Charles and Lady

FIG. 158.

FIG. 159.

Diana Spencer which took place on July 29, 1981. The vase measures 8-3/4" high and is marked WADE on the underside of the base.

No. 1018. "BELL'S WHISKY DECANTER" - issued in 1984 to commemorate the birth of Prince Henry of Wales on September 15, 1984. This 50 cl decanter is marked WADE on the underside of the recessed base.

FIG. 158. MISCELLANEOUS COMMEMORATIVE ITEMS.
A. CUP & SAUCER "QUEEN ELIZABETH II." The cup measures 2-7/8" high and the saucer measures 5-1/2" in diameter. Both items have Mark Type 10 on the base. This cup and saucer was issued to commemorate the coronation of Queen Elizabeth II on June 2, 1953.
B. PLATE "QUEEN ELIZABETH II" - measures 7" in diameter and has Mark Type 10 on the base. This plate was issued as a companion piece to item "A" in this illustration.
C. NAPKIN RING "CHARLES AND DIANA" - measures 1-3/4" in diameter and has a transfer type mark "Wade Made in England" inside the ring.
D. MUG "GEORGE VI AND QUEEN ELIZABETH" - measures 3" high and has Mark Type 5 on the base. This mug was issued to commemorate the coronation of King George VI and Queen Elizabeth on May 12, 1937.

No. 1019. TEAPOT - measures 6-3/8" high and has Mark Type 27A on the base. A very small number of these teapots were issued.

No. 1020. FRUIT BOWL - issued in 1953 to commemorate the coronation of Queen Elizabeth II. The bowl measures 9" across and has Mark Type 10 on the base.

No. 1021. PLATE - issued in 1937 to commemorate the coronation of King George VI and Queen Elizabeth on May 12, 1937. The plate measures 6" square and has Mark Type 5 on the base.

No. 1022. TANKARD - issued in 1977 to celebrate the Silver Jubilee of Queen Elizabeth II. This 1/2 pint tankard has Mark Type 37 on the base.

No. 1023. BEER MUG - issued in 1953 to commemorate the Coronation of Queen Elizabeth II. This 5" high mug has Mark Type 10 on the base.

No. 1024. TANKARD - issued in 1977 to celebrate the Silver Jubilee of Queen Elizabeth II. This 1/2 pint tankard has Mark Type 37 on the base.

FIG. 159. TAUNTON CIDER MUG - measures 3-1/4" high and is marked on the base: Queen's Silver Jubilee. A limited edition of 2,500 produced for the Taunton Cider Company by Wade, Heath Potteries, Staffordshire in the year of 1977. The illustration shows the front and back of the mug.

No.1025. BABY'S CEREAL DISH - issued in 1937 to commemorate the coronation of King George VI and Queen Elizabeth on May 12, 1937. The dish measures 6-1/2" in diameter and is marked Wadeheath on the base.

No. 1026. "SHELL-MEX AND B.P. LTD." CORONATION DISH - produced in 1953 to celebrate the coronation of Queen Elizabeth II and also as an advertisement for the North Eastern Division of the Petroleum company. The dish measures 4-3/4" in diameter by 1-1/8" high and is mold-marked "WADE ENGLAND CORONATION 1953" on the recessed base.

No. 1027. TRINKET BOX - issued in 1981 to commemorate the wedding of H.R.H. Prince Charles and Lady Diana Spencer. The two part trinket box is 1-1/2" high by 3-1/2" across and is mold-marked "WADE PORCELAIN MADE IN ENGLAND" on the underside of the base.

No. 1028. TRINKET BOX - issued in 1990 to commemorate the 90th birthday of Queen Elizabeth the Queen Mother on August 4, 1990. The trinket box measures 3-1/4" in diameter by 1-3/4" high and is marked WADE CERAMICS. This was a special issue produced for Ringtons Limited in the amount of 10,000 pieces.

No. 1029. PIN TRAY - issued in 1990 to commemorate the 90th birthday of Queen Elizabeth the Queen Mother on August 4, 1990. The pin tray measures 4-3/8" in diameter and is marked WADE CERAMICS. This was a special issue produced for Ringtons Limited in the amount of 10,000 pieces.

No. 1030. "BURROWS & STURGESS LTD." CORONATION DISH - produced in 1953 to celebrate the coronation of Queen Elizabeth II and also as an advertisement for the company's Spa Tablewaters.

The dish measures 4-3/4" in diameter by 1-1/8" high and is mold-marked "WADE ENGLAND CORONATION 1953" on the recessed base.

No. 1031.  CORONATION FRUIT BOWL - issued in 1937 to commemorate the coronation of King George VI and Queen Elizabeth. This special edition, 12" diameter bowl was issued in a limited number of 25 pieces with the special decoration as illustrated. The bowl is marked on the base:
Manufactured in England by Wade, Heath & Co. Ltd. to Commemorate the Coronation of King George VI and Queen Elizabeth May 12th 1937 "Long May They Reign" Robert R. Barlow.

No. 1032.  CORONATION FRUIT BOWL - issued in 1937 to commemorate the coronation of King George VI and Queen Elizabeth. This 12" diameter bowl was issued in a limited number of 225 pieces. The bowl has Mark Type 6 on the underside of the footed base.

placed between two different coats of arms, reads: To Commemorate the Visit to Cod Donnington of Her Majesty Queen Elizabeth the Second 4th June 1982. FIG. 161 illustrates both coats of arms.

FIG. 160.

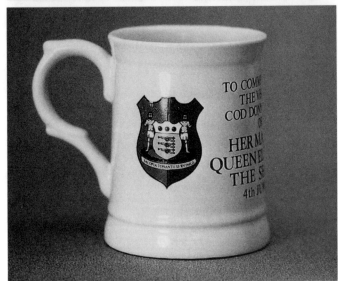

FIG. 161.

FIG. 160.  BOWL - measures 7-1/2" in diameter and has Mark Type 7C on the base. This bowl was issued to commemorate the coronation of Queen Elizabeth II on June 2, 1953.

No. 1033.  STEIN - measures 8-1/2" high and is unmarked. The stein was produced in a very limited number to commemorate Queen Elizabeth II's silver jubilee in 1977.

No. 1034.  COACH DECANTER - measures 6-1/2" high and is unmarked. The decanter was made for Gordon Chaseton in a very limited number.

No. 1035.  "BELL'S MINIATURE WHISKY DECANTER" - issued in 1981 to commemorate the marriage between H.R.H. Prince Charles and Lady Diana Spencer. The miniature decanter is 4" high. Approximately 2,000 pieces only were made.

FIG. 161.  TANKARD - measures 4-1/8" high and has Mark Type 20 on the base. The lettering on the tankard,

216

**WADE (ULSTER) LTD.,**
and
**WADE (IRELAND) LTD.**

## WADE (ULSTER) LTD. & WADE (IRELAND) LTD.

Wade (Ulster) Ltd. was incorporated on January 2, 1950. The pottery, which began its life in a converted linen mill in 1946, was established to produce die-pressed insulators along with other pressed ceramic items needed for the rebuilding of industries stricken by WWII.

In 1953, the pottery began production of pressed and turned ceramic giftware. The giftware, typified by its blue/grey glaze, proved to be a popular seller right up until it was discontinued in 1988. In November 1966, the pottery had changed its name to Wade (Ireland) Ltd.

When the giftware line was discontinued, the pottery completely retooled the production lines for the manufacture of fine ceramic tableware which was introduced at the Birmingham and Frankfurt Spring Fairs of 1989.

Late 1989 saw the takeover of the Wade Potteries by Beauford PLC. This takeover involved a number of changes to the Wade Potteries, one of which was the change of name of the Irish pottery to Seagoe Ceramics Ltd. which then became an independent concern. Seagoe Ceramics however, still continued to manufacture tableware which was sold under the Wade brand name. Unfortunately, the tableware did not become successful and the Irish Tableware Department of the pottery ceased manufacturing in April 1993 to concentrate on engineering ceramics.

In the early 1990's, whilst still producing tableware, Seagoe Ceramics Ltd. reissued the popular Wade (Ireland) Ltd. giftware lines of the Irish Character Figures and the Irish Song Figures. The pottery also began production of a line of self-standing and wall-hung ceramic plaques with applied decoration. The decorations on the rectangular plaques show typical Irish scenes and those on the oval plaques had attractive flower designs. For further information on the early Wade (Ireland) Ltd. products see *The W of W pgs. 157 - 166.*

No. 1036.    EILEEN OGE - shape No.C.509, measures 8" high and is marked: Irish Porcelain Figures Made in Ireland.

No. 1037.    BABY - measures 4-1/4" high and is marked: Irish Porcelain Figures Made in Ireland.

## WALL PLAQUES *early - mid 1950's.*

This series of porcelain wall plaques was designed by Iris Wade Carryer to resemble either hand carvings on stone or carving on wood. Each piece has a transfer type mark reading Made in Ireland by Wade Co. Armagh. Records indicate that this was not a high selling item.

No. 1038.    WALL PLAQUE "HORSE" - measures 11" long by 8" high.

No. 1039.    WALL PLAQUE "ABSTRACT" - measures 15" high by 9-1/2" wide.

No. 1040.    WALL PLAQUE "FISH" - measures 12" long by 7-1/2" high.

## WADEHEATH CHARACTER JUGS
*late 1950's.*

Illustrated in the color section are two designs from the Wade, Heath Design Book. Although illustrated in the section dealing with Wade (Ireland) Ltd., these jugs were produced at the Royal Victoria Pottery. Records indicate that these character jugs had only a limited production run, less than 750 pieces for the Pirate and 1,000 pieces for the Highwayman. Samples of a third character jug in the form of a North American Indian were produced, but records indicate that it never went into production.

No. 1041.    CHARACTER JUG "PIRATE"- measure 6" high and has Mark Type 19A on the underside of the base.

No. 1042.    CHARACTER JUG "HIGHWAYMAN" - measures 6" high and has a similar Mark Type as No.1041 but with the word Highwayman substituted for Pirate.

## IRISH GIFTWARE *early 1950's to late 1980's.*

No. 1043.    ONE PINT TANKARD - shape No.I.P.2 with Mark Type 28 on the base. The tankard measures 6-1/2" high.

No. 1044.    KILLARNEY URN - shape No.I.P.40 with Mark Type 28 on the base. The urn measures 8" high.

No. 1045.    KILLARNEY URN - shape No.I.P.41 with Mark Type 28 on the base. The urn measures 6-1/4" high.

No. 1046.    KILLARNEY URN - shape No.I.P.42 with Mark Type 28 on the base. The urn measures 4-1/4" high.

No. 1047.    KILLARNEY URN - shape No.I.P.43 with Mark Type 28 on the base. The urn measures 3" high.

No. 1048.    STEIN TANKARD - shape No.I.P.3 with Mark Type 28 on the base. The tankard measures 6-3/8" high.

No. 1049.    ONE PINT TANKARD - shape No.I.P.2 with Mark Type 28 on the base. The tankard measures 6-1/2" high.

No. 1050.    ONE PINT "TYRONE" TANKARD - shape No.I.P.10 with Mark Type 41 on the base. The tankard measures 6-1/2" high.

No. 1051.    HALF PINT "TYRONE" TANKARD - shape No.I.P.8 with Mark Type 28 on the base. The tankard measures 5-1/2" high.

No. 1052.    MINIATURE "TYRONE" TANKARD - shape No.I.P.9 with Mark Type 28 on the base. The tankard measures 3" high.

No. 1053.    MUSICAL TANKARD - shape No.I.P.5. This 5-1/2" high tankard is unmarked.

No. 1054.    CHILD'S TANKARD - shape No.I.P.4 with Mark Type 37 on the base. The tankard measures 3" high.

No. 1055.    VINEGAR BOTTLE - shape No.I.P.111 with Mark Type 28 on the base. The bottle measures 6-3/4" high.

FIG. 162.    MISCELLANEOUS WADE (IRELAND) LTD. ITEMS.

A. HOT PLATE - measures 5-1/2" square and is mold-marked: Made in Ireland by Wade.

B. TANKARD - measures 4-1/4" high and has Mark Type 28 on the base.

C. LAMP BASE - measures 6" in diameter and is

FIG. 162.

marked: Irish Porcelain made in Ireland by Wade Co. Armagh. Produced circa 1965 as a regular item in the Wade (Ireland) Ltd. giftware line.

**D. SHAMROCK DISH** - measures 4-1/2" across by 4-3/4" from top to bottom and has Mark Type 28 on the base. No one at the Irish pottery can recall the name and use of this item.

**E. DUCK PLANTER** - measures 4-1/4" high by 7" long and has Mark Type 28 on the base.

**F. DONKEY AND SIDE PANNIERS** - measures 4" high and has Mark Type 47 on the base. The donkey was in production for approx. one year circa 1965.

**G. SELF STANDING ORNAMENTAL PICTURE** - measures 3-5/8" high by 4-1/2" long and is unmarked. Produced by Segoe Ceramics until 1993.

## MOURNE RANGE *1971 - circa mid 1970's.*

A limited range of fifteen pieces described in Wade advertising as "... porcelain carefully nurtured into life by Irish craftsmen with a coloring that reflects the tang of the hills, and a single flower motif etched deep into each design..." For additional information on Mourne Range see *The W of W pg.66.*

No. 1056.  VASE - shape No.C.350 with Mark Type 41 on the base. The vase is 6-3/4" high.

No. 1057.  CREAM JUG - shape No.C.356 with Mark Type 41 on the base. The jug is 4-1/4" high.

No. 1058.  COVERED PRESERVE JAR - shape No.C.353 with Mark Type 41 on the base. The jar is 3-3/4" high.

No. 1059.  HALF PINT TANKARD - shape No.C.351 with Mark Type 41 on the base. The tankard is 4" high.

No. 1060.  ONE PINT TANKARD - shape No.C.352 with Mark Type 41 on the base. The tankard is 5" high.

No. 1061.  DISH - shape No.C.349 with Mark Type 37 on the base. The dish measures 7" long by 5" wide.

No. 1062.  COVERED CANDY BOX - shape No.C.348 with Mark Type 41 on the base. The candy box measures 5" long by 3-3/4" wide.

## MISCELLANEOUS GIFTWARE.

No. 1063.  COVERED JAR - measures 5-1/4" high and has Mark Type 40 on the base.

No. 1064.  COVERED SUGAR SHAMROCK - shape No.C.316 with Mark Type 33 on the base. The sugar measures 4-1/4" high. Other giftware items in the Shamrock range were:
C.313 Coffee Pot
C.314 Open Sugar
C.315 Cream Jug
C.317 Covered Hot Milk Jug
C.320 One Pint Jug
Cup and Saucer

For illustration of some of these items see the advertisement below.

No. 1065.  TEAPOT STAND - shape No.I.P.624 with Mark Type 29 on the base. The stand measures 5-1/2" square.

No. 1066.  COFFEE POT - measures 10-1/2" high and has Mark Type 41 on the base.

FIG. 163.  CUP & SAUCER. The cup measures 3" high and the saucer measures 5-3/4" in diameter. Both items have Mark Type 40 on the base.

FIG. 163.

*IRISH PORCELAIN. Wade (Ulster) Ltd.*

**FIG. 164.**

FIG. 164.   **PROTOTYPE TEAPOTS.** Two 6-1/2" high teapots designed for Wade (Ireland) Ltd. by William Harper in the mid 1950's.

No. 1067.   **TEAPOT STAND** - shape No.I.P.624 with Mark Type 29 on the base. The stand measures 5-1/2" square.

No. 1068.   **PLATE** - measures 7" in diameter and has Mark Type 41 on the base.

## WALL PLATES *late 1980's.*

No. 1069.   **"BLARNEY CASTLE" WALL PLATE** - measures 7-3/4" in diameter and has Mark Type 37 on the base.

No. 1070.   **"WOLSELEY" VETERAN CAR WALL PLATE** - measures 7-3/4" in diameter and has Mark Type 32A on the base. This wall plate illustrates the 1904 6 h.p. Wolseley, No.25 from series 9 of the Veteran Car series.

No. 1071.   **"FIAT" VETERAN CAR WALL PLATE** - measures 7-1/8" in diameter and has Mark Type 32A on the base. This wall plate illustrates the 1907 Fiat F2, No.21 from series 7 of the Veteran Car series.

No. 1072.   **"DUESENBERG" VETERAN CAR WALL PLATE** - measures 7-1/8" in diameter and has Mark Type 19C on the base. This wall plate illustrates the 1933 Duesenberg SJ, No.22 from series 8 of the Veteran Car series.

No. 1073.   **"WOLSELEY" VETERAN CAR WALL PLATE** - measures 7-1/8" in diameter and has Mark Type 32A on the base. This wall plate illustrates the 1904 6 h.p. Wolseley, No.25 from series 9 of the Veteran Car series.

No. 1074.   **"AUSTIN SEVEN" VETERAN CAR WALL PLATE** - measures 7-1/8" in diameter and has Mark Type 32A on the base. This wall plate illustrates the 1925 Austin Seven, No.26 from series 9 of the Veteran Car series.

# RAINDROPS GIFTWARE.

**No. 1075.** TEAPOT - shape No.C.312 with Mark Type 41 on the base. The teapot measures 4-3/4" high.

**No. 1076.** CREAMER - shape No.C.311 with Mark Type 33 on the base. The creamer is 2-3/4" high.

**No. 1077.** SUGAR - shape No.C.310 with Mark Type 33 on the base. The sugar is 2" high.

**No. 1078.** TABLE LIGHTER - measures 3-1/4" high and is unmarked.

**No. 1079.** ONE PINT JUG - shape No.C.305 with Mark Type 33 on the base. The jug measures 4-1/2" high. There were two other jugs in the series. THREE QUARTER PINT JUG shape No.C.306 and a HALF PINT JUG shape No.C.307.

**No. 1080.** COFFEE POT - shape No.C.308 with Mark Type 33 on the base. The coffee pot is 6-1/4" high.

# SELF STANDING PICTURES.

Both Wade (Ireland) Ltd. and later Seagoe Ceramics Ltd. have produced a number of self-standing pictures. The paintings are reproduced from works of talented Irish artists and are mounted on beautifully crafted Irish porcelain. The pictures are also made as regular wall hanging, not self-standing, pictures.

**No. 1081.** PICTURE - measures 4" square with Mark Type 30 on the back.

**No. 1082.** OVAL PICTURE FRAME - measures 4" high and is unmarked.

# LUCKY LEPRECHAUNS *circa 1956 - 1986.*

These miniature "Lucky Fairyfolk" proved to be among the most popular items of the Irish giftware line. The series had a long production life with the figurines being made in a number of color variations and styles. See item No. 112 in the color section for a prototype model and *The W of W pgs. 164 and 165* for additional information on the Lucky Leprechauns.

**No. 1083.** LEPRECHAUN PINTRAY - shape No.I.P.619L with Mark Type 32 on the base. This tray features the leprechaun with the "POT OF GOLD" and measures 1-5/8" high.

**No. 1084.** LEPRECHAUN PINTRAY - shape No.I.P.619L with Mark Type 32 on the base. This tray features the "TAILOR" leprechaun and measures 1-7/8" high.

**No. 1085.** "LEPRECHAUN ON ACORN" DISH - this rare leprechaun dish combination measures 3-1/4" in diameter by 2-1/2" high. The dish is mold-marked Wade England on the underside of the base.

**No. 1086.** LEPRECHAUN ON ACORN - measures 1-1/2" high and may be found unmarked or ink stamped "Made in Ireland."

**No. 1087.** LEPRECHAUN ON RABBIT - measures 1-1/2" high and may be found unmarked or ink stamped "Made in Ireland."

**No. 1088.** LUCKY IRISH LEPRECHAUN - measures 2-1/8" high on a 2" by 1-1/2" marble base. The paper label on the underside of the base reads: Real Connemara Marble, Made in Ireland.

# IRISH CHARACTER FIGURES *early 1990's.*

First issued in the early 1970's through 1986, the Irish Character Figures were reintroduced by Seagoe Ceramics Ltd. in the early 1990's. Although the same tools were used for the reissue, the glaze was much darker with a pronounced all-over honey glaze. Each piece was ink stamped with the Seagoe/Wade mark which, in many cases, would wash off.

**No. 1089.** DANNY BOY - shape No.S.16, measures 4" high and has Mark Type 41A on the base.

FLOWER RANGE

*Additional shapes and designs of the self-standing pictures by Seagoe Ceramics Ltd.*

No. 1090. MOTHER MACREE - shape No.S.19, measures 2-1/2" high and has Mark Type 41A on the base.

No. 1091. MOLLY MALONE - shape No.S.17, measures 3-1/4" high and has Mark Type 41A on the base.

No. 1092. KATHLEEN - shape No.S.18, measures 3-1/2" high and has Mark Type 41A on the base.

No. 1093. EILEEN OGE - shape No.S.25, measures 3-3/4" high and has Mark Type 41A on the base.

No. 1094. PHIL THE FLUTER - shape No.S.20, measures 3-3/4" high and has Mark Type 41A on the base.

No. 1095. PADDY REILLY - shape No.S.26, measures 3-3/4" high and has Mark Type 41A on the base.

No. 1096. ROSE OF TRALEE - shape No.S.24, measures 4" high and has Mark Type 41A on the base.

No. 1097. PADDY MAGINTY - shape No.S.21, measures 3-1/4" high and has Mark Type 41A on the base.

FIG. 165.

## IRISH SONG FIGURES 1962 - 1986.

The full range of these figurines is illustrated in *The W of W pg.67*. The line consisted of eight figures approximately 6" high designed by Wm. Harper and three figures approximately 8" high designed by Phoebe Stabler. All of these figures were reissued by Seagoe Ceramics Ltd. in the early 1990's and all had the Seagoe/Wade backstamp. The figures illustrated in the color section are the original figurines.

No. 1098. EILEEN OGE - shape No.C.509, measures 8" high and is marked: Irish Porcelain Figures Made in Ireland.

No. 1099. WIDDA CAFFERTY - shape No.C.501, measures 6-1/4" high and is marked "Widda Cafferty" modeled by William Harper Irish Porcelain Made in Ireland.

No. 1100. THE BARD OF ARMAGH - shape No.C.510, measures 5-1/8" high and is marked "The Bard of Armagh" modeled by William Harper Irish Porcelain Made in Ireland.

No. 1101. DAN MURPHY - shape No.C.507, measures 8-1/4" high and is marked: Irish Porcelain Figures Made in Ireland.

No. 1102. MOTHER MacCREE - shape No.C.508, measures 8-1/4" high and is marked: Irish Porcelain Figures Made in Ireland. It is of interest to note that the figures of Dan Murphy (No.1101) and Mother MacCree (No. 1102) were advertised in the June 1962 issue of *The Pottery Gazette and Glass Trade Review* as "Himself" and "Herself" modeled from life by Phoebe Stabler.

## MISCELLANEOUS GIFTWARE.

FIG. 165. KINGSFORD'S DECANTER - measures 6-3/4" high and is marked Wade Ireland.

FIG. 166. PHEASANT DECANTER - measures 5-1/2" high and is marked Wade Ireland. This decanter is from a special order of Old Bushmills Irish Whisky which was specially bottled for Wade (Ireland) Ltd. to be given as gifts by the pottery.

No. 1103. "LARRY" BOOKEND - measures 4-1/2" high and is

FIG. 166.

found either unmarked or marked with an ink stamp "Made in Ireland."

No. 1104. "LESTER" BOOKEND - measures 4-1/2" high and is found either unmarked or marked with an ink stamp "Made in Ireland."

No. 1105. LUCKY LEPRECHAUN - shape No.S.11, measures 2-3/4" high and is unmarked.

No. 1106. INK WELL - measures 3-5/8" wide by 3-1/8" long by 1-7/8" high and has Mark Type 28 on the base.

No. 1107. LEPRECHAUN COTTAGE - shape No.S.9, measures 2-1/4" high by 5-3/8" across.

No. 1108. SINGLE EGG CODDLER - shape No.I.P.631, measures 3" high and has Mark Type 35 on the base.

No. 1109. LUCKY LEPRECHAUN - shape No.S.11, measures 2-3/4" high and is unmarked.

No. 1110. FLOWER POT HOLDER - shape No.I.P.37, measures 4" high and has Mark Type 28 on the base.

No. 1111. SHAMROCK CUP & SAUCER - the cup measures

FIG. 167.

2-1/2" high and has Mark Type 33 on the base. The saucer measures 5-1/4" in diameter and has Mark Type 33 on the base.

No. 1112. DUCK POSY BOWL - measures 4-1/2" high by 7-1/2" long and has Mark Type 30 on the base.

FIG. 167. RHINOCEROS ASHTRAY 1962.
This figure, described as a new outstanding design in ashtrays in the March 1962 issue of *The Pottery Gazette and Glass Trade Review* has been found in two sizes. The large size measures 8-1/4" high to the top of the horn by 9" long with a shamrock leaf mark on the base. The small size measures 5-1/2" high to the top of the horn by 6" long and has Mark Type 33A on the base. The rubber stopper in the base of the figure reads: CHEKALEKE REGD. NO. 698795.

No. 1113. CELTIC PORCELAIN DISH - measures 4-1/2" in diameter and has Mark Type 34 on the base.
No. 1114. CELTIC PORCELAIN COVERED BOX - measures 4-1/2" high and has Mark Type 34 on the base.

FIG. 168. GLAXO OINTMENT JAR (circa 1976). This jar was a single run item specially manufactured for Glaxo Laboratories. The 7" high container has Mark Type 37 on the base and the wording: Dermovate Psoriasis and stubborn Eczema, printed around the finial of the lid.

No. 1115. "ROSE" ASHTRAY - shape No.I.P.627, measures 6-3/4" across and has Mark Type 29 on the base.

FIG. 169. CANDLEHOLDER/ASHTRAY (mid 1950's). This 6-1/2" diameter ashtray has Mark Type 28 on the base. It is interesting to note that the applied candle holder is from the same mold as the "Everlasting Candle" base produced by George Wade & Son Ltd. in 1953-1954.

FIG. 170. CANDLEHOLDER/ASHTRAY (early 1960's). This 8" diameter ashtray has Mark Type 33 on the base.

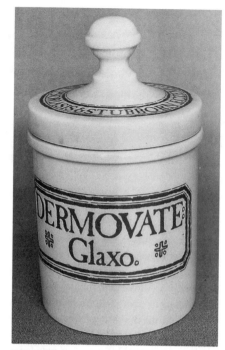

FIG. 168.

FIG. 169.

FIG. 170.

FIG. 171. PADDY McGREDY FLORIBUNDA SET. In the 1960's, Wade (Ireland) Ltd. produced their Gift Pack No. 1 comprising cigarette box, tankard and ashtray. A number of these sets were specially decorated and used as a special order by the Samuel McGredy Nursery famous for their roses.

223

FIG. 171.

One Nursery was located in Portadown with a second Nursery and store located at Derriaghy, near Belfast. The Nurseries closed in 1975 when Sam McGredy, Jr., emigrated to New Zealand.
Sam McGredy had a sister named Paddy so it is most likely this design was named after her.
Each of these items is marked: Paddy McGredy, Floribunda. Raised by Sam McGredy from spartan x Tzigane. Awarded gold medal National Rose Society, Award of Merit, Royal Horticultural Society.

    A. HALF PINT TANKARD.
    B. CRINKLED EDGE ASHTRAY .
    C. CIGARETTE BOX.

No. 1116.    MINIATURE TANKARD - measures 3" high and has Mark Type 28 on the base.

No. 1117.    "PADDY MAGINTY" PIPE REST - measures 3-5/8" high and has Mark Type 40A on the base.

No. 1118.    PIPE REST - measures 2" high and has Mark Type 40A on the base.

No. 1119.    "PHIL THE FLUTER" PIPE REST - measures 3-3/4" high and has Mark Type 40A on the base.

No. 1120.    CRUET SET AND STAND - cruet stand (I.P.629) measures 5-1/4" across and has Mark Type 29 on the base, pepper (I.P.604) measures 2-5/8" high and is mold-marked Irish Porcelain, salt (I.P.605) measures 2-5/8" high and is mold-marked Irish Porcelain. The covered mustard (I.P.606) measures 3" high and is mold-marked Irish Porcelain. As a complete set, this cruet set and stand was allocated a special number I.P.606C.

# YACHT WALL PLAQUES 1955.

    A set of three die-pressed wall plaques produced by the Irish pottery for approximately one year only. The plaques are mold-marked Made in Ireland by Wade and each has a single hole for affixing the item to wall pins. For a prototype self-supporting version of the "Yacht Wall Plaque" see No. 122 in the color section.

No. 1121.    YACHT WALL PLAQUE (large) - measures 4-1/2" high.

No. 1122.    YACHT WALL PLAQUE (medium) - measures 4-1/8" high.

No. 1123.    YACHT WALL PLAQUE (small) - measures 3-3/8" high.

# "PEX" FAIRY 1948 - 1950.

    The figurine of a fairy was produced by Wade (Ulster) Ltd. as a promotional item for Pex Stockings. At the end of the promotion a number of the surplus figurines were mounted on a posy of porcelain flowers which incorporated a candleholder behind the figurine.

FIG. 172.

FIG. 173.

FIG. 172.    THE "PEX" FAIRY - this promotional figurine measures 2-3/8" high and has a black and gold paper label reading Made in Ireland by Wade Co. Armagh.

FIG. 173.    THE "PEX" FAIRY CANDLEHOLDER - measures 3" high and is marked Made in Ireland by Wade Co. Armagh. This photograph illustrates the candleholder behind the figurine. See also item No. 88 in the color section.

# POGO 1959.

    This beautifully hand-decorated but hard-to-find die-pressed figure modelled by Wm. Harper from a design based on the Pogo newspaper cartoon strip. For a prototype figurine of Pogo see item No. 115 in the color section.

No. 1124.    POGO - measures 3-1/4" high and is marked "POGO" copyright Walt Kelly Made in Ireland 1959.

## PINK ELEPHANTS *1959.*

A series of comic elephants was produced with a variety of liquor-related comments printed on the figures. This series of figures, along with white comic pig figures decorated in green and orange, was produced for a limited time only by the Wade potteries under their Shamrock Pottery Giftware line.

No. 1125.   **"NEVER MIX'EM!" PINK ELEPHANT** - measures 1-1/2" high by 3" long and is marked Made in Ireland.

No. 1126.   **"STICK TO WATER!" PINK ELEPHANT** - measures 1-1/2" high by 3" long and is marked Shamrock Pottery Made in Ireland.

## FLYING BIRDS set 1 *circa 1956 - 1959.*

These wall ornaments were originally sold in boxed sets of three, all of a similar color. The birds were unmarked and had two small holes on the back for affixing the item to the wall.

No. 1127.   **GREEN FLYING BIRD** - measures 1" high by 2-3/4" across the wings.

No. 1128.   **YELLOW FLYING BIRD** - measures 1" high by 2-3/4" across the wings.

No. 1129.   **BLUE FLYING BIRD** - measures 1" high by 2-3/4" across the wings.

## FLYING BIRDS set 2 *circa late 1950's.*

This set is comprised of three bird wall ornaments. The off-white and blue glazed birds were unmarked and had holes on the back for affixing the item to the wall. See FIG.174.

**FIG. 174.   FLYING BIRDS - Set 2.**

## ANIMAL FIGURES *1978 - circa 1980.*

This set of six figurines is comprised of walrus, polar bear, koala, rhino, elephant and lion. This set was not connected to the earlier "blow-up" polar bear, polar bear cub and seal which were produced in the early 1960's by George Wade & Son Ltd. See FIG.175.

**FIG. 175.   WALRUS.** This figurine measures approx. 4" high by approx. 6" long and is marked Wade Ireland.

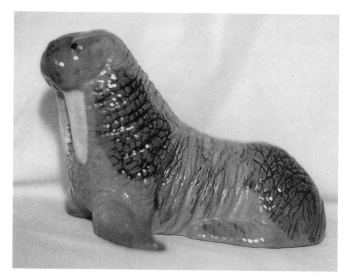

**FIG. 175.**

**WADE (PDM) Ltd.**

**1950 - 1993.**

## WADE (PDM) LTD. *1950 - 1993.*

Wade (PDM) Ltd. began life in the 1950's as Wade Regicor, when Wade, Heath & Co. Ltd. collaborated with Reginald Corfield (Sales) Ltd. to produce and distribute promotional items directed mainly toward the brewery and distilling industries. In 1969, Wade, Heath & Co. Ltd. dissolved the association and established its own Point of Sale, Design and Marketing division.

First located in Purley, Surrey, just south of London, the office later relocated to Burslem, Stoke-on-Trent, so that the distributing arm of the business would be more in touch with the pottery. For further information on Wade (PDM) Ltd. and illustrations of its products, see *The W of W pgs. 3 & 4 and 168-178.*

FIG. 176.

FIG. 176.    NOVELTY ITEMS. These two advertising dishes were based on the 1953 Coronation Dish. The dish on the left is an advertising item for Reginald Corfield including a quote by Ralph Waldo Emerson. The dish on the right was issued to commemorate the founding of the London Zoo in 1829. Both dishes measure 4-3/4" in diameter by 1-1/8" high.

## BELL'S WHISKY DECANTERS.

Wade, Heath & Co. Ltd. and now Wade Ceramics Ltd. have made decanters for Bell's whisky since 1965. The new bell shape decanter was introduced in 1988. For further information on Bell's decanters, see *The W of W pg.69.*

No. 1130.    BELL'S OLD SCOTCH WHISKY - 75 cl decanter measures 8" high and has Mark Type 27A on the base.

No. 1131.    BELL'S OLD SCOTCH WHISKY "CHRISTMAS 1989" - 75 cl decanter measures 8" high and has Mark Type 27A on the base.

No. 1132.    BELL'S OLD SCOTCH WHISKY "CHRISTMAS 1990" - 75 cl decanter measures 8" high and has Mark Type 27A on the base.

No. 1133.    BELL'S OLD SCOTCH WHISKY "CHRISTMAS 1991" - 70 cl decanter measures 8" high and has Mark Type 27A on the base.

No. 1134.    BELL'S FINE OLD SCOTCH WHISKY - 75 cl decanter measures 8" high and has Mark Type 27A on the base.

No. 1135.    BELL'S OLD SCOTCH WHISKY "HAWAII" - 75 cl decanter measures 8" high and has Mark Type 27A on the base.

No. 1136.    BELL'S OLD SCOTCH WHISKY "WEDDING" - 75 cl decanter measures 8" high and has Mark Type 27A on the base.

No. 1137.    BELL'S OLD SCOTCH WHISKY - 5 cl miniature decanter measures 3-3/4" high and has Mark Type 27A on the base.

No. 1138.    BELL'S OLD SCOTCH WHISKY "YEAR OF THE SHEEP 1991" - 75 cl decanter measures 8" high and has Mark Type 27A on the base.

No. 1139.    BELL'S OLD SCOTCH WHISKY "YEAR OF THE MONKEY 1992" - 75 cl decanter measures 8" high and has Mark Type 27A on the base.

## FINDLATER'S WHISKY DECANTERS *1986 - 1990.*

No. 1140.    FINDLATER'S FIRST XI - 750 ml decanter measures 5-1/2" high and is marked: Designed for Findlater's Scotch Whisky Hand Crafted Porcelain by Wade Ceramics.

No. 1141.    FINDLATER'S FIRST XI "WORLD CUP ITALY 1990" - 750 ml decanter measures 5-1/2" high and is marked: Designed for Findlater's Scotch Whisky Hand Crafted Porcelain by Wade Ceramics.

## MISCELLANEOUS DECANTERS.

No. 1142.    JOHN JAMESON & SON IRISH WHISKY - 750 ml decanter measures 7-3/4" high and has Mark Type 41 on the base.

No. 1143.    BENEAGLES SCOTCH WHISKY - this 4-3/4" high miniature brown bear decanter was first issued in 1981 by Wade (Ireland) Ltd. for Peter Thompson (Perth) Ltd. Production ended circa 1987.

No. 1144.    GLENTURRET 25 YEAR OLD SCOTCH WHISKY - 70 cl decanter measures 7-3/4" high and has Mark Type 27B on the base. This decanter was produced in 1991 only.

## TAUNTON'S CIDER.

Two porcelain imitation cider flagons for use as "bar top" decorations. Both items are hollow with an opening at the back for clamping the ceramic flagon to either the bar or a shelf.

No. 1145.    TAUNTON'S "AUTUMN GOLD" CIDER - measures 6-1/4" high and is unmarked.

No. 1146.    TAUNTON'S "DRY BLACKTHORN" CIDER - measures 6-1/4" high and is unmarked.

## PUSSER'S RUM DECANTERS.

The Wade Pottery has made a number of popular decanters for Pusser's Rum in a variety of shapes and sizes. The most renowned of these is the one litre (full size) "Nelson's Ship" decanter. This shape has recently been issued with a new series of decals featuring the famous U.S. sailor, John Paul Jones. See item No.1317 in the color section.

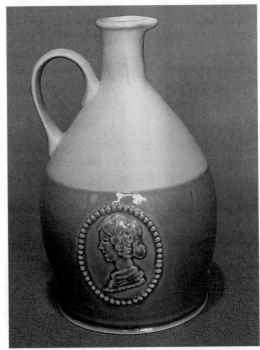

FIG. 178.

FIG. 177.

FIG. 179.

FIG. 177. BRITISH NAVY RUM "VICTORY AMERICA'S CUP CHALLENGE 1983" - HIP FLASK. The flask measures 5-3/4" high and is mold-marked: Hand Cast Porcelain Made in England.

No. 1147. "NELSON'S SHIP" MINIATURE DECANTER - measures 3-1/2" high and is unmarked.

No. 1148. BRITISH NAVY RUM "WEST INDIES" HIP FLASK - measures 5-3/4" high and is mold-marked: Hand Cast Porcelain Made in England.

No. 1149. "BRITISH NAVY" RUM MINIATURE FLAGON - measures 2-1/2" high and is unmarked.

# MISCELLANEOUS DECANTERS and LIQUOR BOTTLES.

FIG. 178. "BRONTE" DECANTER JUG - measures 7-1/2" high and is marked: Created for the James B. Beam Import Corp. by Bronte Liqueur, Yorkshire, England. Made by Wade Ireland.

FIG. 179. "BRONTE" LIQUOR BOTTLES. The miniature bottle on the left measures 2-3/4" high to the top of the plastic stopper. The larger bottle on the right

measures 6-1/4" inches high to the top of the stopper. Not shown is a third, medium sized, bottle.

No. 1150. BENEAGLES SCOTCH WHISKY - this miniature 2-3/4" high curling stone decanter is mold-marked: Beneagles Scotch Whisky Wade. Produced in 1981 by Wade (Ireland) Ltd. for Peter Thompson (Perth) Ltd.

No. 1151. WHYTE & MACKAY SCOTCH WHISKY - this 9-3/4" high decanter is unmarked and was in production between 1983-1989.

No. 1152. GLENFIDDICH® ANCIENT RESERVE SINGLE MALT SCOTCH WHISKY - this 700 ml liquor bottle measures 8-3/4" high and is marked on the underside of the base: Specially Commissioned by William Grant & Sons Limited, The Glenn Turret Distillers, Scotland. This liquor container was in production between 1991-1992. Similar containers were also produced by Spode.

No. 1153. GLENFIDDICH® ANCIENT RESERVE SINGLE MALT SCOTCH WHISKY - this 700 ml liquor bottle measures 8-3/4" high and is marked on the underside of the base: Specially Commissioned by William Grant & Sons Limited, The Glenn Turret Distillers, Scotland. This liquor container was in production between 1991-1992. Similar containers were also produced by Spode.

No. 1154. GLENFIDDICH® ANCIENT RESERVE SINGLE MALT SCOTCH WHISKY - this 700 ml liquor bottle measures 8-3/4" high and is marked on the underside of the base: Specially Commissioned by William Grant & Sons Limited, The Glenn Turret Distillers, Scotland. This liquor container was in production between 1991-1992. Similar containers were also produced by Spode.

No. 1155. ABBOT'S CHOICE SCOTCH WHISKY - this liquor bottle measures 10" high and is mold-marked on the base: M-Made Exclusively for the Abbot's Choice Scotch Whisky. John McEwan & Co. Ltd. Leath, Scotland. Liquor Bottle, Scotland. This liquor bottle was first produced in 1982 by Wade (Ireland) Ltd. and some were still in stock in 1992. A new, second mold was made in 1987 for Low Robertson, part of the Distillers Company Limited who were then absorbed into United Distillers as part of the Guinness Group.

FIG. 180.

FIG. 180. Reverse side of the "ABBOT'S CHOICE" liquor bottle showing the applied paper label.

No. 1156. VILLA COLONNA® - this 9-1/2" high liquor bottle has Mark Type 20 on the base and was in production in 1989 only.

No. 1157. OLD PARR TRIBUTE - this 7" high liquor bottle has the wording "Anno 14 Dec 1635" impressed on the

recess in the base. Old Parr Tribute celebrates the legendary life of Thomas Parr who lived to be 152. Famed for his great age, King Charles I requested he be presented at court. So began the long and arduous journey from his native Winnington to London. He was royally entertained and paid the final tribute by Royal Decree. He was laid to rest amongst the kings in Westminster Abbey in 1635. This special issue bottle was in production between 1990 -1991 over a period of only twelve months.

No. 1158. CARLTON SPECIAL SCOTCH WHISKY - this 750 ml decanter is 9-1/4" high and is unmarked. This decanter was in production between 1981-1985.

FIG. 181.

FIG. 181. THORNTON & FRANCE SHERRY BARREL - measures 11-1/4" long by 8-3/4" high and has Mark Type 20 on the base. This container was made by Wade, Heath & Co. Ltd. in a limited number of two hundred pieces between 1980-1981.

# FINDLATER'S WHISKY DECANTERS
*1986 - 1990.*

No. 1159. FINDLATER'S FIRST XV - 750 ml decanter measures 8" high and is marked: Designed for Findlater's Scotch Whisky Hand Crafted Porcelain by Wade Ceramics.

No. 1160. FINDLATER'S FIRST XV - 750 ml decanter measures 8" high and is marked: Designed for Findlater's Scotch Whisky Hand Crafted Porcelain by Wade Ceramics.

# DIMPLE SCOTCH WHISKY LIQUOR BOTTLES *1987 - 1988.*

No. 1161. DIMPLE SCOTCH WHISKY "HAWAII" - this 75 cl bottle measures 8-1/4" high and is marked: John Haig & Co. Ltd. Edinburgh, Scotland.

No. 1162. DIMPLE SCOTCH WHISKY "1990 YEAR OF THE HORSE" - this 75 cl bottle measures 8-1/4" high and is marked: John Haig & Co. Ltd. Edinburgh, Scotland.

No. 1163.    DIMPLE SCOTCH WHISKY "1989 YEAR OF THE SNAKE" - this 75 cl bottle measures 8-1/4" high and is marked: John Haig & Co. Ltd. Edinburgh, Scotland.

## THE THISTLE AND THE ROSE CHESS SET *1980.*

This set of porcelain chess pieces was made by the Wade Pottery for Peter Thompson (Perth) Ltd. of Scotland. The designs were based on historical characters from the royal houses of Scotland (The Thistle) and England (The Rose) of the 16 th. century, modeled by Frederick Mellor from designs by Ann Whittet.

The original pieces were unfilled and were contained in a presentation box along with a bottle of Beneagles Scotch Whisky and a copper-finished chess board. The principle pieces were also made available individually packaged and containing 50ml of whisky. A great number of these were distributed as a free gift to first class passengers flying British Caledonian Airways.

Toward the end of the production run, boxed sets of one Principle Piece filled with whisky and one solid Pawn, were distributed by Las Vegas Distributing Co. of Las Vegas, Nevada.

No. 1164.    NORMAN ENGLISH TOWER  - measures 4" high.
No. 1165.    SIR FRANCIS DRAKE - measures 5-1/8" high.
No. 1166.    THOMAS A BECKET - measures 5-1/4" high.
No. 1167.    QUEEN ELIZABETH I - measures 5-1/4" high.
No. 1168.    KING HENRY VIII - measures 5-1/4" high.
No. 1169.    PAWN "ROSE" - measures 3-5/8" high.
No. 1170.    PAWN "THISTLE" - measures 3-5/8" high.
No. 1171.    KING ROBERT THE BRUCE - measures 5-1/8" high.
No. 1172.    MARY QUEEN OF SCOTS - measures 4-7/8" high.
No. 1173.    JOHN KNOX - measures 5" high.
No. 1174.    SIR WILLIAM WALLACE - measures 5-3/8" high.
No. 1175.    SCOTTISH TOWER HOUSE - measures 4-1/8" high.

## BLACK & WHITE SCOTCH WHISKY DECANTER *1972-1986.*

No. 1176.    BLACK & WHITE "DOG" GIFT DECANTER - this decanter measures 7-1/2" high by 9-1/2" across and is marked: Scotch Black & White Whisky Premium Distilled, Blended & Bottled in Scotland by James Buchanan & Co. Limited.

FIG. 182.    BLACK & WHITE SCOTCH WHISKY JUGS. The hard-to-find miniature jug on the left measures 2-1/8" high and is marked Wade Regicor Made in England. The large jug on the right measures 4-7/8" high and has Mark Type 45 on the base.

FIG. 182.

## CHIVAS ROYAL SALUTE LIQUOR BOTTLES *1982 - to present.*

No. 1177.    CHIVAS SCOTCH WHISKY - this 750 ml liquor bottle measures 8-3/4" high and is marked Wade England on the recessed base.
No. 1178.    CHIVAS SCOTCH WHISKY - this 375 ml liquor bottle measures 7-3/8" high and is marked Wade England on the recessed base.
No. 1179.    CHIVAS SCOTCH WHISKY - this 750 ml liquor bottle measures 8-3/4" high and is marked Wade England on the recessed base.
No. 1180.    CHIVAS SCOTCH WHISKY - this 375 ml liquor bottle measures 7-3/8" high and is marked Wade England on the recessed base.
No. 1181.    CHIVAS SCOTCH WHISKY - this 750 ml liquor bottle measures 8-3/4" high and is marked Wade England on the recessed base.
No. 1182.    CHIVAS SCOTCH WHISKY - this 200 ml hip flask measures 6" high and is marked Wade England on the recessed base.
No. 1183.    CHIVAS SCOTCH WHISKY - this 50 ml miniature liquor bottle measures 4" high and is marked Wade England on the recessed base.
No. 1184.    CHIVAS REGAL 12 YEAR OLD WHISKY - water jug with recessed handle measures 8" high and has Mark Type 47 on the base. The name appears twice on the jug.

## GILBEY'S WINE BARRELS *1953.*

Additional information on Gilbey's Wine Barrels may be found in *The W of W pgs. 71 & 174.*

No. 1185.    COGNAC BARREL - measures 5-1/8" high and has Mark Type 17 on the base.
No. 1186.    RUM BARREL - measures 5-1/8" high and has Mark Type 17 on the base.

# MISCELLANEOUS WATER JUGS, ASHTRAYS and WAITER TRAYS.

No. 1187.  NICHOLSON'S LAMPLIGHTER GIN - this water jug measures 6" high and has Mark Type 45 on the base.

No. 1188.  LONG JOHN SCOTCH WHISKY - easy clean type ashtray, measures 6" in diameter and has Mark Type 43 on the base.

No. 1189.  PUSSER'S BRITISH NAVY RUM - this water jug with recessed handle measures 5-3/4" high and has Mark Type 20 on the base.

No. 1190.  KEG HARP LAGER - easy clean type ashtray, measures 7" in diameter and has Mark Type 45 on the base.

No. 1191.  IMPERIAL VODKA - water jug, measures 6-1/2" high and has Mark Type 44 on the base. The transfer type decoration appears on both sides of the jug.

No. 1192.  CRAWFORD'S OLD SCOTCH WHISKY - water jug, measures 4" high and has Mark Type 42 on the base.

No. 1193.  JOHN BEGG SCOTCH WHISKY - water jug, measures 5" high and has Mark Type 45 on the base.

No. 1194.  JOHN BEGG SCOTCH WHISKY - pressed ashtray, measures 6" across and has Mark Type 42 on the base.

No. 1195.  "QUANTAS " AUSTRALIA'S OVERSEAS AIRLINE - water jug with recessed handle,  measures 4- 1/2" high and has Mark Type 19 on the base.

FIG. 183.

FIG. 183.  M&B CENTENARY JUG (1979) - measures 5-3/8" high and is marked: "This jug has been produced in a limited edition to mark the 100 years that have passed since beer was first brewed at the Cope Hill Brewery of Mitchell & Butlers. Supplied by Wade (PDM) Ltd."

No. 1196.  JOHNNIE WALKER SCOTCH WHISKY - small square waiter tray, measures 12-3/4" square by 3/4" high and is marked: Wade (PDM) Ltd./Avon Product.

No. 1197.  JOHNNIE WALKER SCOTCH WHISKY - water jug, measures 6-1/2" high and has Mark Type 47 on the base.

No. 1198.  JOHNNIE WALKER SCOTCH WHISKY - easy clean type ashtray, measures 6-3/4" square and has Mark Type 47 on the base.

No. 1199.  JOHNNIE WALKER SCOTCH WHISKY - overhang lip type ashtray, measures 4-3/4" square and has Mark Type 42 on the base.

No. 1200.  JOHNNIE WALKER RED LABEL - water jug, measures 7-1/2" high and is marked: Fine Staffordshire Pottery Duncan Fox & Co. Inc. New York, Regicor Wade, Made in England.

No. 1201.  BELL'S OLD SCOTCH WHISKY - easy clean type ashtray, measures 9" long and has Mark Type 48 on the base.

No. 1202.  BELL'S OLD SCOTCH WHISKY - easy clean type ashtray, measures 7" in diameter by 3-1/2"  high and has Mark Type 47 on the base.

No. 1203.  BELLS'S OLD SCOTCH WHISKY - water jug with ice check spout, measures 8" high and has Mark Type 47 on the base.

No. 1204.  ARTHUR BELL & SONS LTD. SCOTCH WHISKY - water jug, measures 5" high and has Mark Type 45 on the base.

FIG. 184.

FIG. 184.  COFFEE MUG - measures 2-1/2" high by 2-3/4" in diameter and has Mark Type 43 on the base.

No. 1205.  BELL'S SCOTCH WHISKY - water jug, measures 5-1/2" high and has Mark Type 45 on the base.

No. 1206.  BLACK & WHITE SCOTCH WHISKY - water jug, measures 5" high and has Mark Type 45 on the base.

No. 1207.  BLACK & WHITE SCOTCH WHISKY - easy clean type ashtray, measures 5" in diameter and has  Mark Type 46 on the base.

No. 1208.  BERTOLA CREAM SHERRY - sherry container, measures 9" high and has Mark Type 45 on the base.

No. 1209.  JOHN PLAYER SPECIAL CIGARETTES - water jug with ice check spout, measures 6-1/4" high and has Mark Type 46 on the base.

FIG. 185.

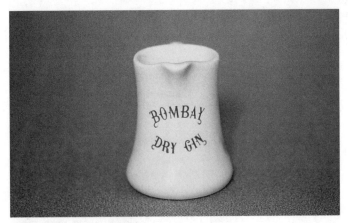

FIG. 186.

FIG. 185.   NELSON FILTER TIPPED CIGARETTES - over-hang lip type ashtray, measures 7" long by 5-1/2" wide by 1-3/4" high and has Mark Type 43 on the base.

No. 1210.   JUBILEE STOUT - water jug, measures 4-3/4" high and has Mark Type 46 on the base.

No. 1211.   VAT 69 SCOTCH WHISKY - water jug with recessed handle, measure 4-1/2" high and has Mark Type 46 on the base.

No. 1212.   VAT 69 SCOTCH WHISKY - easy clean type ashtray, measures 4-1/8" in diameter and has Mark Type 46 on the base.

No. 1213.   THE ABBOT'S CHOICE SCOTCH WHISKY - easy clean type ashtray, measures 5" in diameter and has Mark Type 45 on the base.

No. 1214.   CANADA DRY - easy clean type ashtray, measures 5" across and has Mark Type 43 on the base.

No. 1215.   OLD RARITY DE LUXE SCOTCH WHISKY - water jug, measures 5" high and has Mark Type 47 on the base.

No. 1216.   JOHNNIE WALKER SCOTCH WHISKY - water jug with recessed handle, measures 5-3/4" high and has Mark Type 43 on the base.

No. 1217.   DEWAR'S SPECIAL SCOTCH WHISKY - water jug, measures 6-1/4" high and has Mark Type 43 on the base.

No. 1218.   DEWAR'S FINE SCOTCH WHISKY "THE DEWAR HIGHLANDER" - water jug with recessed handle, measures 5-3/4" high and has Mark Type 45 on the base.

No. 1219.   GRAND MACNISH SCOTCH WHISKY - water jug with recessed handle, measures 5-1/2" high and has Mark Type 47 on the base.

No. 1220.   GRAND MACNISH SCOTCH WHISKY - small square waiter tray, measures 12-1/2" square by 3/4" high and is marked: Wade (PDM) Ltd./ Avon Product.

No. 1221.   CHARRINGTON'S BEERS - toby mug, measures 7-3/8" high and has Mark Type 42 on the base.

FIG. 186.   BOMBAY DRY GIN - miniature water jug, measures 2-1/2" high and is marked: Wade Regicor Made in England.

No. 1222.   TOBY JIM JUG - water jug, measures 4-3/8" high and has Mark Type 43A on the base.

No. 1223.   DEWAR'S® DE LUX ANCESTOR® SCOTCH WHISKY - pressed ashtray, measures 5-1/2" square and has Mark Type 47 on the base.

No. 1224.   DEWAR'S "WHITE LABEL" SCOTCH WHISKY - water jug with ice check spout, measures 5-3/4" high and has Mark Type 45 on the base. The wording around the bottom of the jug reads: The Scotch that never varies! 86.8 proof blended Scotch Whisky. Schenley Imports Co., N. Y., N.Y.

No. 1225.   THE FAMOUS GROUSE FINEST SCOTCH WHISKY - water jug, measures 4-1/2" high and has Mark Type 47 on the base.

No. 1226.   THE FAMOUS GROUSE ASHTRAY - easy clean type ashtray, measures 5-1/2" in diameter and has Mark Type 46 on the base.

No. 1227.   THE BUCHANAN BLEND "THE SCOTCH OF A LIFETIME" - water jug, measures 6" high and has Mark Type 47 on the base.

No. 1228.   BEEFEATER GIN - water jug with recessed handle and ice check spout, measures 6" high and has Mark Type 46 on the base.

No. 1229.   BEEFEATER DRY GIN - overhang lip type ashtray, measures 4-1/4" square and has Mark Type 42 on the base.

No. 1230.   BEEFEATER LONDON GIN - overhang lip type ashtray, measures 8" long and has Mark Type 45 on the base.

No. 1231.   BEEFEATER GIN - water jug with recessed handle and ice check spout, measures 6" high and has Mark Type 46 on the base.

No. 1232.   MCCALLUM'S SCOTCH WHISKY - water jug with recessed handle and ice check spout, measures 5" high and has Mark Type 46 on the base.

No. 1233.   DOUBLE DIAMOND - easy clean type ashtray, measures 4" square by 2" high and has Mark Type 47 on the base.

No. 1234.   JUBILEE STOUT - salt shaker, measures 3-1/8" high and has Mark Type 42 on the base.

No. 1235.   JUBILEE STOUT - pepper shaker, measures 3-1/8" high and has Mark Type 42 on the base.

No. 1236.   JUBILEE STOUT - mustard pot, measures 3-1/8" high and has Mark Type 42 on the base.

FIG. 187.

FIG. 187. MARSTON'S GOOD FOOD - these 4-5/8" high salt and pepper shakers have Mark Type 19 on the base.

No. 1237. WELCOME - salt shaker, measures 4-5/8" high and has Mark Type 19 on the base.

No. 1238. WELCOME - pepper shaker, measures 4-5/8" high and has Mark Type 19 on the base.

# BASS PROMOTIONAL ITEMS.

Established in 1777, Bass PLC is today, one of Britain's largest brewers producing a wide range of beers and lagers. For more information on Bass PLC see *The W of W pgs. 71, 174 & 175*. The publisher and authors acknowledge that Bass Public Limited Company or its subsidiaries are the proprietors of all copyright trade marks and all rights associated with these illustrations and the items depicted therein.

No. 1239. BASS - spun dish type ashtray, measures 5-1/4" in diameter and has Mark Type 42 on the base.

No. 1240. BASS THE GREAT ALE OF ENGLAND - small square waiter tray, measures 12-1/2" square by 3/4" high and is marked: Wade (PDM) Ltd./ Avon Product.

No. 1241. YOU'RE TWICE THE MAN ON WORTHINGTON - spun dish type ashtray, measures 5-1/2" in diameter and has Mark Type 42 on the base.

# MISCELLANEOUS ASHTRAYS and WATER JUGS.

No. 1242. GRANT'S SCOTCH WHISKY - water jug, measures 6" high and is marked: 86 Proof Blended Scotch Whisky Imported by Austin Nichols & Co. Inc. New York, N.Y. Made in Great Britain Wade Regicor.

No. 1243. GRANT'S SCOTCH WHISKY - overhang lip type ashtray, measures 4" triangle and has Mark Type 43 on the base.

No. 1244. GRANT'S SCOTCH WHISKY - water jug with ice check spout, measures 6-1/2" high and has Mark Type 42 on the base.

No. 1245. GORDON'S SPECIAL LONDON DRY GIN - water jug with ice check spout, measures 5-1/8" high and has Mark Type 47 on the base.

No. 1246. GORDON'S SPECIAL DRY GIN - easy clean type ashtray, measures 6-1/4" square and has Mark Type 47 on the base.

No. 1247. CAVALIER PANATELLAS - overhang lip type ashtray, measures 9" long and has Mark Type 42 on the base.

No. 1248. CATTO'S SCOTCH WHISKY - water jug with ice check spout, measures 6-3/4" high and has Mark Type 42 on the base.

No. 1249. KENTUCKY TAVERN THE VINTAGE BOURBON - water jug without handle, measures 7-1/2" high and has Mark Type 45 on the base.

No. 1250. SOMETHING SPECIAL DE LUX SCOTCH WHISKY - water jug with ice check spout, measures 5-3/4" high and has Mark Type 46 on the base.

No. 1251. BENSON & HEDGES - easy clean type ashtray, measures 9-1/2" long by 7" wide and has Mark Type 46 on the base.

No. 1252. BENSON & HEDGES - cigarette lighter, measures 3-1/2" square by 4-1/2" high and has Mark Type 46 on the base.

No. 1253. CHEQUERS SCOTCH WHISKY - water jug, measures 6" high and has Mark Type 46 on the base. It also has the wording: Chequers Blended Scotch Whisky 86.8 Proof Custom Import House Ltd. New York.

No. 1254. BLACK BUSH IRISH WHISKY - water jug with ice check spout, measures 6-5/8" high and is unmarked. This water jug was produced for the "Old Bush Mills" Distillery Co. Limited in 1990.

FIG. 188.

FIG. 188. KRONENBOURG TANKARD - measures 4-7/8" high and has Mark Type 46 on the base. The tankard is multicolored in grey, white and red.

No. 1255. KRONENBOURG - pressed ashtray, measures 5" square and has Mark Type 47 on the base.

No. 1256. KRONENBOURG - easy clean type ashtray, measures 6" in diameter by 3-5/8" high and has Mark Type 46 on the base.

233

No. 1257.   MORLAND - pressed ashtray, measures 5-1/2"
square and has Mark Type 47 on the base.

## WHITBREAD HOPPER *1987*.

Only the ceramic frog of the combination ceramic/
metal pin badge was made by Wade. Records indicate that
only a few thousand frogs were produced as an order for
Enterprise Products, a company specializing in button
badge assembly equipment. After the frog and the pin
badge had been assembled, by means of double-sided tape,
the finished product was forwarded to Whitbread for distribution.

Due to the method of attachment of the two items, it is
most often that the frog alone is found. The full value of
the pin badge is only realized when both the pin and the
frog are found together.

No. 1258.   PIN BADGE AND CERAMIC FROG - the metal pin
badge measures 2-1/4" in diameter and the ceramic
frog is 1-1/2" long.

## MISCELLANEOUS ASHTRAYS, WATER JUGS and WAITER TRAYS.

No. 1259.   AUSTIN - pressed ashtray, measures 5-1/2" square
and has Mark Type 46 on the base.

No. 1260.   MARSTON'S BURTON BITTER - draft beer display sign, measures 3" long by 2-1/4" high and has
the reserved item No.S33 on the back.

No. 1261.   MANSFIELD ALES - plate, measures 8" square and
has Mark Type 46 on the base.

No. 1262.   CELEBRATION ALE - hors d'oeuvres dish, measures 8-1/2" in diameter by 5-1/2" high and has
Mark Type 45 on the base.

No. 1263.   MARSTON'S LOW "C" - small round waiter tray,
measures 10-1/2" in diameter and is marked: Wade
(PDM) Ltd./ Avon Product.

No. 1264.   ALLBRIGHT A GREAT BITTER - small square
waiter tray, measures 12-1/2" square by 3/4" high
and is marked: Wade (PDM) Ltd./ Avon Product.

No. 1265.   SENIOR SERVICE CIGARETTES - easy clean type
ashtray, measures 9-1/2" across and has Mark Type
44 on the base.

No. 1266.   DUNHILL INTERNATIONAL - water jug with ice
check spout, measures 6" high and has Mark Type
46 on the base.

No. 1267.   DUNHILL INTERNATIONAL - easy clean type ashtray, measures 4-1/4" square and has Mark Type 45
on the base.

No. 1268.   DUNHILL INTERNATIONAL - water jug with ice
check spout, measures 5-1/2" high and has Mark
Type 46 on the base.

No. 1269.   SAMUEL WEBSTER 1838 - easy clean type ashtray,
measures 10" long and has Mark Type 47 on the
base.

No. 1270.   BADGER BEER - pressed dish ashtray, measures 5-
1/4" square and has Mark Type 42 on the base.

No. 1271.   BADGER BEER - pressed dish ashtray, measures 8-
1/2" long and has Mark Type 47 on the base.

No. 1272.   BOOTH'S GIN - spun dish ashtray, measures 5-
3/4" in diameter and has Mark Type 46 on the base.

No. 1273.   CARLING BLACK LABEL LAGER BEER - easy
clean type ashtray, measures 8-1/4" long by 7-3/4"
wide and has Mark Type 45 on the base.

No. 1274.   CARLING BLACK LABEL - water jug, measures 6-
1/2" high and has Mark Type 47 on the base.

## BOTTLE POURERS.

Bottle pourers, either purely ornamental or used as
advertising items, were produced by George Wade & Son
Ltd. A small number were marked with a Wade Regicor
transfer type mark but most were either unmarked or had
only the "reserve line" number impressed in the base.

No. 1275.   "BIRD" BOTTLE POURER - measures 5" long.

No. 1276.   "EAGLE" BOTTLE POURER - measures 5-1/2"
long.

No. 1277.   "BUSH BABY" BOTTLE POURER - measures 5"
long.

No. 1278.   "BEEFEATER" BOTTLE POURER - measures 3"
long and is marked Wade Regicor Made in England.

No. 1279.   "CAPTAIN MORGAN" BOTTLE POURER - measures 4-1/2" long and is marked Wade Regicor
Made in U.K.

No. 1280.   "J & B" BOTTLE POURER - measures 3" long.

No. 1281.   "WHITE HORSE" BOTTLE POURER - measures
5" long and was produced circa 1954.

## MISCELLANEOUS ASHTRAYS, WATER JUGS and WAITER TRAYS.

No. 1282.   GREENE KING - easy clean type ashtray, measures
5" in diameter and has Mark Type 46 on the base.

No. 1283.   DISH - measures 4-3/4" across and has Mark Type
42 on the base.

No. 1284.   GREENE KING "ABBOT ALE, HARVEST ALE" -
pressed dish ashtray, measures 5-1/2" square and
has Mark Type 45 on the base.

No. 1285.   WM. YOUNGER'S TARTAN - small square waiter
tray, measures 12-1/2" square by 3/4" high and is
marked: Wade (PDM) Ltd./ Avon Product.

No. 1286.   THE FIRM FAVORITE TETLEY MILD - small
square waiter tray, measures 12-1/2" square by
3/4" high and is marked: Wade (PDM) Ltd./ Avon
Product.

No. 1287.   THE NORTHERN CLUBS - small square waiter
tray, measures 12-1/2" square by 3/4" high and is
marked: Wade (PDM) Ltd./ Avon Product.

No. 1288.   TENNENT'S LAGER - small square waiter tray,
measures 12-1/2" square by 3/4" high and is
marked: Wade (PDM) Ltd./ Avon Product.

No. 1289.   DOWN WITH MARKSMAN - easy clean type ashtray, measures 8-1/2" in diameter and has Mark
Type 47 on the base.

FIG. 189.   PICON-PICON CONTAINER (circa mid 1960's) -
measures 3-1/4" high by 2-1/4" in diameter and
has Mark Type 44 on the base.

# Porcelain Novelties...

...attractive to look at and ready sellers.

These delightful novelties in genuine felspathic porcelain are made by an entirely new process which produces a richness and translucency of extraordinary quality.

Supplied carton packed in convenient quantities. You are invited to send for further details.

# WADE

GEORGE WADE & SON LTD · MANCHESTER POTTERY · BURSLEM · STOKE-ON-TRENT · ENGLAND
Telephone Stoke-on-Trent 97138-9

*PORCELAIN NOVELTIES. An advertisement from the July 1954 issue of Pottery and Glass.*

FIG. 189.

## GUINNESS DISHES *early 1960's.*

The "Bon Bon" dishes were produced as Christmas gifts in late 1961. The decorations were based on illustrations by John Gilroy who designed many of the Guinness posters. Records indicate 2,250 dishes were produced by Wade and were a "special" one-off item and not regular point-of-sale stock. A Guinness-sponsored film, made in 1964, about life in an English country town, features a honeymooning couple (the groom played by well-known British T.V. actor Richard Briers) debating whether they should steal a couple of these "Bon Bon" dishes as souvenirs.

No. 1290. "KANGAROO" BON BON DISH - measures 4" in diameter and has Mark Type 43 on the base.

No. 1291. "TOUCAN" BON BON DISH - measures 4" in diameter and has Mark Type 43 on the base.

No. 1292. GUINNESS STOUT PLATE - measures 8" in diameter and has Mark Type 45 on the base. The description on the plate reads: Sam Weller composing his Valentine. From an illustration by "Phiz" which includes a contemporary Guinness advertisement.

No. 1293. "PELICAN" BON BON DISH - measures 4" in diameter and has Mark Type 43 on the base.

No. 1294. "SEAL" BON BON DISH - measures 4" in diameter and has Mark Type 43 on the base.

## MISCELLANEOUS ASHTRAYS and WATER JUGS.

No. 1295. BREAKER REAL MALT LIQUOR - easy clean type ashtray, measures 8" in diameter and has Mark Type 46 on the base.

No. 1296. GORDON GRAHAM'S BLACK BOTTLE® SCOTCH WHISKY - water jug, measures 5-1/2" high and is unmarked.

No. 1297. CARROLLS NO.1 VIRGINIA CIGARETTES - easy clean type ashtray, measures 9" overall.

No. 1298. WHITE HORSE SCOTCH WHISKY - easy clean type ashtray, measures 8" long and has Mark Type 46 on the base.

235

No. 1299.   WHITE HORSE SCOTCH WHISKY - over hang type ashtray, measures 5-3/4" long and has Mark Type 42 on the base.

No. 1300.   TREBLE GOLD - pressed ashtray, measures 9" long by 5" wide and has Mark Type 42 on the base.

No. 1301.   USHER'S SCOTCH WHISKY - water jug with ice check spout, measures 5" high and has Mark Type 42 on the base.

No. 1302.   ROMANOFF VODKA - pressed dish ashtray, measures 5-1/2" square and has Mark Type 47 on the base.

No. 1303.   TENNENT'S LAGER AND STOUT - glass ashtray, measures 5-1/2" in diameter and is mold-marked Wade (PDM).

No. 1304.   JOHN BULL BITTER - easy clean type ashtray, measures 6-1/2" in diameter and has Mark Type 47 on the base.

No. 1305.   WHITEHALL LONDON DRY GIN - water jug, measures 4-5/8" high and has Mark Type 46 on the base.

No. 1306.   OLD PARR SCOTCH WHISKY - overhang lip type ashtray, measures 6-1/4" in diameter and has Mark Type 46 on the base.

No. 1307.   BOOTH'S GINS - pressed dish ashtray, measures 6-1/4" square and has Mark Type 42 on the base.

FIG. 190.   McCALLUM'S SCOTCH WHISKY WAITER TRAY - measures 12-3/4" square by 3/4" high and is marked: A Wade (PDM) Ltd./ Avon Product.

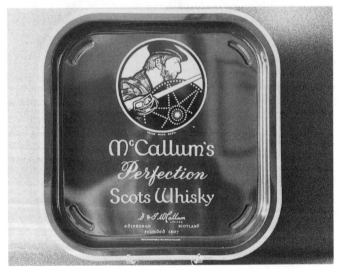

FIG. 190.

# VAUX BREWERIES TANKARDS and TAUNTON CIDER MUGS.

## VAUX TANKARDS and LOVING CUPS

### 1977 to present.

C. Vaux and Sons was founded in 1837 by Mr. Cuthbert Vaux at a brewery located at Matlock and Cumberland Streets in Sunderland. In 1844, Vaux purchased a brewery in Union Street, Sunderland where the firm traded until 1875

when the site was required for Sunderland's new central railway station. Vaux therefore moved once again, this time to their present location between Castle Street and Gillbridge Avenue. The first beer to be brewed at the new site was in June 1875.

In 1878, Cuthbert Vaux died and the business passed to his two sons, John Story Vaux and Edwin Vaux, both of whom had been involved with the business for many years and, under their leadership both the brewery and its trade grew.

After the death of John Story Vaux in 1887, his two sons, Major Cuthbert Vaux and Colonel Ernest Vaux went into partnership with their uncle, Edwin Vaux. In 1896, the business was converted into a private limited company going on to become one of the largest breweries in the North of England and also become one of the first breweries to introduce bottled ales and stouts to the area.

In 1896, C. Vaux and Sons became a limited company. At this time the business expanded significantly and the purchase of many public houses, or "pubs" as they are fondly called by their clients, was also made.

In the twenty years since the move to Castle Street, the brewery had developed from a small Victorian brewery into a modern industrial complex covering over two acres. The Vaux brothers had in-depth experience in the art of brewing but lacked experience in management. To overcome this problem, the brothers, in 1897, engaged Frank Nicholson a local Chartered Accountant, as Manager and Secretary of the brewery. Nicholson later married Amy, sister of Cuthbert Vaux and went on to become Director of the company in 1914 and Managing Director in 1919.

1927 saw a major development in the history of the brewery. At this time Frank Nicholson, who was knighted in 1943, arranged the amalgamation of C. Vaux and Sons with the North Eastern Breweries forming the Associated Breweries. This name was changed to Vaux and Associated Breweries in 1940.

North Eastern Breweries had been established, under the direction of Mr. Richard Murray, in 1896, with the amalgamation of a number of businesses. The original objectives of the NEB was to carry out the business of Hotel, Beer House, Restaurant and Bar keepers through Coal Merchants, Grocers, Brewers and Cement Manufacturers.

In 1928, after the first full year of trading for the merged companies, the new company made a handsome profit but within a few years, due to the depression of the 1930's, these profits dropped to below a quarter of the early years.

In spite of the depression, the company continued to expand and carried on doing so throughout the 1930's. After the war, the company continued to expand with the acquisition of numerous smaller breweries in and around the north of England.

Vaux and Associated Breweries changed the name of the company in 1973, to Vaux Breweries Ltd. and in 1985, the company became Vaux plc. The current Chairman of the Vaux Group is Sir Paul Nicholson, grandson of Sir Frank Nicholson.

Today the Vaux Group is made up of Vaux Breweries in Sunderland, S. H. Ward in Sheffield, Vaux Inns, Swallow Hotels, Percheron Properties and St. Andrews Homes.

Starting in 1977 the Wade Potteries started producing

special issue tankards for the brewery. The first of these special issue tankards was the all-over gold tankard shown in the color section in No. 1308. Starting in 1979 Wade Potteries produced the first Christmas tankard for the Vaux Breweries. With the exception of one year, 1980, Wade has continued to produce Christmas tankards for the brewery, each featuring a different theme or brand of beer.

In 1992 a special tankard was issued and was given as a Christmas present to licensees and friends of the brewery. See item No. 1311 in the color section. Also in 1992 a special tankard was produced for Vaux to celebrate Sunderland being made into a city. The tankard for 1993, will feature the brand "Samson" a popular beer brewed by Vaux breweries.

No. 1308.   **VAUX BREWERIES TANKARDS.** - A selection of 14 special issue tankards produced by the Wade Potteries.
A. Gold Tankard (1977).
B. Sunderland Draught Bitter (1978).
C. Lorimer's (1979).
D. Group Logos (1981).
E. Double Maxim (1982).
F. School of Sport (1983).
G. Vehicles (1984).
H. Vaux Group (1985).
I. Old Brewery Shot (1986).
J. Vaux Breweries (1987).
K. Double Maxim (1988).
L. Maxim Light (1989).
M. Ward's (1990)
N. Brand Logos (1991).

# TAUNTON CIDER MUGS *1974 to present.*

Taunton Cider plc of Taunton, Somerset produces a wide range of ciders. Starting in 1974, Wade Potteries have produced limited edition traditional cider mugs which are presented, by Taunton Cider, as Christmas Gifts to its key company contacts.

Taunton Cider has a collection of approximately 750 mugs, many of which date from the late 18th and 19th centuries. It is from some of these early designs upon which the annual Taunton Cider Christmas mugs are based. These mugs are produced in limited editions of 500 pieces, the first 50 of which are numbered.

In 1992, Wade produced a special mug to commemorate Taunton Cider's listing on the London Stock Exchange. See item No. 1312 in the color section. One special issue produced for Taunton Cider was the "Beyond the Call of Duty" mug. This was especially produced for members of the Taunton Cider staff who were involved in the intensive preparation for the Stock Exchange listing.

No. 1309.   **TAUNTON CIDER MUGS.** - A selection of 13 special issue mugs produced by the Wade Potteries. Following is the year of issue of these mugs:
A (1981), B (1976), C (1982), D (1989), E (1980), F (1983), G (1977), H (1988), I (1980), J (pre-1980), K (pre-1980), L (1990), M (1987).
No. 1310.   VAUX BREWERIES TANKARD (1991) - measures 4-

1/4" high by 4-5/8" in diameter and has Mark Type 49 on the underside of the base. The design includes a number of Vaux beer brand names along with the wording: More Flavour, More Quality, More Choice, More Vaux.

No. 1311.   **VAUX BREWERIES TANKARD** (1992) - measures 4-1/4" high by 4-5/8" in diameter and has Mark Type 49 on the underside of the base. The design shows an "A-Z Good Pub Guide 1992" along with reproductions of a number of famous "pub" signs.

No.1312.   **TAUNTON CIDER MUG** (1992) - measures 5" high by 5-1/8" in diameter. The wording on the underside of the base reads: A limited edition drinking mug copied from an original, dating from 1820, which is held in the Taunton Cider collection. This mug was produced to commemorate Taunton Cider's Listing on the London Stock Exchange -23 July 1992 - Wade No. 20.

No.1313.   **TAUNTON CIDER MUG** (1992) - measures 4-7/8" high by 4-3/4" in diameter. The wording on the underside of the base reads: This mug is one of a limited edition of five hundred specially commissioned by Taunton Cider. It is produced from a 19th century original in the Taunton Cider collection - 1992 - Wade.

*An illustration showing a number of mugs, tankards and loving cups produced by Wade Ceramics Ltd. for distribution by Wade (PDM) Ltd.*

# MISCELLANEOUS DECANTERS, WATER JUGS and ASHTRAYS.

No. 1314.   **"THE ENGLISH GENTLEMEN'S CHOICE" DECANTER** - this single malt Scotch whisky decanter measures 10" high and has the following wording on the underside of the base: The Foxhunting decanter is handmade by The Royal Victoria Pottery, Staffordshire, England - Designed by Gordon Highlander Ltd. - Collector's Series.

No. 1315. "IRISH MIST" DECANTER - measures 9" high and has the following wording molded on the underside of the base: This is a fine piece of Irish Porcelain made by Wades - Liquor bottle - Tullamore Ireland. Records indicate that 25,000 decanters were produced between 1965 - 1966.

No. 1316. BRITISH AIRWAYS LIQUOR BOTTLE - measures 2-1/4" high by 5-1/8" overall. The bottle, in the form of BA's Concorde, contains 50ml of "The Balvenie" Single Malt Scotch Whisky.
This container was also used for another Scotch Whisky but "The Balvenie" was only issued in a very limited number.

No. 1317. PUSSER'S RUM "JOHN PAUL JONES SHIPS DECANTER" - measures 8-3/4" high by 8" in diameter at the base. This decanter is from a similar mold as the popular "Nelson's Ships Decanter." The lettering on the underside of the decanter reads: Pusser's Ltd. British Virgin Islands, West Indies. Hand cast & Hand decorated Made in England - "The John Paul Jones" U.S. Navy and Marine Corps Ships Decanter.

No. 1318. BELLS'S OLD SCOTCH WHISKY "CHRISTMAS 1988" - this 75 cl decanter measures 8" high and has Mark Type 27A on the base.

FIG. 191. BELL'S OLD SCOTCH WHISKY "CHRISTMAS 1993." This 75 cl decanter measures 8" high and has Mark Type 27A on the base.

No. 1319. CANADIAN CLUB - water jug, measures 5-1/2" high and has Mark Type 46 on the underside of the base.

No. 1320. CANADIAN CLUB - overhang lip type ashtray, measures 2" high by 4" square and has Mark Type 46 on the base.

No. 1321. CANADIAN CLUB - water jug, measures 6-3/4" high and has Mark Type 45 on the base.

No. 1322. ROYAL SALUTE SCOTCH WHISKY -this water jug with ice check spout measures 4-3/4" high and has Mark Type 47 on the base.

No. 1323. KEG HARP LAGER - easy clean type ashtray, measures 3" high by 5-3/4" across at the widest point. The ashtray has Mark Type 43 on the inside of the recessed base.

No. 1324. "CREAM OF THE BARLEY" SCOTCH WHISKY - pressed ashtray, measures 5-1/4" across and has Mark Type 43 on the underside of the base.

No. 1325. BELL'S FINEST OLD SCOTCH WHISKY - water jug, measures 6" high and has Mark Type 49 on the base.

No. 1326. BASS & CO'S. PALE ALE - water jug, measures 6-1/4" high and has the wording: "This jug was produced in 1977 to celebrate the two-hundred years that have passed since William Bass first brewed in Burton-upon-Trent." Supplied by Wade (PDM) Limited. England.

FIG. 192. BELL'S OLD SCOTCH WHISKY "CHRISTMAS 1993" This 75 cl decanter, produced for the South African market, measures 8" high and has Mark Type 27A on the base.

FIG. 191.

FIG. 192.

No.1327. IMPERIAL - water jug, measures 6" high and has Mark Type 46 on the base.

No.1328. IMPERIAL - cigarette lighter, measures 4-1/4" high and has Mark Type 46 on the base.

No.1329. 75 th ANNIVERSARY OF THE FIRST CAMP OF THE SCOUTS - 1982. This loving cup measures 3-1/4" high and is marked: Produced for Commemorative House by Wade Potteries England.

No.1330. 75 th ANNIVERSARY OF THE OF THE FIRST CAMP OF THE SCOUTS - 1982. This tankard measures 4-3/4" high and is marked: Produced for Commemorative House by Wade Potteries England.

No.1331. VAUX BREWERIES TANKARD - measures 4-1/8" high and has Mark Type 49 on the underside of the base. This tankard was issued in 1992, in a limited number of 2000 and shows the official crest of The City of Sunderland.

No.1332. VAUX BREWERIES TANKARD - the reverse side of No. 1331.

No. 1333. "LEAPING TROUT DECANTER" - measures 10-3/4" high. A prototype decanter, with a removable head containing the stopper. As of this writing, this decanter has never actually been produced as a "production model."

FIG. 193. PETER ENGLAND ASHTRAY (1977 - 1978). This hard-to-find ashtray was produced for Peter England Shirts of Wakefield, England in a very small quantity, not exceeding 1,000 pieces.
A. This yellow lion ashtray, highlighted in black, measures 7-1/4" x 7-1/4" and has Mark Type 46 on the base.
B. Ashtray showing name on the lion's tail.

FIG. 194. BACARDI ASHTRAY - measures 7-1/2" long by 4-3/4" wide by 1-3/4" high and has Mark Type 47 on the base. This ashtray was produced for Bacardi International for their then distributor Charles Hosie based in Hamburg, Germany. The ashtray would then have been distributed throughout Europe.

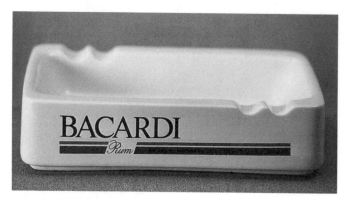

FIG. 194.

FIG. 193A.

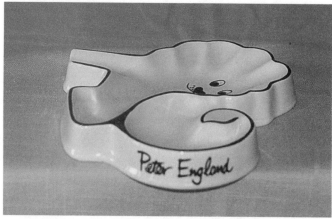

FIG. 193B.

*Prototypes by Wade, Heath & Co. Ltd. for Wade (PDM) Ltd.*

**REPRODUCTIONS and RE-ISSUES.**

early 1980's - 1993.

# REPRODUCTIONS and RE-ISSUES.

When a collectable item gains acceptance by the trade and wide popularity with the collecting public, it often happens that reproductions soon begin to appear on the market. This phenomena can have a devastating impact on novice collectors and a feeling of rage and frustration by the more experienced collector.

Reproductions of popular collectables, especially the higher priced items, are, unfortunately, a fact of life. All collectors and dealers can do is to seek out and publicise the reproductions and learn the differences between the original article and the fake. It is usually only a matter of time before the distributor/manufacturer of the fake items is located or identified, maybe not publicly but often through the collector "grapevine," and the eventual lasting harm is then brought home to rest on the shoulders of the parties concerned.

First, some words of warning to the novice collector along with some suggestions that may help avoid some of the pitfalls in buying through the mail. First and foremost, join well-established and reputable Wade clubs publishing newsletters. It is often in the pages of these newsletters that word is first mentioned about fakes and possible reproductions. Secondly, know your dealer.

As the old saying goes "if it sounds too good to be true, it probably is."

Before sending for either small or large orders from a new source, especially if including payment, check out the vendor. If there is no telephone number listed in the advertisement, take this as a real warning. In the past year, prior to publication of this book, a number of advertisements of "Wade for sale" have appeared in trade papers, along with lists sent directly to collectors that have not included the phone number of the vendor. A number of collectors have written to the addresses given asking for further information, but in each case no reply was forthcoming. The message here is obvious.

Prior to sending payment, verify in writing with the vendor that pieces not as advertised can be returned for full reimbursement of funds. Also, come to a mutual agreement on dealing with possible breakages or loss in the mail.

First we would like to enlarge on the word "reproduction." Webster's dictionary defines reproduction as "1. a reproducing or being reproduced., 2. something made by reproducing a copy, close imitation, duplication, etc." The dictionary defines the word "re-issue" as "to issue again (v.t.) or: a second or repeated issue (n)". We thereby conclude that any item made from an original or a re-tooled mold, by the original manufacturer, is a re-issue. Any item made by a person or company other than the original manufacturer, and made to copy or resemble an original of another source, is a reproduction.

Probably the first official re-issues were the Happy Families series. This series was first introduced starting in 1961 comprising The Giraffe Family, The Tiger Family, The Hippo Family, The Rabbit Family and The Mouse Family. Between 1978 and 1984 four of these sets were re-issued along with three new families, The Frog Family, The Elephant Family and The Owl Family. Not re-issued in the second issue was the original Tiger Family.

In the early 1980's, six of the original Disney Hat Box characters from the movie *"The Lady and the Tramp"* and two characters from the movie *"Bambi"* were re-issued. The figurines were Lady, Jock, Dachsie (Dachie in the original issue), Scamp, Bambi and Thumper.

## NURSERY FAVOURITES RE-ISSUE
*1990-1991.*

In the mid 1980's Wade re-issued a number of the Nursery Favourites as a special order for two private concerns, one located in North America and the other in England. The figurines re-issued were The Three Bears, Little Tommy Tucker, Cat 'n the Fiddle, Mary Lamb and Little Boy Blue. Approximately 8,000 each of these figurines were re-issued. There was no change in decoration or mold-mark.

Nursery Favourites Mary Mary, Polly Kettle and Tom Piper were re-issued as a special order for a U.S. based dealer in 1990. In each case, the original tool was amended to include the year of issue. Each figurine is therefore mold-marked Wade England 90. For the same client, Wade re-issued in 1991, Nursery Favourites Old Woman in a Shoe and Goosey Gander. The original molds were amended to have the mold-mark read Wade England 91. The glazes used for these 1990 and 1991 re-issues were similar to the original issues except for Old Woman in a Shoe which had the dog sitting beside the old woman in a similar color glaze to the shoe rather than the roof color used on the original issue.

It has been reported that a number of collectors have purchased the re-issue figurines with either the 90 or 91 removed and a type of clear finish applied to the area affected. When purchasing the highly-priced original issues, carefully check for any possibility of the mold mark having been tampered with. As an added precaution, the client for whom Wade produced the Old Woman in a Shoe and Goosey Gander, applied an ink stamp on the underside of the base. The mark is reproduced here.

## EARLY WHIMSIE SHIRE HORSE and SWAN REPRODUCTIONS *1992.*

Beginning in the early 1990's, unauthorized reproductions of a number of Wade figurines have started to appear. Most notorious of these are the reproduction "Shire Horse" and "Swan" from set 10 of the early Whimsies.

It has been suggested that the reproduction Shire Horse and Swan could be variations of the original Wade figurines. This is not the case. Wade personnel state that the possibility of two tools being used for the 1950's Shire

Horse and Swan was quite improbable. Records show that only 89,000 of set 10 were sold in 1959 and only 19,000 sets were forecast for 1960. The average life of a tool is 200,000 pieces, well above the actual amount produced.

The Wade miniature figurines are made, one at a time, by hand-operated steel pressing tool and not by the multiple cast mold system as used in many potteries. It appears that the reproduction Swan and Shire Horse may have been made using the cast mold system. The Wade figurines are hand-decorated and, therefore, some slight variations in overall finish might occur. However, due to the use of the steel tool, the shapes would be virtually identical for all the original figurines. This is certainly not the case with the reproductions of the Shire Horse and Swan.

The Wade Whimsies, Red Rose Tea figurines, etc. are fired differently from traditional potting which separates bisque and glost firings. The firing temperature for Wade porcelain miniature figurines is 1,250 degrees Celsius and is a once-fired process where the glaze is applied directly to the clay article. A single firing cures the clay body and the glaze at the same time.

# SHIRE HORSE REPRODUCTION. *1992.*

The reproduction "Shire Horse" has been found in two versions. The first attempt at trying to fool collectors was an extremely poor model which was crudely formed and appeared almost as if the horse were about to sit. The figurine also wobbled when standing on a flat surface, something the original "pressed" model would not do. The second version was a slight improvement over the first but the differences are basically the same. The major differences between the reproduction "Shire Horse" and the original can be seen in FIGS.195, 196, 197 and 198. In each case the reproduction figurine is on the left and the original on the right.

**FIG.195.** This shows the much cruder head on the reproduction with lumpy ears and the neck set back. There is a noticeable difference in the hooves, larger and chunkier on the reproduction. The difference in the size of the tail is also apparent, the reproduction having a longer tail.

**FIG.196.** This shows again the difference in ears, head and height. The height of the reproduction Shire Horse is 2-1/16" as opposed to 1-15/16" for the original Wade figurine. The photograph also shows the decidedly backward slant of the reproduction, it almost appears as if the horse were about to fall backwards. The poorly formed hooves are also apparent in this photograph.

**FIG.197 and FIG.198.** These illustrate the differences in height, and the rounded, poorly formed head, ears and hooves on the reproduction. The body and main colors are quite good matches however, the eye color on the reproduction is a brighter orange brown whereas on the original, it is a very dark brown, almost black.

FIG.195.

FIG.196.

FIG.197.

FIG.198.

# SWAN REPRODUCTIONS. *1992.*

The reproduction Swan has also been found in two versions, a white and a black version. The original swan was never issued in black. FIGS.199, 200, 201 and 202 illustrate the major differences between the reproduction Swan and the original. The reproduction figurine is on the left and the original on the right.

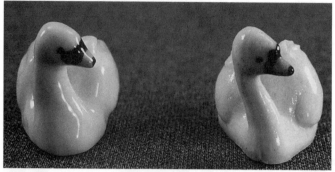

FIG.199.

FIG.200.

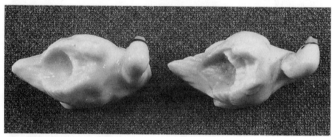

FIG.201.

FIG.202.

FIG.199.　This shows the reproduction Swan having a shorter, thicker and straighter neck with a smooth transition from head to beak. The original swan has a thinner, more curved and angled neck with a noticeable bump separating the head from the beak.

FIG.200.　This shows the reproduction Swan to have wings which are more rounded and lumpier than the original. The neck is also much thicker. The original Swan

shows the wings to be much better defined with the feathers much more detailed.

FIG.201.　This shows the reproduction Swan with shorter, rounded tail feathers and a lack of detail between the wings. The original Swan has longer and more pointed tail feathers and much more detail between the wings. Not apparent in the black and white photographs is the difference in color; creamy white for the reproduction and greyish white for the original.

FIG.202.　This shows the two reproduction versions: the white on the left, the black in the centre and the original on the right.

# EASTER BUNNY and BO-PEEP REPRODUCTIONS *early 1990's.*

Two hard-to-understand reproductions are the Easter Bunny and Easter Bo-Peep. These are difficult to understand due to the fact that they are not "hard-to-find" items and, therefore, do not command a high price. During one of our visits to the Wade Potteries, we discussed these reproductions with Wade personnel, and came to the conclusion that someone had made a mold using the original figurines as a model. This assumption came from the fact that the fakes are approximately 12% smaller than the originals and have most of the detail along with the mold-mark Wade England on the Bo-Peep figurine. This would be consistent with a "one size shrink" when making a new mold from an original figurine.

FIG.203.

FIG.203.　This illustrates two fake Bo-Peeps alongside the original figurine. Note the difference in height between the two fakes. This could not have occurred when using the original steel tool. The difference in size of the base of the reproductions is due to the use of a "cast-mold" process of manufacture.

The reproduction Easter Bunny is shown in the color section as item No.217 and is located beside the Wade original, item No.216. As with the reproduction Bo-Peep, this unauthorized Easter Bunny appears to be approximately 12% smaller than the original and would therefore have been made using the "cast-mold" process of manufacture.

## "KISSING RABBITS" REPRODUCTION.

Over the past few years, a number of very suspect "Kissing Rabbits" have appeared. The fake "Wade" rabbits are smaller than the 2-1/2" original Wade figures and many have a crude "Wade" ink stamp on the underside of the base. For an example of the the fake rabbits, see item No.152 in the color section. This fake is positioned along-side an original Wade figure, item No.151. Notice the variation in the shape of the ears. The ears on the original are pointed and well-divided at the ends whereas the fake figure has rounded ears not nearly so well-divided at the ends. The form of the ears on the smaller rabbit also differs considerably.

## RECENT FAKES *mid 1993.*

Just before the manuscript of this book went into print, a number of brightly colored "Nurseries" appeared on the North American market purporting to  be prototypes. So far those seen are "Humpty-Dumpty" with orange hands and feet and red bow tie, "Little Bo-Peep" with a light blue dress, "Old Woman in a Shoe" with red skirt and hat and "Little Red Riding Hood" with a bright red enamel cape. There are probably more. Although the original figurines were manufactured by Wade, the bright enamel finish has been applied by someone other than the original manufacturer. These are definitely not prototypes. They are Wade stock bought by an outside concern which then had enamel paint applied over the original glaze. Much of the original detail is lost due to the second applied finish and any chips or defects are also painted over. These items, along with other fake Wade items, have little or no commercial value and should, in the opinion of the authors, be avoided at all costs.

As was stated at the beginning of this section, reproductions are a fact of life in the field of popular collectables. All that can be done is for collectors to become educated in their particular field of interest and, above all, know and trust their sources and have a predetermined agreement regarding the return of suspect items if purchased through the mail.

# MISCELLANEOUS ITEMS.

by

George Wade & Son Ltd.,

Wade, Heath & Co. Ltd.

and

Wade Ceramics Ltd.

mid 1940's - 1993.

# MISCELLANEOUS ITEMS.

**FIG. 204.** ARTHUR HARE (1993). This limited edition of 2,000 slip-cast figurines, was made by Wade Ceramics exclusively for C & S Collectables. The figurine measures approx. 5" high.

**FIG. 205.** FESTIVE TEAPOTS (1993). Two teapots, produced by Wade Ceramics for Boot's Drugstores, in the form of a stylized Christmas tree with an all-over gold Fleur-de-Lis decoration on a white or dark green body glaze. The teapots measure 6" high and have Mark Type 27B on the base.

CLOWN RANGE (1993). A set of four co-ordinated items made by Wade Ceramics Ltd. exclusively for Boot's Drugstores. These items utilized the earlier "Bow" and "Kipper" clown designs used for the designer teapots in the Wade retail line. See FIGS. 206 and 207.

**FIG. 206.** CLOWN RANGE.
A. BOWL - measures 6-3/4" in diameter.
B. PLATE - measures 7-1/2" in diameter. Both items have Mark Type 27B on the base.

**FIG. 207.** CLOWN RANGE.
A. MUG - measures 3" high and has Mark Type 27B on the base.
B. EGG CUP - measures 2" high and has Mark Type 19 on the base.

**FIG. 208.** DOLEFUL DAN POSY BOWL (circa late 1940's) with "Basket Ware" mustard bowl. The posy bowl measures 4-1/4" high by 4" overall and has Mark Type 10 on the base.

**FIG. 209.** HIGHLAND PARK SINGLE MALT SCOTCH WHISKY (1993) - water jug with ice check spout, measures 6" high and has Mark Type 49 on the base.

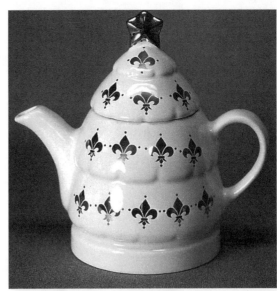

FIG. 205.

FIG. 206.

FIG. 207.

FIG. 204.

**FIG. 210.** TULLAMORE DEW® IRISH WHISKY (1993).
A. WATER JUG - measures 4-1/2" high and has Mark Type 49 on the base.
B. WATER JUG - this hard-to-find miniature jug measures 3" high and has Mark Type 49 on the base.

**FIG. 211.** VAUX BREWERIES TANKARD (1993) - measures 4-1/8" high by 4-1/2" in diameter and has Mark Type 49 on the base.

FIG. 208.

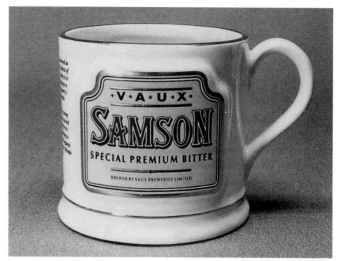

FIG. 211.

FIG. 209.

FIG. 212.

FIG. 210.

FIG. 212.    TAUNTON CIDER MUG (1993) - measures 5" high
             by 5" in diameter. The mug has the following
             inscription on the base: This mug is one of a limited
             edition of five hundred specially commissioned by
             Taunton Cider. It is produced from a 19th century
             original in the Taunton Cider collection. 1993
             Wade.

FIG. 213.    "FALSTAFF" CLARET JUGS (circa 1970).
             A second size jug has recently surfaced. As with the
             large companion claret jug shown as No. 807 in the
             color section, this smaller jug has the red rose decal
             decoration.
             A. LARGE CLARET JUG - measures 10" high and is
             mold-marked Wade Falstaff England on the base.
             B. SMALL CLARET JUG - measures 6-1/4" high
             and is mold-marked Wade Falstaff England on the
             base.

FIG. 214.    BALLANTINE'S® VERY OLD SCOTCH WHISKY
             (1993). This 70 cl liquor bottle is dark blue with
             gold lettering and measures 9-1/2" high and has
             Mark Type 27A on the base.

FIG. 213.

FIG. 216.

FIG. 214.                     FIG. 215.

FIG. 217.

FIG. 215.  **THE FAMOUS GROUSE SCOTCH WHISKY**
(1993). This 9-3/4" high liquor bottle has an all-over
yellow glaze with a multi-colored decal around the
bottle. The bottle has Mark Type 27A on the base.

FIG. 216.  **"HIGHLAND GATHERING"** (1993). This 8-3/4"
high bottle has an all-over maroon glaze decorated
with gold bands and multi-colored decal. The bottle
has the following inscription along with Mark Type
27B on the base: Made Exclusively for Lombard
Scotch Whisky Ltd. by Wade England.

FIG. 217.  **"YEAR OF THE DOG"** (1993). This limited edition

of 4,000 decanters measures 9-1/4" tall and has an
all-over white glaze with gold and blue decoration.
Along with Mark Type 27A the following inscription
appears on the base: LANGS® Select 1861 Founders
Reserve Scotch Whisky Genuine Wade Porcelain.

FIG. 218.  **SPIRIT OF ROBYN HOOD** (1993). This limited edition two piece decanter in the shape of a hunting
horn measures 14-1/8" long and has an all-over white
glaze with gold lettering. The stopper forms the
mouth piece of the horn and the funnel end has the
following inscription: Spirit of Robyn Hoode Aged
Malt Whisky Specially Selected for Robyn Hoode

248

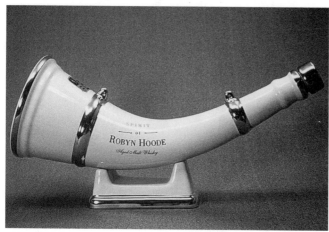

FIG. 218.

FIG. 220.

Distilleries, Elston, Newark, Nottinghamshire NG23 5PG followed by Mark Type 27B.

The stand, which also has gold decoration on an all-over white glaze, measures 2-1/4" high by 5" long and is unmarked.

FIG. 219. POLICE MAN (1993) - measures 3-5/8" high and is mold-marked Wade on the underside of the base. This figurine was produced with two decorations.
A. POLICE MAN with eyes, eye brows, moustache and mouth decoration. Approximately 1,600 pieces were produced. See also FIG. 14.
B. POLICE MAN with moustache decoration only. Approximately 400 pieces were produced.

FIG. 219.

FIG. 221.

FIG. 220. ANDY CAPP (1994) - measures 3" high and is marked 1994 ©Mirror Group Newspapers Ltd., C & S Collectables, Wade England.

FIG. 221. HARRODS DOOR MAN MONEY BOX (1994) - measures 7" high and is marked Harrods Knightsbridge on the underside of the base. This is a larger version of the Harrods Egg Cup shown as No. 80 in the color section.

249

# INDEX

# V

# W

# Y

# Z